MW00770880

The Last Eunuch of China

The Life of Sun Yaoting

Jia Yinghua
Translated by Sun Haichen

China Intercontinental Press

Sun Yaoting with the Author

Sun Yaoting at the Temple of Great Deliverance, 1992

国正天心順
官清民自安

末代太監孫耀庭九十有一

In a well-governed nation the heart of heaven is content.
Under uncorrupt officials the people remain at peace.

Sun Yaoting, the Last Eunuch, at 91

Pu Yi

Wanrong

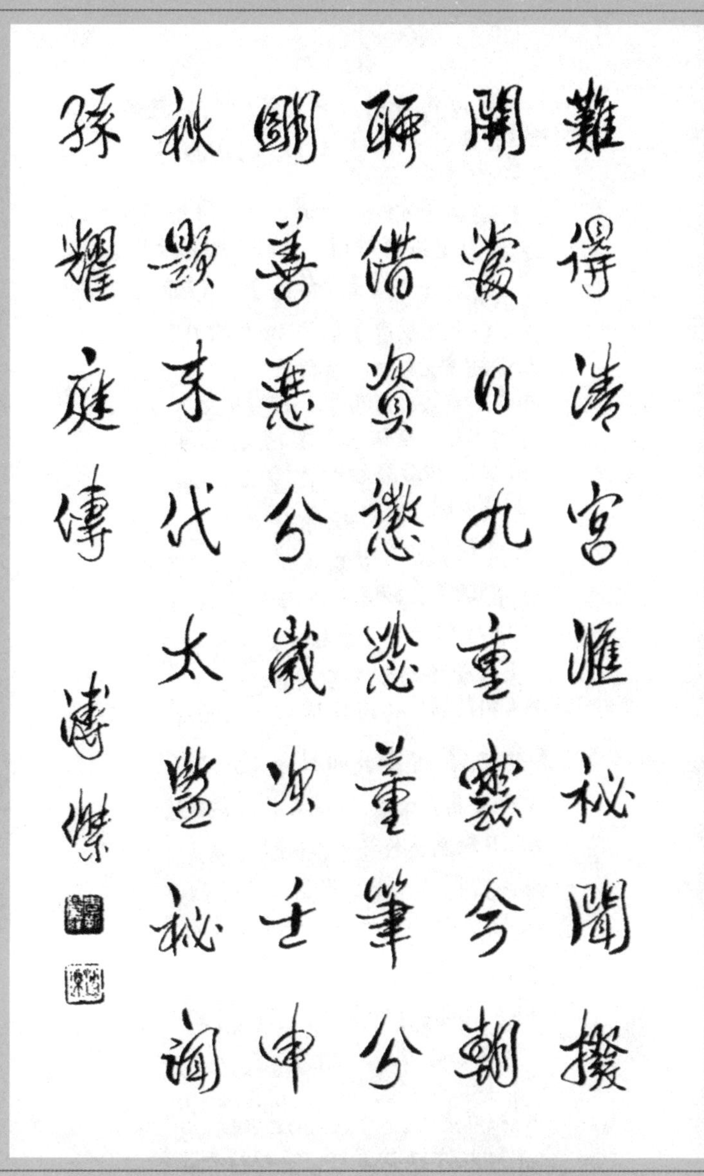

How precious is this secret account of the Qing Palace,
Uncovering the days bygone behind nine layers of clouds!
It enables us to learn from past mistakes for a better future,
With good and evil deeds marked out for all to see.

Written for *The Last Eunuch of China*: *The Life of Sun Yaoting*, autumn 1992
Aisin-Gioro Pu Jie

自序

我作為中国历史上最后一个太監在世上已度过九十載春秋，追溯往事，滄桑感慨良多。

光緒二十八年十一月三十日我出生于天津静海県西双塘村。八歲那年我净身，十五歲我抱着荣华富貴梦想进了京城，先是进了濤貝勒府，次年进了紫禁城，开始我伺候九堂嗣督大总管任德祥，后来去了司房。在此前后先伺候端康皇貴太妃、婉容，与遜帝溥仪也有頗多的接触。如今這些人的音容仍历历如昨。在皇上退位的小朝廷，我目睹了宫内的种种内幕，也亲历了溥仪被逐出紫禁城那一幕。

我在北府呆不多日子又回到太監們聚集的京城的兴隆寺，尔后与小德張也有了来往。當溥仪在偽滿称帝后又去長春内廷伺候溥仪，耳闻目睹了一些外間所不知之事。因病我回北京，先后居兴隆寺、立馬关帝廟等处，又与太監們長期相处。总之，我這一辈子都没有离开过太監朋友。一生中我飽尝了酸甜苦辣。新中国成立后我竟成了国家的宗教干部。

多年来，我与晚清史研究者賈英华結成了忘年之交，成了無話不談之摯友，經常相互一吐衷腸，陆續我向他談了許多从未向旁人透露过的太監秘聞。据此，他多方考証，撰寫了我一生的經历。虽然記述我的不只限于此書，但是唯此書最為翔实，亦絶无任何随意編造或穿鑿之处，可以作為信史来讀的。有感于此，欣然命笔為之作序。

末代太監孫耀庭

辛未年五月二十六日

As the last eunuch in Chinese history I have lived for over ninety years. All sorts of feelings welled up in my mind as I look back on the past.

I was born in western Shuangtang of Jinghai County in Tianjin on the 30th day of the 11th month in the 28th year of Emperor Guangxu's reign. I was castrated at eight and came to Beijing at fifteen, dreaming of riches and honors. I served Prince Zai Tao in his residence for some time before entering the Forbidden City the following year. I first waited on chief eunuch Ren Dexiang, then went to work at the Accounting Office. Afterward I became an attendant of High Consort Duankang and Empress Wanrong and came into close contact with the abdicated Emperor, Pu Yi. All these people remain fresh in my memory as if it all happened only yesterday. I saw with my own eyes many behind-the-scenes occurrences in Pu Yi's little court and witnessed the episode when he was driven out of the Forbidden City.

After a short time in the Northern Mansion I went to stay at the Temple of Prosperity, where a lot of eunuchs lived. I also came into contact with Xiaode Zhang. When Pu Yi proclaimed himself Emperor of the puppet state Manchukuo, I went to Changchun to serve him. Much of what I saw and heard there was unknown to the public. I returned to Beijing on account of illness and stayed along with other eunuchs in various places such as the Temple of Prosperity and the Temple of Mounted Lord Guan. I have spent most of my life in the company of my eunuch friends. I have tasted both joys and sorrows. After the founding of New China I began to work for the government and became a religious cadre.

Jia Yinghua, a researcher of late Qing history, has been a friend of mine for many years. We feel close in spite of our age difference and often bare our hearts to each other. Over a long period of time I disclosed to him, for the very first time, a lot about the secret life of eunuchs. Based on my account and his research, he has completed this book about my life. Though many people have written about me, this is the most reliable and best-researched book yet. It is a truthful history free of fabrications or farfetched conclusions. Therefore I have composed this foreword in my own handwriting.

The Last Eunuch, Sun Yaoting
May 26, 1991

CONTENTS

PROLOGUE

It was an early winter day in 1916, five years after the collapse of Qing Dynasty, the last Imperial dynasty of China. Within the high palace walls the last Qing Emperor, Pu Yi, continued to live in pomp and extravagance, and the ancient palatial buildings, their yellow and green glazed tiles glittering in the sunlight, looked as imposing as ever. For hundreds of years the Imperial Palace, also known as the Forbidden City, had witnessed the vicissitudes of history, impassive and unmoved.

A handsome young boy wearing a gray gown and a broad-rimmed hat appeared on the road in front of the Gate of Divine Prowess. The ground was covered in fallen leaves from the Chinese scholar trees lining the road. He stopped to stare at the giant red gate and the armed guards checking the identification of everyone passing through. He took off his hat. The towering palace wall made him feel small and insignificant.

It was a time of great change and turbulence. The 1911 Revolution had put an end to the Manchu rule of China. The following year the Republic of China was established. Empress Dowager Longyu issued an edict proclaiming the abdication of Pu Yi, or Emperor Xuantong, then only six years old. In return the imperial house was awarded the Articles of Favorable Treatment, by which the child Emperor got to retain his title and stay in the Imperial Palace to preside over his "little court".

The downfall of the Qing Dynasty did not bring peace to the nation.

An octagonal corner tower in the Forbidden City

There were entangled fights among different military cliques. Yuan Shikai, President of the newly founded republic, proclaimed himself Emperor in 1916 but died soon afterward. The various warlords, backed up by foreign powers and representing their conflicting interests, waged wars against one another incessantly. The common people were thus plunged into misery.

Amid the chaos the Imperial clan enjoyed relative peace and security in the secluded quarters of the Forbidden City, waited on by hundreds of eunuchs and palace maids. Eunuchs continued to be recruited in secret despite the prohibition in the Articles of Favorable Treatment. It was in the hope of entering the palace someday that the young boy had come to Beijing and stood before the Gate of Divine Prowess, his heart filled with awe and apprehension. Little did he know what fate and fortune had in store for him.

He was born in a peasant's family on the Grand Canal, near the port city of Tianjin. For him, the dethroned Emperor remained a godlike figure, and entry to the Forbidden City would be a childhood dream come true. He remembered not only his father's ashen face and his mother's loud wails when he was castrated but also the splendor and glory of Chief Eunuch Zhang's homecoming trip. At the thought of the fame and wealth awaiting him, he was flushed with excitement, his eyes misty with tears.

Hadn't he been dreaming for this moment all along?

As he walked away, his mind was awash with memories of what he had gone through all those years that finally brought him to the Imperial Capital.

Empress Dowager Cixi before the Hall of Joyous Longevity in the Summer Palace (Cui Yugui, front left; Li Lianying, front right)

1

CASTRATION

1. The Chief Eunuch Comes Home

The Grand Canal flowed south past the city of Tianjin and made a turn at Jinghai County, winding its way through Lüguantun, a village with over two hundred households.

"Hurry to the river! Chief Eunuch Zhang is coming!"

At the news the villagers put down their sickles and pickaxes and swarmed to the banks of the canal. A huge crowd soon gathered, staring anxiously upstream for the sight of the renowned eunuch.

A few days before, news of Zhang's imminent return had spread to every corner of Jinghai County. It was said that the chief eunuch would come home to show off his wealth and give opera performances to his fellow villagers for free. Early in the morning people from all over the county flocked to Lüguantun.

A previously unknown village, Lüguantun had become famous for being the hometown of Zhang Yunting, popularly known by his palace nickname Xiaode Zhang, a powerful chief eunuch in the Imperial Palace of Beijing.

Among the crowd of people on the canal bank was a tall, hefty middle-aged man carrying a small boy on his back. By his side stood another boy of twelve or thirteen.

"Dad, when are they coming?" asked the small boy.

"Be patient, Liujin!" The man patted the boy. "Listen to all those gongs and drums. They are not far from here."

As the sound of gongs and drums grew louder, there was a stir among the crowd as people pushed against each other to get a better view.

"Look, brother, they are coming!" cried the small boy, who was now standing on his father's shoulders.

"Where?" The big boy stood on tiptoes and strained his eyes, just in time to see a large wooden boat emerging at the turn of the canal, the first of a fleet. The boats moved very slowly, towed by boat trackers along the bank shouting a work song to synchronize movements.

"How grand!" exclaimed a young man in the crowd.

"Grand indeed!" echoed a middle-aged man who appeared to be a private tutor judging by his attire. "Almost everyone on the boats is dressed in silk and brocade!"

"Xiaode Zhang has certainly made it! He's the chief superintendent of the whole Imperial Palace!"

"Have you heard the news? He's going to feast the village with steamed meat dumplings and give opera performances for three days on end!"

As a six-year-old boy Liujin only half understood what the people were saying. Standing on his father's shoulders, he got a good view of the approaching boats and the excited villagers thronging on both banks. The first boat was still too distant to for him make out the features of people on board, but their entrance was already a dazzling sight. He had never seen anything like it before.

"Where's Zhang?" he asked his father.

"You silly boy! You think he'd stand outside in the sun? He must be taking a rest somewhere in the cabin. Those on the deck are all his servants."

Liujin found this hard to believe. He tugged at the hem of his tattered shirt and tilted his head. "Dad, why is he so rich?"

"Oh well, he's been a eunuch for dozens of years. That's why!"

"What's a eunuch?"

"A eunuch's a palace-person."

"Palace-person?" The boy repeated the word a few times. "What's a palace-person, Dad?"

"You're too small to be told these things!" The father caught hold of the boy's penis and squeezed it lightly. "You have this thing cut off and enter the palace to serve the Emperor – that'll make you a palace-person!"

"Oh!" The boy fell silent.

It did not occur to the father that this conversation would leave a lasting impression on the mind of his six-year-old son, Liujin. With the penis cut off, one could enter the palace to wait on the Son of Heaven and eventually grow as rich as Chief Eunuch Zhang, or at least rich enough to free the family from all worries. The novelty of such an idea haunted the small boy for days.

This was a typical example in which a small incident in a person's life produces far-reaching consequences. The brief exchange between the small boy and his father on that fateful autumn day in the 34th year of Emperor Guangxu's reign (1908) eventually led Liujin, whose full name was Sun Yaoting, to follow in the footsteps of Chief Eunuch Zhang. He was to become the last surviving eunuch in China in the final years of the 20th century.

Nothing unusual happened that day. Liujin saw swarms of people wherever he looked. Carried along by the crowd, the father and sons spent the whole day at Lüguantun. They failed to push their way close to the theatre platform and had to climb up a mound to watch from a distance. Liujin again searched the crowd eagerly for the chief eunuch, but gave up in disappointment when he was told that Zhang was sitting inside a big tent in front of the platform. The opera performance, they later found out, did last three whole days.

Though Liujin did not get to see the chief eunuch, he learned quite a lot about him from the animated chatter of the spectators.

"You know why Zhang is giving us this performance? To fulfill a pledge he made when he left to become a palace-person!"

The village of West Shuangtang in Jinghai County, a prosperous area today

"This is nothing but a sideshow, you know. He's back home this time mainly to attend the opening ceremony of the temple built with his money! He had sworn a secret oath about it before he went into the palace!"

Before he left for Beijing, as the story goes, Zhang had knelt in front of the clay figurine of Buddha in a small temple outside the village to pray for a prosperous future. He promised to come back to rebuild the temple and have the Buddha covered in gold if he should attain wealth and status in the imperial capital.

As for what had prompted Zhang to become a eunuch, Liujin heard the following "story of the whip".

Zhang Xiangzhai was born into a poor family in Lüguantun. His father made a living by fishing and doing odd jobs. The second of three sons, he was a very headstrong boy. One day he saw a mule cart in front of the house of Wang, an obnoxious rich man in the village. He picked up a whip from the cart and flung it a few times, trying to make it crack. While he was thus amusing himself a man in his twenties, the younger son of the Wang family, walked out of the gate.

"What are you doing with the whip?"

"I'm just playing with it," said the twelve-year-old boy nonchalantly.

"Playing with it? What if you break it?"

"I'll pay you back!"

"And you think you can afford it?" Wang sneered.

The boy put back the whip. He ran home and threw himself into his mother's arms. "Mum, why do we always get bullied in the village? How can I get rich?"

His mother shook her head. "Poor folks like us never get rich. Unless one becomes a eunuch and goes to the imperial capital to serve the Emperor."

Early the next morning Zhang left home, saying he would go and cut some grass. Instead, he made his pledge in a small Buddhist temple outside the village, then went into a cowshed where he castrated himself with his sickle.

Shortly afterward Empress Dowager Cixi ordered forty eunuchs to be recruited in Changzhou. That was the starting point of Zhang's miraculous career in the Imperial Palace. He finally became Chief Superintendent in charge of all personnel of the inner court, enjoying special favor of the

Empress Dowager and wielding more power than many high-ranking ministers.

On his homecoming visit Zhang was treated with the utmost respect wherever he went. Yang Yide, Military Commissioner of Tianjin, received the eunuch in person. Song Gongdi, Magistrate of Jinghai County, tugged the eunuch's boat along with his subordinates. Imagine having a county magistrate among one's boat trackers!

Zhang returned to Beijing after a short stay, leaving behind numerous legends. According to one story the county magistrate, who was no drinker, downed one cup after another at the banquet given by Zhang. When a subordinate tried to stop him, he said, "Don't be so dumb! How can a humble person like me refuse to drink when His Highness wants me to?" Some said the magistrate got dead drunk in the end and collapsed under the table.

Riding on his father's shoulders, Liujin listened attentively to the gossip of the villagers. "Xiaode Zhang is no ordinary eunuch. As head eunuch for Empress Dowager Longyu, he is equal to a third-rank mandarin, and he wears a bright blue hat with a peacock feather! When he comes home this time, he has a retinue of a few dozen eunuchs and a dozen cooks from the imperial kitchen!"

"Have you heard the story about the Wang family? They were scared witless! When the son of the family kowtowed and begged for mercy, Zhang waved his hand and said he didn't even remember the incident. But the son remained on his knees and dared not get up!"

Liujin was filled with admiration. Xiaode Zhang is such a remarkable man, he thought. He has got rich and famous on his own and made his family proud of him! The only difficulty he went through was having the thing cut off... But is it really difficult? What he could do, I can do also!

It was dark when they got back home. The elder brother chattered excitedly about what he had seen and heard, but Liujin was silent.

It had been a tiring day. Liujin went to bed and soon fell asleep. Late at night he woke up and went to the toilet. Back on the kang, half-asleep, he overheard a conversation between his parents.

"Liujin is a good boy!" said his father. "He has a mind of his own!"

"What are you talking about? Stop all this nonsense! Becoming a eunuch is no way to make a living! Let me make this clear: Don't lead my boy onto that cursed road!" Liujin's mother was a simple, illiterate peasant woman, but she had a clear mind and a strong will.

"Why are you so worked up? Just listen to me. If the boy is willing to do it himself, then..."

"What does a small child know about it? Does he know it would make him a cripple all his life? Or that everyone would look down on him because he'd die sonless?"

"Being a cripple is better than starving! Look at us. When will this life of poverty come to an end?"

Liujin listened, his heart thumping. He was torn between conflicting thoughts and emotions. His father's words sounded quite reasonable. His mother seemed to be worried, but he did not understand why. Mother had always loved him dearly. But he was also his father's favorite. Didn't he ride on his father's shoulders for a whole day? It was some 25 to 30 kilometers from their village to Lüguantun and back.

In the quiet night Liujin continued to hear the hushed arguments of his parents. He knew they were still talking about the question of "eunuch". Not daring to speak, he just stared at the stars outside the window until he finally drifted back into sleep.

2. A Childhood Dream

At dawn on December 29, 1902, or the 28th year of Emperor Guangxu's reign, Sun Yaoting was born at West Shuangtang Village of Jinghai County in Tianjin. It was the year of the tiger. The baby received the pet name Liujin ("Retaining Gold"). He took after his father, Sun Huaibao, looking rather strong and robust.

Sun Huaibao was the youngest of three sons. A bold, upright man, he earned his living by sheer hard work. The family owned a two-room earthen house with a thatched roof at the eastern end of the village. Sun Huaibao milled flour at home and sold the flour to pancake shops in the county seat, riding a donkey bought with many years' savings. In this way he barely managed to support the family. The eldest of the three brothers, Sun

Huairong, was a carpenter who could make carts. The second brother, Sun Huaizhen, earned a living by fishing and farming. Their father's name was Sun Youxing. The Suns had lived in Jinghai County for six generations.

Life was hard for Sun Huaibao and his family. The room where Liujin was born was built entirely of sun-dried mud bricks and had only three beams for support. The furniture consisted of a stove, a water tank, an unpainted wooden chest for storing flour, a table, a broken chair and a bench.

Liujin grew up to be a sensible child. One day when he was quite small, he worked all morning in the flourmill driving the donkey. After lunch he put down the rice bowl and left the table at once. "Where are you going?" asked his father.

"I'm going to put in some hay for the donkey!" he answered.

His parents could not help feeling proud of their young son. Like other children in poor families, he had a precocious ability to share life's burdens with his parents.

At the approach of winter Liujin and his elder brothers had to go out collecting firewood. They always managed to gather two big piles. In spite of their poverty Liujin was a cheerful boy who seldom complained about anything.

One day his father took him to a village fair. "Dad, the corn cones are not dry yet," Liujin said. "Let's buy some sorghum instead."

"Don't you worry about it, my boy," his father replied.

Back home Sun Huaibao praised Liujin to his wife. "He's a good boy! He surely knows sorghum is cheaper but does not taste as good as corn!"

From his grandfather Liujin learned something about his ancestry. One day Grandpa called him over and told him to take off his shoes.

"What for?" asked Liujin.

"Take a look. Does the little toe of your left foot tilt outward?"

Liujin looked carefully. "Yes, it does!"

"Now look again. Is the little toe much shorter than other ones?"

"Yes, Grandpa!"

"Remember, everyone who has such toes comes from a big willow tree in Shanxi."

Liujin took Grandpa at his word. Later he learned that the so-called "big willow tree" referred to Hongdong County of Shanxi Province.

Liujin's father was an industrious and honest man. At twelve he began to work as a hired hand for Liu Fadi, a landlord in a nearby village, earning only two strings of coins a year. At eighteen he went to serve Guan Fenglou, a big landlord nicknamed "Local Emperor". He had been to the city of Tianjin, where he worked as rickshaw boy, docker, and temporary laborer. To make ends meet Liujin's mother also had to go out to do odd jobs, even during her pregnancy. Their eldest son, born in the courtyard of the landlord she was working for at the time, got the name Changyuan, or "Courtyard". Their second son was named Posheng, or "Born on a Mound". Only Liujin was properly delivered at home.

This life of poverty and hard labor was going on peacefully when a misfortune befell the family. Sun Huibao was thrown into prison.

In the village lived a landlord and ex-official, Shang Buyin, who terrified the local people. According to a story, a vagabond peddler was foolish enough to hawk his wares in front of Shang's house. Shang's wife took ten pairs of earrings into her room but returned only eight pairs, saying she didn't find any to her liking. The poor peddler had no way to get back the two missing pairs. Another landlord, nicknamed Monkey, had a knack for falsifying contracts. He used his talents to seize other people's land and estates, and no one in the village dared stand up against him.

Unfortunate for Sun Huaibao, the two powerful landlords took a fancy to a small piece of land owned by his family. When Monkey offered to buy it, Sun Huaibao flatly refused. So the two landlords had someone set fire to an open court, then sued Sun Huaibao at the county yamen, accusing him of arson.

While jailed, Sun received a severe beating before he had a chance to say anything. He struggled to his feet and tried to reason with the official in charge, but his accusers ridiculed him, taking out some silver dollars. "You've got any of these? If you do, maybe someone would listen to you!"

Filled with anger and despair at his father's arrest, Changyuan broke into Monkey's house, where he tried to commit suicide by drinking kerosene. But he was brought back to life and also thrown into prison. To win his case Shang Buyin extorted some money from the villagers and used it to bribe the county officials. When Sun Huaibao's big brother took Liujin and his mother to Shang's house, pleading for him to have some mercy, Shang refused to open the gate. The family was forced to leave the village as vagrant beggars.

Liujin's father and brother were finally released from prison and reunited with the rest of the family. But they had no money and no home. So they wandered from place to place, even staying in Beijing for a period of time. In eight years they moved a total of fourteen times. They finally settled down in a village called Changtun by renting an old thatched house opening to the north. The house leaked in summer and was freezing cold in winter, when the family had to cuddle together under the only cotton-padded quilt to keep warm. Sun Huaibao earned a little money by running a ferryboat, but it was not enough to feed all the mouths in the house. Sometimes they went hungry for a whole day and felt too weak to talk. "Poor people like us have no hope!" Sun Huaibao often sighed. "The world belongs to the rich and heartless!"

Listening to his father's words, Liujin felt helpless and indignant. He had been yearning for revenge ever since his father was thrown into prison on a false charge. He would like to break into Shang's house with a kitchen knife, killing everyone standing in his way. Or maybe he could slip in and set fire to it. But these were mere fantasies. Even if he could bring it off, he knew his family would not be able to get away with it. That seemed to leave him only one option.

"I want to be a eunuch like Xiaode Zhang!" Liujin declared to his father. "If I enter the palace, we can surely take our revenge someday!"

"You don't know what you're talking about," Sun Huaibao said. "I'd rather not take revenge if it means turning you into a cripple."

"But I want revenge!" Liujin insisted, wiping away his tears. "I will enter the palace and make you proud!"

Sun Huaibao also wept. "If you have it cut off," he gestured toward Liujin's groin, "the pain will kill you!"

"I can bear the pain!" Liujin clenched his fists. "I'll do anything for revenge!"

"Sometimes things go wrong, and people just die!"

"Even death is better than living in this way!"

Sun Huaibao sighed deeply and fell silent.

After this conversation Liujin was often lost in thought. In his mind he became a head eunuch who enjoyed the Emperor's favor. Like Xiao Dezhang, he came home in grandeur to settle accounts with his enemies in the village. No sooner had he arrived than Shang Buyin came to beg for mercy, kneeling and kowtowing nonstop. Liujin vowed to turn his dream into reality.

3. The Castration

"Dad, I'll kill myself if you don't let me do it!" Liujin said to his father. His mother was not home.

"This is no joke!" Sun Huaibao said. "If something goes wrong..." He began pacing up and down the room.

"I'll do whatever you tell me!"

"Well, you must not breathe a word to your mother, you know."

Liujin understood. His mother did not want him to be a eunuch and would do anything to stop it. They had to keep her in the dark about it.

From ancient Chinese records inscribed on bones and tortoise shells, we learn that victors in tribal wars sometimes had their prisoners castrated as a form of punishment. According to the Confucian classic *Rites of Zhou*, eunuchs emerged as a "profession" more than three thousand years ago. In the Qing Dynasty the court had an institution in charge of the recruitment of eunuchs, and a few households in Beijing specialized in handling such affairs for generations. However, in many cases castration was carried out "in private", especially among poverty-stricken families. The procedure was crude and brutal, often resulting in death. If the boy survived, his family would report the matter to the county yamen and have his name entered into a waiting list.

Many methods of castration were adopted. As a general rule the boy must be deprived of his manhood at an early age, for a technique that worked on a child might cause death in an adult. To become a eunuch the boy must not only have his genitals removed but also lose his reproductive function and sexual traits completely.

In certain remote areas the "castration knot" technique was once widely adopted. People used a hemp thread to tie a tight knot at the root of the baby boy's testicles, thereby obstructing the growth of his reproductive system. The testicles gradually atrophied until they could be easily removed. The boy retained his penis for urination.

A more bizarre method usually carried out by a babysitter: The babysitter would knead and squeeze the boy's testicles until he felt completely numb down there, then increase the pressure until the testicles were crushed.

There was also a way to deprive the sexual organs of their function without removing them. In this case the baby boy was given an oral medicine with an anaesthetic effect, then stabbed in testicles by a needle. Gradually the testicles lost their function, and castration was considered successful.

However, functional castration techniques did not always achieve the desired effect. There were stories of incompletely castrated eunuchs who retained their sexual function and got involved in scandalous affairs in the Imperial Court. Thus in successive dynasties almost all eunuchs chosen to enter the palace had to undergo a thorough castration, with their genitals completely removed.

In the early years of Emperor Guangxu's reign two households in Beijing were authorized to castrate and recruit eunuchs for the imperial court: the Bi family at Kuaijisi Alley of Nanchang Street and "Dagger Liu" at Fangzhuan Alley of Di'anmennei Street. Bi and Liu, who both enjoyed the status of a seventh-rank official (equivalent to a county magistrate), provided the palace with at least forty eunuchs every year. They almost monopolized the eunuch business. If a family wanted to send their boy into the palace, they would take him to Bi or Liu. If considered bright and good-looking, the boy would undergo castration if it had not already been done "in private".

House of the Bi family on Kuaijisi Alley of Beichang Road

The operation was generally safe in the houses of Bi and Liu, for people there had achieved a level of proficiency by constant practice; at least they always sterilized the knife by heating it over the fire.

In the 26th year of the Guangxu reign, two years before Liujin was born, the Bi and Liu houses lost their lucrative job. The castration of would-be eunuchs was assigned to the Office of Palace Justice under the Imperial Household Department located at the north end of Beichang Street.

Apparently Sun Huaibao had made up his mind. He spoke little and looked grim all day.

One early morning before the Mid-Autumn Festival Liujin got up to find his father standing pale-faced at the door. "Your mother has left for the yard," he muttered, not daring to look Liujin in the eye.

Liujin realized the moment had come. He would be castrated that day. All of a sudden Sun Huaibao bent over and began to cry. After a while he stopped and got on his feet. He laid out a few pieces of paper on the matted kang and took a sharpened razor in his hand.

"Dad, I'm ready." Liujin took off his trousers and lay down.

"Liujin!" His father whispered softly.

"Yes, Dad!" Liujin answered in a clear voice, staring at the roof.

"Keep still! Don't move!"

"I won't move!" Liujin nodded emphatically.

With beads of perspiration forming on his forehead, Sun Huaibao tied up Liujin's hands and feet with a rope. The young boy broke into a cold sweat, suddenly seized with terror. The coarse cotton shirt on his back was drenched.

Sun Huaibao looked at his son nervously. "Brace up, my boy." He almost choked on his words. He tightened his grip on the handle of the razor. With one hand he fumbled between Liujin's legs to take hold of his genitals, and with the other hand he brought down the razor. Blood oozed out from between Liujin's legs and dripped all over the kang. His body twitching in agony, Liujin uttered a shrill cry and blacked out.

Sun Huaibao dropped the razor to the ground and stood there in a daze, staring at his son's face drained of all color. Then he came to his senses and began to move frantically. He changed the sheets of paper under Liujin's body, wiped off the blood from the wound, and covered the boy with a blanket. He had no idea what else to do, though he had consulted the relatives of eunuchs in a neighboring village.

The door was suddenly pushed open. It was Liujin's big uncle, who had just learned the correct procedure from the nearby Nanliumu Village. He heated the sesame oil he had brought and threw in a few pieces of prickly ash. When the prickly ash got burnt, he removed the oil from the fire and waited for it to cool off. Then he took a piece of paper, dipped it in the oil, and placed it between Liujin's legs. The oiled paper served as a kind of bandage that must be changed frequently.

The sesame oil was put back on the fire. The severed genitals were carefully boiled, wrapped up in a piece of paper, and put into a container filled with chaff. After a while the string tying up the packet was pulled gently, a ritual performed to signify a "rise" in the boy's future career.

All eunuchs attached great importance to their mutilated genitals, which they preserved carefully at home. Whether they eventually achieved high status or remained poor all their life, they wanted to be buried with the genitals placed between their legs, so that they would be reborn a complete man to enjoy a prosperous afterlife. This practice had long been held sacred among eunuchs, and Liujin's father and uncle knew better than to ignore it.

Liujin's mother came home that day to find the house packed with villagers. The moment she realized what had happened, she threw herself on the kang and broke into an uncontrollable wail. Then she turned her tearful face to her husband, her eyes burning with fury. He took her into his arms and wept silently, not daring to look her in the face. "Let's take good care of our boy!" he finally said. Liujin was lying on the kang, still unconscious.

At the news many sympathetic neighbors called on the family until the courtyard was filled with people. Many uttered deep sighs, and a few elderly women wept out of pity. "It's lucky for the poor boy that you've done it in autumn," someone said to Sun Huaibao. "Otherwise it would be hard for him to lie in bed all day!"

Liujin remained in a coma for three days. For two months he could not get up from bed. He lay perfectly still at first, as the slightest movement gave him a piercing pain. The pain gradually subsided. During this time the oil-soaked paper covering his wound had to be changed regularly, and he had to prepare for the searing pain when the paper was torn off.

What Liujin went through was perhaps typical of those who were castrated "in private". After the genitals were cut off with a sharp knife, a siphon, usually a goose's quill, was planted in the urethra to prevent it from getting blocked. It took about a hundred days for the wound to heal. Medicated plasters should be applied regularly, but if they were not available, such as in the case of Liujin, people used paper treated with wax, sesame oil, and prickly ash powder. After the wound festered, new flesh would grow. Throughout the child lay in bed unable to move, kept dry by plant ash placed underneath his body. Though plant ash was replaced several times a day, the child often developed bedsores. When he finally got out of bed, he was often haggard and skinny, and had a good chance of fainting the first time he walked out of the house.

When Sun Huaibao came to change the oiled paper one morning, he frowned, staring at Liujin's wound. "Now what shall I do?" he muttered to himself.

"What's the matter, Dad?" asked Liujin.

"This is my fault. I should have changed the paper sooner. It's stuck to the wound. What shall I do?"

"Tear it off, Dad!"

"Can you take the pain, my boy?"

"Yes I can!" Liujin said, clenching his teeth.

Sun Huaibao took hold of the paper and yanked forcefully. With a cry of pain Liujin passed out, for the paper had come off together with his flesh and blood.

A few days later the wound began to fester. Not knowing what to do, Sun Huaibao hurried to Nanliumu, where several families had sent eunuchs to Beijing. He was lucky enough to find an old eunuch named Dong Menglan, who had just returned home from Beijing.

"There's no need to worry," Dong said after hearing him out. "Everything is fine with your boy. I congratulate you!"

"What are you talking about?" Sun Huaibao thought Dong was making fun of him.

"It always works in this way," the old eunuch explained. "Only after the wound has festered and formed pus will it start to heal."

Greatly relieved, Sun Huaibao came back home. He killed the only hen in the house to cook broth for Liujin. Some relatives also brought food, which Sun Huaibao cooked carefully and fed to the boy with a spoon.

For two months Liujin was unable to move. Liujin had to endure excruciating pain when relieving himself. He felt as if the bones in his body had turned to cinder and could not help crying out in agony at the slightest movement. A neighbor named Zhang Suocheng was hired to take care of him. Zhang, an old man who had worked as a hired hand all his life, showed genuine concern for the boy.

The castration was a success. At the end of two months Liujin finally got up from bed. Weak and limp, he had to lean on the wall to prevent himself from falling. He was totally unprepared for the catastrophic news his father would soon bring home.

"Heaven is blind!" Sun Huaibao staggered into the house and fell with a flop on the kang. "Your dad is a beast!" he muttered to Liujin. "Your dad is a scoundrel!"

"Dad?" Liujin stared at him in dismay.

"I've ruined your life, my son!" Sun Huaibao started to weep, stamping his feet and beating his chest like a madman. "I must have done something terrible in my past life to deserve all this!"

"What's the matter with you?" asked his wife.

"Our boy has suffered for nothing! It's all my fault!"

"Tell us what's happened!" Liujin's mother grew impatient.

"The Emperor has stepped down!" As if exhausted by uttering these words, Sun Huaibao collapsed on the kang again.

"What?"

"The Emperor was overthrown by rebels! Our boy will never enter

Empress Dowager Longyu (seated in the middle)

Emperor Xuantong, Pu Yi, who abdicated a month after Sun Yaoting's castration

the palace! They don't need eunuchs anymore!"

The news rendered Liujin's mother speechless. They had castrated their child at the risk of his life, dreaming of a bright future for him, but all of a sudden the world was turned upside down. If eunuchs were no longer needed, Liujin was simply a cripple. How could he support himself when he grew up?"

Lying on the kang, Liujin heard everything. He felt drained of all strength, his mind a total blank.

History often plays cruel pranks on ordinary people. Emperor Xuantong's abdication had taken place two month before, but news from the imperial capital did not travel fast to the small village where the Sun family lived. An armed uprising in the city of Wuchang had touched off the famous 1911 Revolution, which put an end to Qing, the last imperial Dynasty of China. The last "imperial edict", issued by Empress Dowager Longyu, proclaimed the abdication of Emperor Xuantong. All this took place a month after Liujin's castration. Even if news of the revolution had spread instantly to the village, it would still have been too late.

Li, a married young man in his twenties living at Nanliumu, had castrated himself several months before. Recommended by a fellow villager, old eunuch Dong Menglan, Li went to the capital to wait on a high-ranking eunuch in the palace. After the revolution Li received a "severance fee" of twenty silver dollars and came back home. He enjoyed talking about his life in the imperial capital. "You wouldn't believe how many rules one has to obey in the palace!" he once remarked. But the villagers often ridiculed him. "First you got married, then you became a eunuch. Now look what you've got yourself into!" Sun Huaibao knew nothing about the Emperor's abdication until he overheard Li bantering with a neighbor.

Li gradually found out to his distress that life could never be the same again after his return from Beijing. In summer days the villagers often went naked down the river to catch fish. One day, when Li slipped out of his trousers by the river, people around all burst out laughing. "Take a look at him!" one of them jeered. "He's not afraid to take off his trousers because he has nothing to hide between his legs!" Li never divorced his wife, but they did not get along well. He died prematurely a few years afterward.

As the initial shock subsided, Liujin calmed down and did not complain to his parents. "If I had done it at six," he said, "I would have entered the Imperial Palace already."

Sun Huaibao would not give up on his boy. The road to the Imperial Palace might be permanently blocked, but there must be other roads to a better life. "I'll take good care of him!" he declared. "The boy will learn to read and write. He will be somebody when he grows up!"

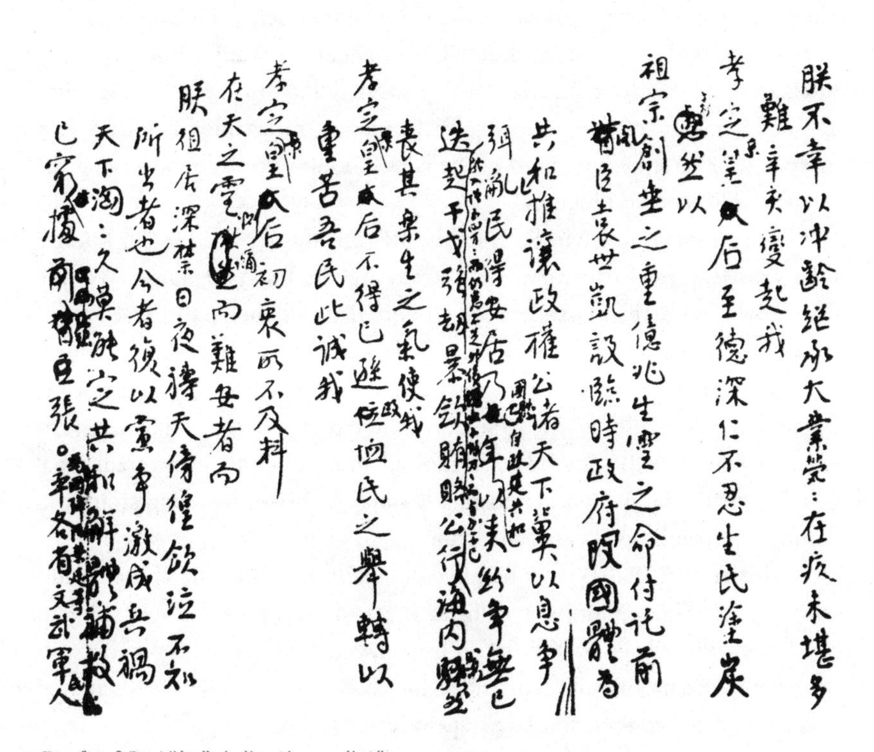

Draft of Pu Yi's "abdication edict"

4. Private School

Sun Huaibao made up his mind. "My son will learn to be a scholar! That's the only way to make a poor family like ours prosper!" He went to see Fu Xueshun, a private tutor in the village. "Please accept Liujin as your pupil. He is smart and sensible and respects the elders."

"All right, I'll take him." Fu agreed with alacrity.

Though his family was not rich, Mr. Fu enjoyed high prestige in the village for his knowledge and learning. On important occasions such as weddings and funerals he was the indispensable master of ceremonies. The villagers, mostly illiterate, relied on him to write invitations and formal letters, and often consulted him when selecting the site of a house or tomb. His status as the learned scholar of the village was widely acknowledged.

Along with a few other boys, Liujin began to study under Mr. Fu's tutelage. Each family paid Mr. Fu five silver dollars in lieu of tuition fee. The boy in charge of the group was Fu Chongwu, nicknamed Baldie. A very lively boy, he later became head of the village. Liujin's best friend among the pupils was his cousin Liuchun.

After a short time Mr. Fu Xueshun left and was replaced by Fu Xuelan. Like great figures in history, the new master had a style name, Wenpo. Conversant with the classics and well versed in all the traditional arts of music, chess, painting and calligraphy, he enjoyed widespread fame as a talented scholar. He modeled his handwriting on a well-known calligrapher Zheng Banqiao, and was able to sell his calligraphic works at Liulichang, the antiques market of Beijing. He also showed an intense interest in traditional Chinese medicine. After a period of self-study he began traveling around in Beijing and Tianjin practicing medicine.

This erudite master now had five disciples: one from the Gong family, one from the Shang family, two from the Sun family, and a very diligent pupil from the village of Xiliumu. His son, Shuangshen, who was born in the year of the monkey, also attended his classes. The pupils always arrived on time to listen to their tutor's eloquent lectures.

Mr. Fu proved an excellent teacher who was both strict and patient. The boys made steady progress under his guidance. Liujin completed three volumes of *The Book of Poetry* in a short time. He could read out all the poems aloud although he did not always understand the underlying message.

Mr. Fu won the admiration of his pupils. Among other things, he had a highly retentive memory. It was said that after getting a copy of Zhang Zhongjing's *Study of Pathogenic Cold* from Tianjin, he read it carefully for a few days until he knew the whole book by heart. The boy from Xiliumu, who was the same age as Liujin, excelled in his ability to write poetic quatrains. Vowing to catch up with the boy, Liujin worked hard and soon became quite good at composing poetic couplets.

The composition of poetic couplets was one of the basic skills for a pupil to acquire in classical training. The teacher posed the question by offering an "upper line", and the pupil must come up with a corresponding "lower line". For starters the pupils learned to respond to single words, using "wind" against "rain", "heaven" against "earth", and "eating meal" against "wearing clothes". As the pupils grew proficient, the teacher gradually increased the number of words in the upper line.

Liujin seemed to have an aptitude for such wordplay. One day, when Mr. Fu gave the upper line, "The spring breeze carries the twittering of swallows", Liujin responded with "The rain forces the croaking of frogs." "Not bad," said Mr. Fu, "though I would substitute 'induce' for 'force'."

Mr. Fu taught in a leisurely manner, always wearing a smile. He never really got angry with a pupil who gave an awkward answer to his question. Once he offered the upper line "spring swallow", and a pupil responded with "spring bird". "Why don't you use your brain?" Mr. Fu said. "Think harder."

Liujin raised his hand, and Mr. Fu was pleased. "You have a try."

"My lower line is 'autumn duck'".

"Not bad. Let me give you another one: Light comes from the sun and the moon."

After a while Liujin replied, "Good comes from women and children."

The above couplet plays on the composition of some Chinese characters: just as "sun" and "moon" combined becomes "light", "women" and "children" combined becomes "good".

Mr. Fu offered another line. "The tiger moves across the snow, leaving footprints like plum blossoms".

"The chicken perks on the bridge, leaving footprints like three-part leaves."

"Your line is fine except for one word," commented Mr. Fu. "Why don't you say 'crane' instead of 'chicken'? That would make the line sound more graceful!"

One of Mr. Fu's favorite heroes was Zhang Zhidong, a renowned court official who led the Westernization Movement in the latter half of the 19th century in an attempt to revitalize the empire. "Although he was not a top candidate in the county-level examination, he had truly great learning, " Mr. Fu remarked. When discoursing on the art of writing poetry, he told the following story about Zhang. "At nine he went to take a local examination, and the examiner had him brought over for a test. The moment the examiner finished the upper line, 'The young pupil from Nanpi County is nine,' Zhang came up with a lower line, 'The Son of Heaven in Beijing City lives ten thousand years.' The examiner was amazed. Only a bright and diligent boy like Zhang Zhidong could have done such a feat! Now you may not be as talented as Mr. Zhang, but the least you can do is to emulate his diligence as a child!"

Mr. Fu charged an annual tuition of fifteen dollars, which the Sun family could hardly afford. Sun Huaibao did farm work on eighty mu of land owned by Mr. Fu, and Liujin's mother cooked for the Fu family. In return, the boy was exempted from tuition. Both sides were happy with the arrangement.

Mr. Fu was very fond of Liujin and took pity on him for what he had gone through. One day he suggested to Sun Huaibao, "The Imperial Palace in Beijing doesn't seem to need eunuchs anymore, and your boy cannot do heavy farm work. If he has nothing better to do, why don't you let him study medicine with me?"

"Well, we'll wait and see," Sun Huaibao said noncommittally. He was expecting something to come up to change his son's fate for the better.

Something did come up. One day Sun Huaibao was lamenting Liujin's plight in his big brother's house. "Yes," his big brother said with a sigh. "Your boy went through hell for nothing!" Then an idea occurred to him. "Maybe I can find a way out for him!" He had an in-law who was acquainted with He Deyuan, a eunuch in the Northern Mansion, the residence of the Emperor's father. He asked the in-law to write a letter to He asking him to find a place for Liujin.

The reply came quickly. The message was short but encouraging: "Send him to the capital!"

At the news Liujin was so excited that he did not sleep a wink that night. He Deyuan, an illiterate, low-ranking eunuch, had once waited on Pu Yi's mother and was therefore no ordinary person in the eyes of the Sun family. With his help, Liujin suddenly seemed to have a very promising future.

After careful consideration the family made up their mind. They sold what little property they had to raise money for the trip to Beijing. Liujin would travel by train, accompanied by his big brother. The tickets cost them one dollar twenty cents.

Liujin's mother saw the two brothers off at the county seat of Jinghai. At the news Mr. Fu left the village on his donkey and arrived at Jinghai, where he took up lodging at a drugstore and sent for Liujin.

At the drugstore Liujin met Mr. Fu. After giving him some fatherly advice, Mr. Fu handed him five silver dollars. "Take this. You'll need money on your trip."

"No one has ever been so kind to me!" Liujin fell on his knees and kowtowed to Mr. Fu. "I'm forever indebted to you, master!" With tears in his eyes Liujin bade his teacher farewell.

2

PRINCE ZAI TAO'S MANSION

1. Arriving in the Capital

It was the 16th day of the 12th lunar month in 1916, the fifth year of the Republic. The imperial capital was dressed in white amid heavy snow and strong wind. Carrying a small baggage roll on his back, Liujin, or Sun Yaoting, stood with his brother before the giant red gate of the Northern Mansion north of Shichahai Lake. They were covered in a thick layer of snow, and even their eyebrows had turned white. After staring at the gate for a long time, they finally plucked up the courage to walk up and knock on it.

The gate opened slightly, and a bespectacled man wearing a felt hat popped out his head to scrutinize the two brothers. "Who are you?"

Though ignorant of the codes of behavior in a princely mansion, they put on their best manners by bowing with clasped hands. "We've come to see Mr. He. Please take the trouble to pass on the message for us!"

"Where are you from?" The man with the felt hat continued to study them coolly, with no intention to open the gate.

Sun Yaoting put on a big smile. "We are from our hometown, Jinghai County."

The man told them to wait, and the gate clanked shut.

After a while He Deyuan came out to greet them. "Here you are! I was thinking you'd come one of these days."

Sun Yaoting was happy and relieved to see the old eunuch, who at the moment almost seemed like a long-lost friend. Not daring to say anything, the two brothers entered the gate and followed the old eunuch into a side

Prince Zai Tao's Mansion

room. There they learned that He Deyuan's job in the mansion was to wait on the Emperor's younger brother Pu Jie, a very smart and diligent boy of seven. The old eunuch gave them some water to drink and told them to stay in the room while he went around looking for a position for Sun Yaoting. "Do not leave the room," he warned. "Never go anywhere else in this house!"

His big brother soon left Beijing for home, and Sun Yaoting stayed alone in the room like a prisoner. Three days later He Deyuan finally brought good news. "Hey, you're very lucky! Prince Zai Tao's house happens to need someone, and I've recommended you. You'd better go there as soon as you finish eating. It's not a good idea to be late!"

Sun Yaoting began to panic. After all, it was the first time he had left his home village on his own. "What shall I do when I get there?"

"It's quite easy," He Deyuan said. "I've arranged everything for you. A friend of mine has passed on the message, so you'll have no problem."

"But I'm afraid of getting lost in the capital. Could you please take me there? You'd be doing me a big favor!"

"All right," He Deyuan agreed. "I'll take you there, though I've many other things to do."

"Thank you so much," Sun Yaoting bowed with clasped hands, feeling genuinely grateful.

Late in the day Sun Yaoting followed He Deyuan to Prince Zai Tao's mansion. When they got to the main hall, the old eunuch stopped and turned to him. "Stay here and keep silent! I'll go in first."

Sun Yaoting stood there staring at the spacious main hall divided into nine sections. A short moment later He Deyuan returned with a smile. "The prince is home. You may go in now. Don't forget to kowtow when they take you to the prince!"

Stepping into the hall, Sun Yaoting looked up to see a tall, strongly built man in the middle seat, wearing a silk gown and a pair of cloth shoes. He had a square face with a ruddy complexion, and his erect figure in the chair made a towering presence. "This is the Master," He Deyuan said. Sun Yaoting fell on his knees and kowtowed several times.

Zai Tao turned to He Deyuan. "So it's you who brought him here?" He had a stentorian voice with a slight tinge of hoarseness.

"Yes, Your Highness. He's from my home village. He's very honest."

"Get up," Zai Tao told Sun Yaoting. Then he turned to a servant. "Get him something to eat."

Sun Yaoting was overjoyed, knowing that he had been accepted.

"Have you brought your bedding?" The prince was surprisingly attentive to details.

"Yes." Sun Yaoting pointed to the small baggage roll on the ground.

"It looks too thin." Zai Tao sent for his housekeeper at once. "Are there any more quilts in the storeroom? Get one for him at once."

By this time Sun Yaoting had already learned the basics of palace etiquette from He Deyuan, so he knelt again to express his gratitude. He was happy to have such a kindly master.

"What's your name?"

"My name's Sun Yaoting."

"You need another name for use in this house," Zai Tao said. "Let's see. You'll be called Shunshou." The name consisted of two auspicious characters, "shun" for smoothness and "shou" for longevity. Sun Yaoting found out later that "shou" designated a rank of junior eunuchs to which he belonged.

"Now you need to pay respects to the Mistress," He Deyuan said, and Sun Yaoting followed him out of the hall. He Deyuan told him that the prince had agreed to pay him one and a half silver dollars each month.

Coming before the room of the princess-consort, He Deyuan whispered, "The family name of our Mistress is Jiang. Her late father, Jiang Chongli, was a high-ranking minister. Mind your tongue when you speak to her!"

They walked into the room to find the princess-consort sitting on the kang. He Deyuan saluted her while Sun Yaoting stood behind. The princess-consort was a young woman with a handsome face and creamy white skin. She looked Yaoting up and down, then turned to He and asked him a few questions. After a while Sun Yaoting felt very tired, so he sat down on the floor. "So you have seated yourself?" said the princess-consort. "Feeling sleepy? You'd rather lie down, wouldn't you?" She spoke Pekinese with a little southern accent. She seemed more amused than offended.

"I'm tired," Sun Yaoting explained.

"How can you sit down before the Mistress?" He Deyuan scolded him in a mild tone, then turned to the princess-consort. "He's still a child and knows no manners!"

"Don't sit on the floor!" the female attendants standing around chanted in unison.

"All right," Sun Yaoting got to his feet and brushed off the dust off his bottom. Again the attendants rebuked him. "Don't you know how to talk? Do not say 'all right'. Say 'yes'!"

"Yes!" Sun Yaoting said immediately.

Just then Zai Tao walked in, and he burst out laughing along with the others in the room. He then called over an old eunuch named Zhang and pointed to Sun Yaoting. "This is Shunshou. He has just arrived today. You can take him as your last disciple."

"Yes, master." The old eunuch bowed to Zai Tao, then eyed Sun Yaoting closely.

"From now on, you'll learn everything from him," Zai Tao told Sun Yaoting.

At this Sun Yaoting knelt and kowtowed three times to Zhang, his first eunuch-mentor, calling him "master." Zhang waved his hand. "Don't call me master. Call me elder brother instead."

Zhang had been a eunuch attendant for over forty years. His job was to wait on Zai Tao and keep him company, following him everywhere. In the house he was known as "Escort Zhang", and no one remembered his full name. Before Sun Yaoting's arrival, there had been only four old eunuchs in the house: Escort Zhang, Jia Runqing, Li Shun'an, and Liu Jiexuan. Every morning Zhang ate breakfast with an old woman named Cai, who had been Zai Tao's wet nurse. These two old servants seemed to be the most respected people in the house apart from the princely couple.

Without much work to do, Zhang often slipped out of the house by the rear gate to play chess or mahjong on Louyi Alley. He called Jia Runqing "master" and the other eunuchs "brother". He alone used to occupy three rooms: a dining room, a living room, and a bedroom, but now he had to share his bedroom with Sun Yaoting. Despite their age difference, they got along well and became good friends.

The oldest eunuch, Jia Runqing, or Mingshun as he was known in the house, was a native of Hengshui in Hebei. He had a sonorous voice, an agile mind, and great practical abilities. On important occasions such as wedding or birthday celebrations in the princely mansions, he often acted as a messenger and coordinator. Nothing ever went amiss when he was in charge.

"Shunshou," said Jia one day. "Now that you have joined us here, you should be called nest-pad!"

"What's a nest pad?" asked Sun Yaoting.

"You want to know what a nest pad is? Well, you must have seen a bird hatching eggs, or a sow giving birth to piglets? Nest pad is the name for the last hatchling or the last piglet to come out."

This brought a roar of laughter among the eunuchs. After that Sun Yaoting was often called by that nickname in the absence of Zai Tao and his wife.

Sun Yaoting's first assignment was to help the princess-consort comb her hair. After getting up in the morning, he went immediately to her room. He finished his job around ten o'clock and was free for the rest of the day.

Zai Tao soon decided that Sun Yaoting was quite honest and dependable. Not well unacquainted with the rules of proper behavior, the young boy nevertheless seemed trustworthy due to his naivete and simple-mindedness. Zai Tao even allowed his two sons, Pu Jia and Pu An, to play with him.

"What do you do in the evening?" Zai Tao asked Sun Yaoting one day.

"I don't have anything to do, so I just play!"

"And who do you play with?"

"I play with Second Young Master and Third Young Master."

"You've been here for some time and should start to learn some manners. For example, you can't use the word 'I' for yourself; instead, when you answer a question, start your reply with 'your humble servant'."

"Yes! Your humble servant understands!"

Zai Tao then sent for his two daughters. The girls bore a striking resemblance to each other. "Now tell me," Zai Tao said. "Which is the First Young Mistress, and which is the Second Young Mistress?"

"Well," Sun Yaoting hesitated for a few seconds but finally gave the right answer. However, when he saw them a few days later, he got them mixed up again. Then he noticed that the elder sister had a small mole at the tip of her mouth. She married young and died shortly afterward.

In their spare time Zai Tao and his wife liked to chat with the attending women and eunuchs. Because of his ignorance and naivete, Sun Yaoting often made a fool of himself to the amusement of everyone present.

One evening he was waiting on the princess-consort when he sneezed. "Go out and take a look at the sky, Shunshou, " she said with a smile. "Is it clear or cloudy?"

Sun Yaoting ran out of the room and soon returned. "Your humble servant has taken a look outside. I see a bright moon in the sky, so it must be clear."

At his words everyone in the room burst into laughter. He looked at them in puzzlement.

"Let me tell you a secret which you must not disclose to anyone!" said the princess-consort, still laughing. "Haven't you heard the saying, 'The sneeze of a dog forecasts a clear day'?"

Zai Tao, with his wife and children, had three meals a day. For breakfast they had pancake, cookies, bread, and deep-fried dough sticks. Chinese dishes were served at lunch, but Zai Tao always had Western food for supper. The servants, on the other hand, had only two meals a day. In the morning they ate noodles, and the second meal was served between three and four o'clock in the afternoon. As Sun Yaoting later learned, this practice was modeled after the regimen of eunuchs in the Imperial Palace.

Though a little unused to having two meals a day, Sun Yaoting was happy to eat noodles for breakfast. At home he would consider himself lucky if they had cornmeal porridge for lunch. Zai Tao, who seemed to be an expert cook, sometimes went down to the kitchen to oversee the preparation of quick-boiled gravy for the noodles. For the first few days Sun Yaoting gobbled down several large bowls of noodles every morning while the others stared at him in disbelief. However, continuous overeating of the same meal gradually took its toll. He grew so satiated with noodles that the moment he took up his bowl in the morning, he felt convulsions in his stomach.

In the morning Sun Yaoting was free to roam around in the house. One day he strolled into Pu Jia's room to find him eating bread for breakfast. "You want to taste this?" Pu Jia asked by way of politeness. The proper thing to do was to decline the offer, but Sun Yaoting took some bread and ate it, not knowing any better.

One day Zai Tao was eating mutton dumplings with Sun Yaoting in attendance. "Master, the food in your bowl smells so good!" Sun Yaoting said.

"All right, come on and have a bite."

"Your humble servant thanks the master!" Sun Yaoting picked up a pair of chopsticks and put two dumplings into his mouth.

"Shunshou, do you eat this at home?"

"No, your humble servant has never eaten it."

"Is it delicious?"

"Very delicious!"

"Well, have some more if you like."

Sun Yaoting picked up the chopsticks again and ate his fill while Zai Tao watched him with a smile.

The other servants in the house liked to make fun of Sun Yaoting. They would make him pronounce the name of something and laugh at his Tianjin accent, which they found very funny. Quite a few things, such as the sweet potato, had different names in Beijing and Tianjin dialects, and this was also cause for ridicule for Sun Yaoting. To all this derision and mockery he just responded with a good-natured grin.

Though the other servants often amused themselves at Sun Yaoting's expense, they meant no harm. In fact, he soon established himself in their good graces, for he treated all of them with respect and never loafed on his job. The eunuchs addressed each other brother regardless of age difference. One day a eunuch said to him, "Nest-pad, you've never left the house since you came here. There is much fun out in the street!"

Sun Yaoting felt tempted. When he learned that the Protect-the-Nation Temple nearby had a fair on the 7th and 8th days of each month, he went to the princess-consort to ask for a leave. "Your humble servant would like to go and have a look at the Protect-the-Nation Temple."

"Who will go with you?"

"Brother Jia."

"You may go, but don't stay out too late." The princess-consort was good-natured and never made things difficult for the servants.

They found the temple fully packed, with people coming and going in every direction and vendors hawking their wares and all kinds of refreshments. A peddler selling candied haws on sticks caught Sun Yaoting's eye, and Jia was cajoled into buying one for him. Nibbling on the stick and staring at all the hustle and bustle around him, Sun Yaoting had a good time until he knocked into a wire pole and got an egg-sized bump on his forehead. For fear that he would run into further trouble, Jia took him back.

Zai Tao was about to leave the house when the two eunuchs came in. "Shunshou," he said, "Have Blossom Pair harnessed to Number Three Carriage at two this afternoon, and tell Sissy Li to make ready to drive it."

"Yes, yes!" Sun Yaoting answered hastily, staring downward to hide the bump on his forehead.

Zai Tao looked at him doubtfully. "Shunshou, repeat what I've just told you."

Sun Yaoting grew nervous. "Two o'clock this afternoon, Blossom Pair and... and Sister Li..." He tried again but still could not get the words right.

Smiling, the princess-consort said to her husband, "Don't worry, you can leave. He understands your order even though he cannot repeat it."

After Zai Tao left, the princess-consort told Sun Yaoting to state what he was supposed to do. She was puzzled when he spoke fluently without missing a word. "Why did you stutter just now?" she asked.

"Your humble servant was afraid that the master might notice it," he pointed at the swelling on his forehead. "I bumped into a wire pole at the temple fair!"

The princess-consort laughed. "So you know what Blossom Pair is?"

"Yes, it's the name for two of the master's favorite horses."

"And you know who Sissy Li is?"

"Yes, he's the son of Mr. Li, the steward." Sun Yaoting knew both the father and the son quite well.

He Deyuan nodded with approval when he saw Sun Yaoting a few days later. "It's not easy being a eunuch, you know. From my experience, I've found out that no matter how capable, smart or good-tempered you are, you may still fail to win the master's favor. However, you seem to have a special gift that makes people like you. Maybe one of these days you'll get lucky and rise above the likes of us!"

Sun Yaoting said nothing but prayed silently for these words to come true.

2. The Imperial Uncle

Though several years had gone by since the fall of the Manchu Dynasty and the founding of the Republic, Prince Zai Tao's residence located at Longtujing Alley in western Beijing retained much of its former grandeur and magnificence. When going out Zai Tao rode in his carriage or limousine. On his return the driver always honked loudly before they reached the alley, and the gate to the house would be wide open by the time they got there.

At the gate stood fully armed guards dressed in uniform, who were assigned by the Republican government; some soldiers were also stationed inside the house. Zai Tao was Pu Yi's uncle by lineage, and successive rulers of the Republic treated him with great respect.

The mansion had a well-planned layout. A pair of stone lions, a male and a female, greeted visitors at the gate, which opened to the west, facing the residence of Prince Qing across a broad asphalt road. One walked in through the gate to find "Janitor's Office" on both sides and "Steward's Office" just ahead. This design was similar to that of the Imperial Palace. Going farther, one saw the main hall with nine sections. On the western side was Zai Tao's dining room, and on the eastern wing, the bedrooms of his two daughters. A dozen meters to the west was a study, where the child Zai Tao had studied the classics under a private tutor. Pines, cypresses and fruit trees gave the spacious courtyard a pleasant shade in the summer.

A turn to the south took one to a courtyard where a big awning was kept all the year round, providing warmth in winter and coolness in summer. Next to this courtyard was a stage for theatrical performances. A plan to build a canopy over the stage was cancelled because of the 1911 Revolution. Walking west down the corridor, one came to the largest open space in the mansion. In winter the princess-consort and Pu Jia flew kites there, often with Sun Yaoting in attendance.

On top of a small hill in the rear stood a pavilion built many years ago, when Zai Tao was a minister in the Qing court. He liked to sit here on hot summer days. In front of the pavilion was a big fish pool, and a few more rooms stood to the west.

Prince Zai Tao, Pu Yi's seventh uncle

Keeping goldfish was one of Zai Tao's hobbies. He had several dozen fish tanks of various sizes, and he took care of his fish personally. In the morning he cleaned the tanks by dredging up fish dung, and in the evening he added fresh water to the tanks. He insisted on doing everything himself, though he sometimes told Sun Yaoting to fetch water for him. Every now and then he put his hand into the tanks to test water temperature. In summer he draped the tanks with linen to shade the fish, and in winter he had the tanks moved indoors. He often stopped in front of a tank and gazed at the goldfish for a long time.

Regardless of weather conditions, Zai Tao got up early for his morning exercises every day. On a piece of open ground under the wall about eight to nine meters long, he kicked the shuttlecock and practiced somersaults.

One day Sun Yaoting accompanied the princess-consort to the study, where they found Zai Tao in a pleasant mood. Patting him on the shoulder, Zai Tao said, "Shunshou, can you do the handstand?"

"No, your humble servant can't," Sun Yaoting answered timidly. He was not very athletic as a child.

"Come over here," ordered Zai Tao.

Sun Yaoting was made to stand close to the wall and place both hands on the ground. With Zai Tao helping him, he managed to stand on his hands, his feet resting against the wall. Zai Tao did not let him get down until he cried out, "I can't keep it up anymore!"

"Get up early tomorrow morning," Zai Tao said. "I'll teach you to do some physical exercise!"

"Yes!" Sun Yaoting answered. Early the next morning he came, a bit reluctantly, and was again made to do handstands by the wall.

There were many rooms behind the nine-section main building occupied by Zai Tao. Pu Jia had three of these rooms. The attending women, including Cai, occupied the rooms on the west wing. On the eastern side was a toilet for Zai Tao and his wife. In a small courtyard to the east lived the female servants who did cooking, washing and other chores. Zao Tao sometimes took a walk in this courtyard accompanied by Sun Yaoting.

There were two stables in the front courtyard. In one of them Zai Tao kept his two favorite horses, Painted Eye and Big Red Horse, each with a servant assigned exclusively to it. In summer the ground was covered with sand, and in winter the stable was draped over to provide shield against wind and snow. The two horses made fine steeds for the stout prince.

The other stable held seven or eight horses for drawing carriages. Among them was a large horse named Black Chrysanthemum, which neighed thunderously when it got excited. The Blossom Pair were two horses of the same size and appearance except that one was red and the other white. When in a good mood, Zai Tao harnessed his horses to a carriage and drove them out of the house, shouting orders and riding at full speed in the streets of Beijing.

As the horses knew their way around the city, Zai Tao sometimes let them roam aimlessly on the street. Occasionally Sun Yaoting was made to escort the princess-consort on such a free-rein ride. The two young masters of the house, Pu Jia and Pu An, were about seven or eight years old. For them Zai Tao bought two small Yili horses, which were lively and docile. The boys enjoyed riding on horseback in the courtyard. To leave the house they must be accompanied by the grooms, otherwise the servants would get punished. It was Sun Yaoting's responsibility to keep an eye on the young masters.

Most of the time Zai Tao traveled in his limousine, whose rear door seemed to have been designed to accentuate the status of the rider as it could only be shut from the outside by a servant. When going to the Imperial Palace, Zai Tao always rode in his limousine.

Sitting in his study one early morning, Zai Tao sent for Sun Yaoting. It was a spacious room bathed in sunlight. "I've been told that you can read and write. Is it true?"

"Your humble servant was tutored for a couple of years."

"Aha, so we have a young scholar here!" Zai Tao said, putting down the book in his hand.

"Your humble servant knows a few characters, that's all."

"Good, very good," Zai Tao nodded. "From now on I'll have you with me when I practice calligraphy here. Do you understand?"

"Your humble servant understands!"

After breakfast Zai Tao took a walk around the house and came back to the study. He sat down in front of his desk to practice calligraphy, with Sun Yaoting preparing the "four treasures of the study", i.e., writing brush, ink stick, ink slab, and paper. Zai Tao began to copy phrases from *Thousand-Character Primer*. Sun Yaoting noticed that one of the characters, Yi, had a missing stroke, so he pronounced it to draw Zai Tao's attention. But Zai Tao ignored him and went on writing.

Sun Yaoting thought he had to speak out. "Your humble servant has something to say but does not dare to say it."

"Humph," Zai Tao snorted.

"Master, you did not write the character Yi correctly! A stroke is missing!"

"Nothing is missing," Zai Tao said.

"A stroke is missing," Sun Yaoting insisted.

"Well, you can go and ask the Mistress!" Zai Tao said without looking up.

Sun Yaoting found the princess-consort in her room and explained the problem to her. "His Highness didn't put in the last stroke of the character Yi, but he said nothing was missing and told me to come here."

"There has to be a missing stroke in the character Yi in order to avoid infringing on His Majesty's name. This is something you must bear in mind. In an imperial examination, if anyone failed to observe the taboo on the Emperor's name, he would be beheaded!"

Sun Yaoting cringed at her last remark. "Now you understand, don't you?" Zai Tao asked when he came back to the study.

"Yes, your slave understands now. The Mistress told me that if I took part in the imperial examination, I would lose my head."

"Now you're talking!" Zai Tao gave him a quick glance and burst into a hearty laughter.

Unlike many other members of the imperial clan who led erratic, decadent lives, Zai Tao was a calculating man of great practical ability. He was absent from home most of the time. Rather than indulge himself in sensual pleasures, he worked hard cultivating influential friends and building a network of connections with governmental officials and military strongmen. His friends included Zhang Zuolin, the powerful warlord based in Northeast China and his son Zhang Xueliang, who later astounded the world by holding Chiang Kai-shek hostage in Xi'an. He often acted as a representative for the imperial clan, and Pu Yi relied heavily on him to handle affairs outside the palace.

Among the Manchu princes Zai Tao was one of the first to have telephones installed in his house. There was a switchboard with extensions in his study, his bedroom, and several offices. When something needed to be done by servants, he would pick up the phone, saying, "Get me the Janitor's Office." When the call got through, he would give his order. While playing in the courtyard, Sun Yaoting was sometimes summoned by a phone call to go and wait on Zai Tao.

Zai Tao seemed to be on good terms with President Li Yuanhong, who occasionally telephoned him at his house. It was Li who awarded Zai Tao a large medal about 13 inches in diameter. At the year's end the President sent an envoy to the Imperial Palace to offer New Year greetings to Pu Yi, who always chose Zai Tao to return the courtesy as his representative. Zai Tao would put on a tailcoat, leather shoes and the giant medal and leave for the President's office in his chauffeured limousine.

As representative of the imperial house Zai Tao received a monthly salary of eight hundred dollars from the Republican government. One of his main duties was acting as a go-between for President Li Yuanhong and Pu Yi.

When Feng Guozhang succeeded Li as the President, he awarded Zai Tao the title of general with a monthly salary of six hundred dollars. Feng showed a strong interest in cultivating Zai Tao's friendship and paid him frequent visits, but Zai Tao seemed to treat Feng with a cool politeness.

From his six-hundred-dollar salary Zai Tao gave one dollar to Sun Yaoting, who was overjoyed when he first received it. Shortly afterward Zai Tao's salary was raised to eight hundred dollars, and he increased the tips to the servants. As a senior eunuch Jia Runqing got five to ten dollars each month, and Sun Yaoting got two. "Fancy that!" Sun Yaoting bragged. "I get paid every month by President Feng!"

The eunuchs played an important role in running the household. Many guests had to butter up the eunuchs before they could secure a meeting with Zai Tao. A few prominent guests could make appointments by telephone, but most visitors had to wait at the Janitor's Office inside the main gate while the eunuch on duty went in to announce their arrival to Zai Tao. If Zai Tao did not want to see the visitor, the eunuch would say, "His Highness will not see you" or "His Highness is not in at the moment". The visitor who was granted a meeting would be led to a small study that Zai Tao used for receiving guests. Zai Tao had met quite a few distinguished guests there. Sun Yaoting remembered ushering in Premier Xiong Xilin and Jiang Guiti, Military Governor of Jehol.

Ladies from the families of other Manchu princes did not have to stop at the main gate but could go straight to the "Inner Janitor's Office". Zai Tao's nephews also enjoyed such privileged treatment. As for ladies from Prince Chun's house, they always went to the inner compound without being announced.

Zai Tao was a great fan of Beijing opera and an amateur performer of high caliber. Thanks to his proficiency in martial arts, which he had been practicing since early childhood, he played the role of Monkey King very well, dazzling the audience with continuous somersaults. Li Wangchun, a famous Beijing opera actor nicknamed "Living Monkey King", spent several months with Zai Tao learning to perform Longevity Peach Feast, a classic Monkey King drama.

Zai Tao also had a special penchant for playing female roles, notably Yang Guifei, an imperial consort in the Tang Dynasty whose fabulous beauty was a little on the plump side. In *Lady Yang Intoxicated*, Zai Tao played the consort, with eunuchs cast in the supporting roles. Even professional performers admired his graceful postures and full, mellow voice. He had a large number of fans in Beijing. When the curtain fell, a lot of people swarmed backstage in order to get a glimpse of "Lady Yang".

Zai Tao was not only a good performer but also an excellent teacher. Whenever he wanted to rehearse a play, the entire house was mobilized. Servants who had no dramatic training were assigned various supporting roles, and they always managed to carry it through with a little instruction from the prince. Jia Runqing told Sun Yaoting that the first time he was given a role to play he knew nothing about Beijing opera, but he became quite good at it after Zai Tao gave him a few lessons.

Princess Rongshougulun, Empress Dowager Cixi's adopted daughter

Once Zai Tao ordered all the eunuchs and servants who worked in his study to join him in staging a military play titled *The Iron Rooster*. Though all the players were amateurs, they used real weapons instead of props for acrobatic fighting. Their performance was far superior to that given by ordinary amateur groups.

For birthday celebrations it was customary for the Manchu princes to hire a famous Beijing opera troupe for in-house performance. On his thirtieth birthday, Zai Tao staged his favorite plays with himself cast in the leading role. Guests from all the princely mansions in Beijing sat down in front of the stage to enjoy one show after another, sipping tea and eating watermelon seeds. The performance lasted from two o'clock in the afternoon to nearly three the next morning, cheered and clapped by the enthusiastic audience. Sun Yaoting spotted Princess Rongshougulun, the Regent's eldest daughter who had been adopted by Empress Dowager Cixi. Among the many distinguished female guests she stood out with her fair visage and resplendent attire. A great fan of Beijing opera, she kept her gaze on the stage from beginning to end.

For three whole days Zai Tao and his "art troupe" entertained the members of the imperial clan, which included many Beijing opera connoisseurs. His birthday celebration was turned into an in-house drama festival.

3. Loss of the Pigtail

The first outdoor assignment Sun Yaoting got after his entry into Zai Tao's house was escorting his wife on a visit to the Northern Mansion, residence of Zai Feng, the Regent. The princess-consort had to pay a monthly courtesy visit to the Regent's wife, who was the Emperor's natural mother.

They arrived in the limousine and were taken to see the Regent's wife. The princess-consort saluted her hostess by dropping her right arm at the front and bending the left knee. The woman attendant who had come along saluted in the same way, but with only a slight bend of the knee. After an exchange of greetings, the Regent's wife turned her attention to Sun Yaoting. "When did you acquire this boy?"

"He came to our house at the end of last year," the princess-consort replied hastily. "A fellow villager of Mingshun recommended him." She did not, however, mention He Deyuan's name.

The Regent's wife said nothing, but she was determined to look into the matter. The next day she sent for Jia Runqing. "Where is that fellow villager of yours?" Her voice was harsh. "Bring him here immediately!"

"Which fellow villager?" Jia Runqing asked in puzzlement.

The Regent's wife demanded to know how Sun Yaoting had come to work in Zai Tao's house. She flew into a rage on learning that He Deyuan, a eunuch in her own house, had arranged everything. He Deyuan was brought over and given a severe reprimand. "You did not take the child-eunuch to me first. Instead, you took him to Prince Zai Tao. Well, if you like him so much, you can leave me to serve him!"

He Deyuan tried to plead with her, but in vain. A few days later he came to Zai Tao's house, luggage on back. After hearing him out, Zai Tao agreed to let him stay.

Though he did fairly well in Zai Tao's house, Sun Yaoting never gave up the idea of entering the Imperial Palace someday. Then a little incident happened that dashed his hope, at least for the time being.

At the end of his morning walk Zai Tao entered Sun Yaoting's room. He acknowledged Sun Yaoting's salute and came up to poke at his pigtail. "Why are you still wearing your pigtail? It's such a nuisance!"

"But master, I've worn it since I was a baby," Sun Yaoting replied. "I've grown used to it." A wave of panic ran over him. He wanted to keep his pigtail, without which he would not be allowed into the Imperial Palace.

"I prefer a child like you to look neat," Zai Tao said as he went away. Sun Yaoting was wondering what the prince had in mind when Zai Tao returned with a pair of scissors. "Come over, Shunshou, let me cut that thing off." He beckoned Sun Yaoting to sit down.

"No, master, please don't!" Sun Yaoting was scared out of his wits.

"Come here." Zai Tao pulled him over and took hold of his pigtail.

"Please don't! Please don't!" Sun Yaoting babbled, covering his head with both hands. Unmoved, Zai Tao brought down the scissors, and the long queue dropped to the floor.

"Now you look nice and neat." Zai Tao wiped his hands and walked away.

After cleaning up the floor, Sun Yaoting went to see Jia Runqing. "Now you look neat all over, don't you?" Jia said in half-jest.

"Please tell me what this is all about!" said Sun Yaoting.

"It was the master's idea, wasn't it?"

"How do you know?" Sun Yaoting asked in surprise.

"How do I know? I have not stayed in this house for so many years without learning something!"

"But you wouldn't believe it! The master cut it off himself!"

"That's only too natural. The master really likes you!"

"What do you mean?"

"You think you can keep your little secret from our master? Everyone knows a eunuch must retain his pigtail to be accepted into the Imperial Palace! That's what you're thinking about all the time, isn't it? But the master could read your mind, so he cut off your pigtail. Without it you cannot leave for the palace, at least not till you've grown another!"

"Oh!" Sun Yaoting cried out. "So that's why the master did it! Thanks for telling me."

One day Zhao Rongsheng, a eunuch attendant in the palace, came to visit. He looked like a beautiful young woman with his handsome features, slim figure, and creamy white skin. At the gate he nodded politely to Sun Yaoting though they had never met before.

Sun Yaoting had heard of this "Brother Zhao", who was five or six years his senior. Zhao was quite a celebrity among the servants in the house, and his visit caused a sensation. "Why is he here?" said a servant. "He stopped coming long time ago, didn't he?"

"Well, who knows? He had a big quarrel with the master when he left!"

Sun Yaoting listened to the gossip with great interest. "What happened?" he asked. "Is this the first time Brother Zhao has come back after he left for the palace?"

"Now this is between you and me," Jia Runqing pulled him aside and said in a hushed voice. "Brother Zhao came here in the thirty-first year of Emperor Guangxu's reign, when he was only eleven or twelve years old. Well, he was smart and good-looking, and the master and his mother, the Ancestress, both liked him and treated him with special favor. But he still wanted to leave for the palace! I don't blame him. For people like us, the only hope for a bright future lies in the Imperial Palace!"

"Why hasn't he come back to visit until now?"

"Well, the master and the Ancestress were greatly offended because they failed to keep him. They thought they had lost face. The master cut him dead in the palace. Brother Zhao did something to make up. His first job in the palace was at the imperial kitchen, making steamed bread, fried dough-cakes, and things like that. Well, he brought some of those cookies to the master as a token of respect. Of course the master was mollified. A great man does not stoop to bear a grudge with a petty man, so the saying goes."

"Our master seems to be quite tolerant," Sun Yaoting remarked.

"Sure he is! You wouldn't believe what he said to Brother Zhao: 'Water flows downward but man moves upward. I don't blame you for leaving, but you could at least have said goodbye!' Well, Brother Zhao apologized, and that was it. He's come back this time just to pay his respects."

A moment later Zhao left Zai Tao and came to see his old acquaintances at the Inner Janitor's Office. "Is he new here?" he asked, pointing at Sun Yaoting.

"He came here not long ago," Jia Runqing replied.

"What's it like in the palace?" one of the eunuchs asked.

"There's a world of difference between the palace and the house of a prince. You have to follow a lot of rules and watch your every step."

"Have you got your name into the book?" He Deyuan asked. However much he toiled, a eunuch would have no future in the palace until his name was formally registered.

"I've bought a name already. I'm now listed under Duankang."

"Congratulations!" The eunuchs were genuinely impressed, and even Escort Zhang said a few words of compliment.

"But it was not easy. I waited on Herald Xia for some time and worked my fingers to the bone! What do they say about a servant's servant? 'A servant used by a servant will be a dead servant.' I was half dead when I left him."

"Now your hard time is over!" several eunuchs said. The look of envy on their faces left a deep impression on Sun Yaoting.

What Zhao Rongsheng said was true. For a long time after he entered the palace he remained an unregistered eunuch doing the most menial jobs, until High Consort Duankang noticed him due to his fine appearance and ingenuity. After Zhao became a personal attendant of Duankang, even Zai Tao had to take him more seriously.

Zhao was nimble-minded and dexterous with his hands. In Zai Tao's house one of his duties had been helping the mistress dress her hair in the morning, and she was quite satisfied with him. When it came to handiwork no attending woman could rival him. Among other things, he knitted covers for the steering wheel and armrests of the limousine with woolen threads. "You are so clever with your hands!" the princess-consort used to say. "No one in this house is your match!"

In addition to his fair complexion, Zhao had a long braid that went all the way to his heels when loosened, his glossy black hair the envy of every woman in the house. High Consort Duankang was over fifty and started to lose hair when he came to wait on her. He cut off his long braid and made a wig for her. Therefore she treated him with special favor, as was illustrated by the following incident.

He was combing her hair in the morning when she heard his stomach rumble. "Are you hungry?" she asked.

"Yes," Zhao replied. Like other eunuchs, he did not eat his first meal of the day until noon. But from then on he got up every morning to find breakfast on his table.

Zhao Rongsheng lived frugally and in a few years saved enough money to build a big house in his hometown, Changzhou. He also bought a housing compound on East Jingshan Road in Beijing. Like many well-to-do eunuchs, he adopted a son in order to "continue the family line". "Zhao has made it!" was the comment from his fellow eunuchs.

After he made up with Zai Tao, Zhao Rongsheng often called on the house. He liked to stop in Escort Zhang's room for a leisurely chat over a cup of tea. "Do you still remember the time when you were here with us?" Zhang once asked.

"Of course I do! Without your help I would never have got what I have today!" Zhao said.

"Glad to hear you say that," Zhang nodded.

At this Zhao turned to Sun Yaoting sitting nearby and explained that he had entered the palace with Zhang's recommendation. He had asked Zhang for help, feeling he had reached a dead-end in Zai Tao's house. Zhang promised to do his best and soon found him a position in the Imperial Palace.

"You have a lucky star!" Sun Yaoting could hardly conceal his envy.

"Don't worry," Zhao comforted him. "Ask Brother Zhang to put in a word for you, and you'll be all right!"

These words gave Sun Yaoting renewed hope. He often met Zhao in Zhang's room and grew well acquainted with him. One evening he waited outside until Zhao came out. Pulling Zhao aside, he pleaded in a whisper,

"Brother, please give me a hand!"

"I'll keep it in mind," Zhao said. "But you must remember one thing. You know what I went through when I left this house. Don't let the master hear a word of it."

"I won't! You can trust me! I'll never breathe a word about it even after I leave!"

In the end Sun Yaoting's dream of entering the palace came true, though it had nothing to do with Brother Zhao.

4. The Restoration

In the summer of the 6th year of the Republic of China (1917) a piece of astounding news spread quickly in the capital. "General Zhang Xun has marched into Beijing to restore the Emperor to power!"

As Viceroy of Jiangxi, Jiangsu and Anhui and Provincial Governor of Jiangsu, Zhang Xun was one of the powerful warlords who merely paid lip service to the central government in Beijing. After the death of Yuan Shikai, the successive Presidents of the Republic were figureheads generally held in disdain by the Manchu aristocracy, who had been dreaming for a comeback all along. Zhang Xun's arrival in Beijing filled them with joy. In the houses of Zai Tao and other Manchu princes, people talked excitedly about Zhang Xun's exploits.

"General Zhang once defeated the revolutionaries with his troops! Even Yuan Shikai had to treat him with respect!"

"They say all his men are still wearing queues in the style of Great Qing. Even General Zhang himself wears one!"

"That's why he's known as the Pigtailed General!"

"The queue is the mark of his loyalty to the Emperor, and he carries it wherever he goes!"

In the eyes of the imperial clan Zhang Xun became a superhero who was going to bring the Qing Dynasty back to life. All this excitement and anticipation filled Sun Yaoting with curiosity.

One day Zhang Xun made a phone call saying he would come to pay respects to the "imperial uncle". The news caused a great excitement in the house. "The Pigtailed General is coming!"

Zhang Xun, the "Pigtailed General"

Hearing several cars honking outside the gate, a eunuch at the Outer Janitor's Office ran out. At the sight of the cars he rushed back to the Inner Janitor's Office, where Sun Yaoting had been waiting. Sun Yaoting then made a dash for Zai Tao's room. "Your Highness, General Zhang has come. He's waiting outside the gate." He was short of breath from running.

"Invite him to come in!"

Sun Yaoting raced to the Outer Janitor's Office to deliver the order, then headed back. A moment later Zhang Xun walked in with a swagger, and Zai Tao received him down the steps outside his big study.

"Your Highness!" Zhang saluted the prince in the Manchu style.

"No need to stand on ceremony," Zai Tao said.

Zhang had very thick eyebrows and a ruddy complexion. Contrary to popular imagination, he was short and stodgy, wearing a long gown and a hat. He looked more like a fur dealer than a great general.

Without being told, Sun Yaoting went away and returned with the finest "dragon-well" green tea for Zai Tao and his honored guest. Then he left the room and closed the door lightly behind him. Zai Tao usually received guests in the small study to the east and seldom used the big study for this

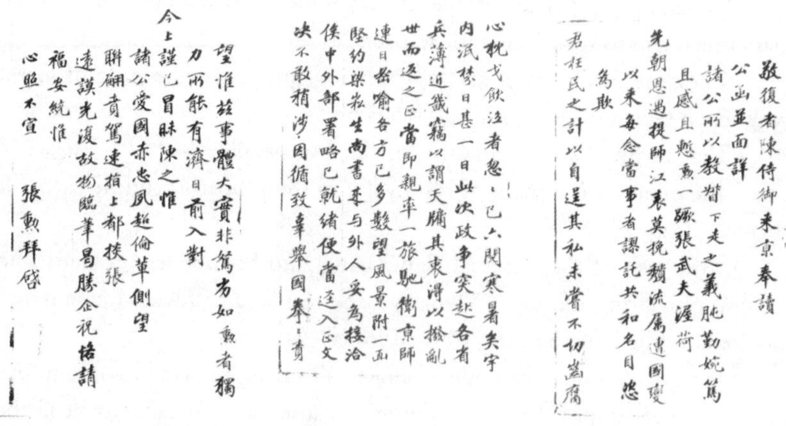

敬復者陳侍御來京奉讀
公函並面詳
諸公所以教督下走之義肫勤婉篤
且感且慚勳一疏張武夫渥荷
先朝恩遇提師江表莫挽頹流屬遭國變
以來每念當事者謀託共和名目恐
為欺
君在民之計以自遂其私未嘗不切齒腐
心枕戈飲泣者忽忽已六閱寒暑矣字
內派禁日甚一日此次政爭突起各省
兵潮迭鐵竊以謂天牖其衷得以撥亂
世而返之正當即親率一旅馳衛京師
連日諮喻各方已多數望風景附一面
堅約梁崧生尚書專與外人妥為接洽
俾中外部署略已就緒便當逕入正文
決不敢稍涉因循致辜舉國奉責
望惟茲事體大實非篤方如勳者獨
力所能有濟日前入對
今上謹已冒昧陳之惟
諸公愛國赤忠夙越倫輩側望
聯翩責駕速指上都挾張
遠謨光復故物臨筆曷勝企祝語請
福安統惟
心照不宣
張勳拜啓

Zhang Xun's letter to Pu Yi about restoration

purpose. There was no sofa in the room, only a few high-back hardwood chairs. A few works of painting and calligraphy decorated the walls. Zhang Xun had brought several bodyguards dressed in yellow military uniforms. They kept patrolling the courtyard throughout the meeting.

Behind closed doors Zai Tao and Zhang Xun discussed the restoration plan, though no one knew the details. Shortly afterward Zhang went to the Imperial Palace, where he kowtowed to Pu Yi, acknowledging him as the ruling Emperor. However, among the powerful warlords at the time Zhang had few sympathizers and many enemies. The nominal restoration of the Qing Dynasty lasted only a few days.

Before he marched into Beijing Zhang Xun had paid several visits to Xiaode Zhang, who lived in retirement in Tianjin. They had known each other for a long time. While stationed in Xuzhou, Zhang had invited the famed eunuch to attend the one-month celebration of his newborn son. Xiaode Zhang came to Xuzhou in such a hurry that he did not bring any present, so he took a ring off his finger and gave it to the general. The ring was said to be worth at least twenty thousand taels of silver.

"Come with me to the capital," Zhang Xun urged. "We shall offer our service to His Majesty again!"

"No, I'm not going anywhere," the old eunuch shook his head. "Whether or not I go with you will make little difference, after all. Now tell me, have you made a deal with the provincial leaders?"

"I've talked with every one of them," Zhang said confidently. "They all promised to sign up once the Emperor is enthroned. No problem at all!"

"You'd better think twice about it. If you ask my advice, I'd tell you to either give it up or take more troops with you!"

"I've tried my best," Zhang Xun said, spreading out his hands. "I'm sure I can manage with the troops I have!"

Zhang Xun then described what he regarded as his secret weapon. He had enlisted the support of General Cao Kun by promising the latter a high post in the imperial court once Pu Yi came back to power. Stationed in Baoding about a hundred kilometers southwest of Beijing, Cao could send timely reinforcements to the capital.

"Is that all?" the eunuch shook his head. "I'm definitely not going with you! I've lived in the capital for many years, and I know what I'm talking about. You won't be able to control it with just a few thousand men! Take my advice. Send a strong force to Beijing and find someone to command it for you: Wang Shizhen, Duan Qirui, Kang Youwei – any of them will do. Whoever you choose will take orders from you, while you stay in Xuzhou and control everything from a safe distance."

"So you don't think I will succeed?"

"Capture the capital with your personal guards? Your chance of success is very slim." The eunuch shook his head again. "Well, if you really want to enter Beijing in person to restore the Emperor to power, you have to take all the troops in Xuzhou with you. Otherwise I want no part in it!"

The bullheaded general ignored the eunuch's advice and went along with his plan. His occupation of Beijing lasted only a few days. He took refuge in the Dutch embassy before fleeing to Tianjin. There he called on Xiaode Zhang again. "Oh brother!" the general broke into tears. "I suffered an ignominious defeat because I didn't listen to you!"

"There's no need to grieve for what is beyond remedy," the eunuch said. "Since you can't change the past, why not accept it with grace?"

Zhang Xun never recovered from his defeat. A few years later, in September 1923, he died of illness and a broken heart in Tianjin. Pu Yi issued a commemorating edict, wrote his epitaph, and awarded him a posthumous official title.

Many years afterward Sun Yaoting was in Xiaode Zhang's house when the old eunuch commented on Zhang Xun's defeat. "He was too headstrong and had too much faith in his troops. If he had taken my advice, he would have seized the initiative, and the outcome would have been different. Well, I suppose we shouldn't blame him. It was meant to be like that!"

5. Leaving Zai Tao

In winter Sun Yaoting's second brother came to Beijing bringing news from home and a pair of cotton-padded trousers handmade by his mother.

"Soon after you left, Mr. Fu stopped teaching. Last autumn there was a big flood in Tianjin, and a man by the name of Kang Zhenfu opened a 'porridge mess' to feed the refugees. Mr. Fu joined him and treated the refugees free of charge. He did not went there to make money, but as he gained a big name money just kept coming in. He has become quite rich and bought several hundred mu of land!"

"A good man like him gets what he deserves at last!" Sun Yaoting felt genuinely happy for his former tutor.

"Here's a pair of trousers Mum made for you. Try it on."

The cotton-padded trousers made Sun Yaoting feel warm all over, but he had no way to repay his family. He took out two dollars, explaining in embarrassment, "I get paid only a couple of dollars a month here." His brother refused to take the money.

Sun Yaoting saw his brother off, feeling rather guilty. "I can't go on like this," he said to himself. "I must find a way to help support the family."

As the days grew warmer, Sun Yaoting became increasingly agitated. He went to the princess-consort to ask for a leave, but there was mockery in her eyes as she mentioned how a senior eunuch Liu Peilian had left the house for the palace with Zhao Rongsheng's help. She seemed to know what Sun Yaoting had in mind.

Unable to get a leave, Sun Yaoting decided to slip away on the sly. To his astonishment, the guard at the gate stopped him. "You cannot leave the house. We have Mr. Jia's instructions." Sun Yaoting then found out that Jia Runqing was merely passing on an order from the princess-consort, who was determined to keep him. Convinced that he had no future in Zai Tao's house, Sun Yaoting was determined to leave. "I have not stolen any money or taken anything from the house," he said to the guard. "Why do you stop me?"

"Take it easy, brother," the guard said. "I just follow orders. It's not up to me to decide whether or not I can let you go."

"But I'm going out to take a bath," Sun Yaoting said. "Surely you have no reason to stop me!" As the guard stood there at a loss, Sun Yaoting walked out triumphantly.

For the first time in his life Sun Yaoting experienced a thrill of freedom. He felt "like a bird flying in the high sky or a fish swimming in the wide ocean." But excitement soon gave way to anxiety. How could he make a living? After eating his fill at a restaurant, he went to Prince Zai Xun's mansion near Xidan to look for a eunuch friend, Shunxi.

After hearing him out, Shunxi shook his head with disapproval. "It's not a good idea for you to leave in that way. What you should have done is to make a plan and carry it out step by step. People like us cannot afford to offend our masters, especially someone as powerful as Prince Zai Tao, otherwise no one in whole capital would hire you, and your future would be ruined." He paused, thinking for a moment. "All right, here is my advice. Before doing anything else, go back and say good-bye to your master. Otherwise how could you look him in the face again?"

"I suppose you are right," Sun Yaoting conceded. "I'll go back to say good-bye, then see what I can do."

After Sun Yaoting kowtowed and explained his intention, Zai Tao gave his consent at once. He sent for the chief steward, saying, "Let the boy go. Who knows? Maybe he'll find something better to do somewhere!"

Sun Yaoting went back to his room to pack up his belongings. After the steward had gone through the house to make sure that nothing was missing, he was allowed to leave.

Standing at the crossroads on Xisi Street in downtown Beijing, Sun Yaoting did not know what to do. It would be embarrassing for him to go home empty-handed; he could not even afford the fare. But where else could he go? Finally he walked into a pawnshop where he pawned his quilt and cotton-padded trousers for a few dollars. With this money he returned home the same day.

That evening the family sat under a kerosene lamp in their thatched house, torn between sadness and joy. "Our child is back home again, safe and sound," Sun Yaoting's mother said. "That's more important than anything else."

"Yes," agreed his father, Sun Huaibao. "At least you have seen the world and gained a lot of knowledge and experience."

When putting away his clothes, his mother was dismayed to find the receipt from the pawnshop. "How come? Why did you have to go to the pawnshop?"

Sun Yaoting sighed deeply. "Life was not easy for me in the capital. I want to tell you all about it, but I just don't know where to begin."

"Take it easy," his second brother said. "The hardships are all behind you. Now you are back home."

For all that they said, Sun Yaoting was unable to calm down and relax. He had left for the capital with high hopes and come back empty-handed. He knew he had let his parents down. He tossed and turned on the kang that night, and got up in the morning with a new determination. "I'll go back to the capital!" he announced. "I'll never come back until I make it!"

Unable to dissuade him, his parents borrowed a hundred dollars for him. With this money Sun Yaoting left for Beijing a second time.

3

THE FORBIDDEN CITY

1. Entry into the Palace

Sun Yaoting had a distant uncle who lived on Nanheng Road just outside the Forbidden City, with a small business selling homemade pastry. For the first three months after his return to the capital, Sun Yaoting stayed with this uncle, working the stoneroller to husk grain and learning to make cakes and cookies. In the evening he smelled the fragrance of flowers in the courtyard and prayed silently for his future.

His luck turned at an accidental visit from another distant uncle named Chen Jitang, who had a job at the Baizhifang Printing Press. Informed of his intention to find a place in the palace, Chen promised to lend a hand. Chen had a friend whose adoptive father, a fellow villager of Xiaode Zhang, was among the several hundred remaining eunuchs in the Imperial Palace. Because of this connection Chen got to know quite a few eunuchs from the palace, including Xin Hengru, the head eunuch in charge of the Imperial Garden.

Chen invited Xin Hengru to come over and explained the situation. "Mr. Xin, look at my nephew. He's already sixteen years old. Could you find him a place in the palace?"

"All right," Xin glanced at Sun Yaoting and agreed with alacrity. "No problem."

"Wow!" Sun Yaoting jumped with joy. "I'm going to the palace!"

"Wait a minute," Xin waved his hand. "Before you enter the palace you must first learn the rules, or you'll lose your head without knowing why!

I'll come here tomorrow to teach you some of these rules. And you must get yourself an outfit."

The next day Sun Yaoting's uncle prepared some good dishes for Xin. After the meal the head eunuch began to tutor Sun on palace etiquette. "First, you must know the way to address all kinds of people. Once you enter the palace, you will be apprenticed to a senior eunuch, and you will call him master. To be polite, you address eunuchs of your own rank as mister, such as Mr. Li or Mr. Zhao. You call the Emperor Your Majesty and high consorts madam. If you make the slightest mistake, you would pay a high price for it!"

Xin took a sip of the strong tea he was served, then went on with his instructions. "You can never be too careful. Most important, you must observe the taboo of the Emperor's name. Never say any word that sounds the same as the names of the Emperor, the Empress dowager, or the high consorts. Ever heard of Xiaode Zhang?"

"Yes! He and I come from the same county," Sun Yaoting said.

"He used to go by the name Chunxi, but it had to be changed because Empress Dowager Longyu had the milk name Xige". Xin paused to take another sip of the tea. "So the first thing you have to do after you get into the palace is to find yourself a eunuch-mentor. Be prepared to work hard. You must get up at dawn and fetch water for your mentor to rinse his mouth and wash his face. You wake him up and help him get dressed. In the evening you must serve him until he goes to bed. While you sleep in bed in the outer room, stay alert. When he calls for you, go in at once. You must be at your mentor's beck and call. If you hear him cough, bring over the spittoon and gently pound his back. Is that clear?"

"Yes!" Sun Yaoting nodded.

Sun Yaoting and his uncle walked the old eunuch all the way to the Eastern Flowery Gate and saw him disappear into the Forbidden City.

"Look," said the uncle, "that's where the Emperor lives! Once you are in the palace, work your way up until you get to serve His Majesty. When that day comes, don't forget about your uncle!"

"I won't forget to repay your kindness!" Sun Yaoting pledged.

On their way back, Sun Yaoting pondered over a remark the old eunuch had repeated with great emphasis: "No one can attain wealth and fame without suffering aches and pains." Though he was too young to fully appreciate the truth of the saying, it gave him an idea of what life might be like for a junior eunuch.

A few days later Xin Hengru came in the evening to give Sun Yaoting another lesson on palace manners. "The rules are rather complicated, so you must take care never to get them mixed up. For example, there are different modes of salutation. To the Emperor you must get down on both knees, just like this." Xin lifted his gown to make a demonstration. "Pay attention. Bend the left knee first, then the right knee. Straighten up your back. The more upright your stature the better. Remember to take off your hat before getting down on your knees; put it on the floor at your right-hand side. Pick it up when you get on your feet, but do not put it on until the Emperor has left. Lift the hem of your gown before you kneel so that it won't wrap around your knee, and keep your eyes lowered all the time. Kneel three times and kowtow nine times when you salute the Emperor. Sometimes it is a good idea to knock your forehead hard against the floor to show your loyalty. When you are dismissed, make your exit by stepping backward. Never point your bottom toward His Majesty, or you'd get a good thrashing! As for your mentor and the head eunuch, you salute by bending one knee, like this."

"There's something I don't quite understand," Sun Yaoting said. "If someone sees the Emperor all the time in the palace, the rules would require him to kowtow nonstop. Is that so?"

"Well, you must kowtow to His Majesty when you meet him for the first time in the day. It would be easier if a head eunuch is present, for you can watch what he does and follow suit. Pay attention to your every posture and move in front of the Emperor. A small mistake could get you into big trouble!"

After a few cups of wine the old eunuch became very chatty. "Watch your tongue in the palace! Don't greet others by asking whether they have eaten, as you do outside the palace, or you'd be laughed at. Instead, wish them good luck. When you see your mentor, say 'Good luck!' When he finishes eating, say 'Good appetite!' When he gets up in the morning, say 'Good sleep!' When you take an order or instruction, always say 'Yes!' with your head lowered. Cock up your ears and listen attentively, for you cannot ask your superiors to repeat their words unless you want to get a beating. In addition, you must learn by heart all the rules on serving tea, preparing meal, laying out the table, fetching things, and so on."

Xin also told Sun Yaoting to be prepared for corporal punishment. "This is something you must bear in mind. If the master gets angry and

The Imperial Garden

swears at you, stand still and say 'yes'. If he slaps you on the face, don't dodge! Lower your head and say, 'Your slave is wrong.' Otherwise you'd be taken away for a heavy beating and maybe end up crippled for life!"

The old eunuch went on to choreograph Sun Yaoting on the proper way for eunuchs to carry out their daily routines such as serving tea. Sun Yaoting tried his best to copy Xin's every move and posture until he felt dizzy in the head and sweated all over. Xin seemed to be satisfied with Sun Yaoting's progress. "I'll try to get you into the palace in a few days," he said before he left. "Wait for my message!"

In the Imperial Palace an old eunuch nicknamed "Big Qi" had the sole official duty of burying the afterbirths of Imperial consorts. That left him plenty of spare time to run a profitable opium trade. Officially, opium consumption by eunuchs was strictly forbidden and punishable by death, with family members of the offender exiled to remote areas. However, by the time Sun Yaoting was about to enter the palace the ban existed on paper only, making it possible for Big Qi to procure opium outside the palace and selling it to other eunuchs.

One day Xin Hengru told Big Qi about Sun Yaoting, describing him as "a good sixteen-year-old boy who can read and write". Delighted, Qi agreed to accept Sun Yaoting as his disciple. Though he was making big money, Qi was illiterate and could not do his own accounts. So the first job Sun Yaoting got in the palace was bookkeeping for an opium trader.

After Xin told him the news, Sun Yaoting was too excited to sleep at night. He got up early and put on his best clothes. Escorted by Xin Hengru, he got through the Gate of Divine Prowess and stepped into the Forbidden City for the first time. After a short walk, they arrived at the Imperial Garden, where Qi lived. Qi seemed to find the young boy to his liking and agreed to let him stay.

Taking Xin's advice, Sun Yaoting bought a hat and two gowns, one blue and the other gray. By palace rules the complete outfit of a eunuch consisted of a pair of boots, an outer gown, a hat, a long inner gown and a short inner gown, a sleeveless shirt, a riding jacket, a sleeveless jacket, a pair of trousers, and narrow and broad leg strings. One could often tell the rank of a eunuch by his clothes. For instance, only chief eunuchs and head eunuchs were entitled to wear riding jackets; the low-ranking and ungraded eunuchs could only wear sleeveless jackets instead. The boots were all black in color, but only a chief or head eunuch got to wear high boots. The eunuchs were also required to wear different colors for various occasions. Blue and gray were all right for ordinary times, but on the birthday of a member of the Imperial family, all eunuchs must be dressed in dark reddish purple.

The garments and accessories of eunuchs used to be made to order at the expense of the palace. In the late Qing Dynasty the depletion of the Imperial treasury meant that the eunuchs had to pay for their clothes out of their own pockets. Therefore one could usually tell the rank and financial status of a eunuch by the quantity and quality of his clothes.

The day after he entered the palace Sun Yaoting was taken to the "Fowling Piece Office", where Qi had turned two large adjoining wing rooms into an opium lounge, the only one in the palace. More than ten eunuchs were lying on the long kang, smoking and chatting. There was a sickening sweet smell in the air. Under Qi's instructions, Sun Yaoting soon learned to tell at a glance the status of the various eunuch-customers.

"Hey, get me a dose." A eunuch in a skullcap walked in, flung himself on the kang, and threw over a few strings of coins.

"Just a second," Sun answered, bringing over a smoking set at once. The first customer he served was apparently not very well off.

A young eunuch saw the little account book in Sun Yaoting's hand. "Big Qi is surely making big money now! He's even hired a bookkeeper!"

"How did you come here?" another eunuch asked Sun Yaoting.

"Tell me, little brother," an old toothless eunuch asked. "What places have you been to?"

The eunuchs gathered around, showing a strong interest in Sun Yaoting. He lowered his head and answered their questions courteously. "I spent a period of time in Prince Zai Tao's mansion."

"That's a very prestigious house!" a eunuch said. "Everyone knows the prince is the Emperor's uncle! Why on earth did you leave?"

"What's the use of being prestigious?" Sun Yaoting blurted out. "I was making only a couple of dollars a month. When the master celebrated his birthday, I went to him and kowtowed several times, and he sent me away with two strings of coins. Why on earth should I stay?"

"You have a point there," a eunuch looked up from his smoking pipe and sighed sympathetically. "It's not easy to make a living nowadays!"

"The prince was a bit too tightfisted, wasn't he?" said another eunuch.

"Big Qi may look sloppy, but he has brains. Keep working for him, and you'll probably get rich someday!"

Qi paid little attention to his appearance and was often slovenly dressed, but he had true business acumen. Now that he had Sun Yaoting to help him, he decided to stop accepting credit at his opium lounge. A notice in Sun Yaoting's handwriting was posted on the door:

Due to small capital and thin profit, no credit will hitherto be given. Cash payment only. Sorry for causing any inconvenience.

Business at the opium lounge did not suffer any decline as most opium smokers had ready money. Some customers showed an interest in the handwriting of the notice.

"Who wrote it for you, Big Qi?" a eunuch asked. "What a nice hand!"

An old eunuch, pipe in hand, walked up to Qi to rebuke him. "You're making a fortune, but why do you keep the child here? What a future does he have with you?"

"Don't give me that!" retorted Qi. "Without me he wouldn't have been able to enter the palace! He didn't have a thing to do, and he was willing to be my disciple, so I took him. If there is a better place for him to go, I'll not stop him. Mark my word for it!"

A few days later Zhu, a regular customer, came into the lounge and threw over several strings of coins. "Get me two doses!"

"Just a second!" Sun Yaoting, who had been standing by the door, hurried over to wait on him. Zhu was a broad-faced, white-haired old eunuch. As his family name, Zhu, was a homonym of the character for "pig", he went by the nickname "White-haired Pig" in the palace.

"You must be new here," he said to Sun Yaoting. "What's your name?"

Sun Yaoting answered the question with a smile. Somehow he felt an affinity to the old eunuch, who had a familiar Tianjin accent.

"How old are you?" Zhu stretched out on the kang.

"Sixteen." Sun Yaoting lit the pipe for him dexterously.

"Judging by your accent, I'd say you've been in the capital for quite a while."

"Yes. I worked in Prince Zai Tao's mansion for a period of time."

"A sensible and clever child," Zhu nodded with approval. He inhaled deeply on his pipe, then turned to Qi. "If you listen to me, Big Qi, send this boy to Chief Ren." He was talking about Ren Dexiang, Deputy Chief Superintendent and second-in-command of all the eunuchs in the Imperial Palace.

"You're not really serious, are you?" Qi said. "Will you be the go-between? Or are you just talking nonsense?"

"I mean every word I say! You just wait and see!" Zhu got down from the kang and left in a huff. A short moment later, he came back and took Sun Yaoting aside. "Tomorrow I'll take you to see Chief Ren," he whispered. "Don't forget!"

2. Chief Eunuch Ren

Ren Dexiang turned out to be a bedridden paralytic. When Sun Yaoting and Zhu walked into his room, he raised his head slightly and gave them a dazed look.

"This is the boy I mentioned to you yesterday," Zhu said. He turned to Sun Yaoting. "What are you waiting for? Salute Chief Ren!"

Sun Yaoting got down on one knee. "Good fortune, master!"

"Where are you from?"

"Your disciple is from Jinghai County of Tianjin."

"I heard that you spent some time in Prince Zai Tao's house. Is that true?" Ren seemed quite clear-minded.

"Yes."

"Well," Ren leaned back and heaved a deep sigh. "This illness has kept me in bed for many years now. If you come here, it'll be your job to clean the bed pan and everything."

"Chief Ren is well-known for his fiery temper," Zhu said. "He'll scream and yell at you. Are you sure you can take it?" Obviously Zhu did not want Sun Yaoting to make a hasty decision and blame him for it afterward.

Sun Yaoting's reply was rather tactful. "If I make a mistake I deserve to be blamed. But what if I do nothing wrong?"

Ren looked pleased. "The child's not bad. I'll let him stay."

"Hurry," Zhu gave Sun Yaoting a shove. "Thank Chief Ren!"

"Thank you for your great kindness!" Sun Yaoting knelt and kowtowed, formally acknowledging Ren as his mentor.

"The two of you can eat here," Ren said.

A small table was placed on the kang, and Zhu sat down to eat with Ren. Thanks to long-time practice, Ren had no difficulty eating in a lying position. He often sipped wine from a silver bottle. Sun Yaoting had his meal in the kitchen with two young eunuchs. One of them, the cook, had to dish out food for Ren and Zhu and clear the table afterward, all the while tending the fire in the stove. He did not get a chance to eat until the two old eunuchs had finished their meal.

Sun Yaoting stayed to work for Ren. Though he was nominally Ren's "disciple" and "brother" to the other junior eunuchs, he did not yet have a registered name in the palace, which means he received no salary and was the very lowest in rank among all eunuchs.

Eunuchs in the palace were strictly graded and could be roughly divided into chief eunuchs, head eunuchs, and ordinary eunuchs. The most senior eunuch at the time was Chief Superintendent Zhang De'an, whose position made him equal to a court official of the second rank. The palace was having financial difficulties, so the eunuchs did not always get their monthly salary on time. The payroll included the names of many long-dead eunuchs, whose salaries became extra income for the head eunuch in charge. When a senior eunuch needed a servant to do menial jobs, as in the case of Sun Yaoting, he often had to hire one with his own money.

Sun Yaoting soon found out how hard life could be for an ungraded, unregistered eunuch like him. He waited on the bedridden Ren all day, making tea, serving meals, and cleaning the bedpan. He also discovered that some palace rules were not easy to follow. For instance, eunuchs must observe a strict dress code. They could not wear only a vest in hot summer, but had to put on a short hemp shirt, with a vest inside to absorb sweat and prevent the outer garment from being soaked. The elderly eunuchs had all become very adept at "keeping the sweat inside", but it gave new recruits like Sun Yaoting a hard time. In addition, a pair of satin-faced boots and cotton socks must be worn all the year round.

Another item of the all-season outfit of eunuchs was a special sort of leggings stretching from the ankle to a few inches above the knee and attached to the belt with strings. A purse on the left side of the belt contained, among other things, a watch and a box of matches. The watch, bought at the eunuch's expense, enabled the eunuch to go on duty on time, and the matches were used to light pipes or cigarettes for the ones he served. A handkerchief folded into a triangle was suspended on the right side of the belt. It was used as a pad when the eunuch had to support the Imperial Master or Mistress. Direct body contact with a member of the Imperial clan was considered an act of contempt and subject to severe penalties.

In the old days, when the Bi and Liu families monopolized the eunuch recruitment business, they charged up to a hundred taels of silver per head for their service: performing the castration, securing a palace position, and providing a complete eunuch's outfit. If one was unable to pay the cost forthright, he had the option of paying by installments, with a certain amount deducted from his stipend once he became a registered eunuch in the palace. He would be poorly paid as a junior eunuch and would have to give presents to the head eunuch in charge of him on festivals, so that he might find himself still in debt after a dozen years. The only hope lay in earning promotions by hard work, which was exactly what Ren Dexiang had succeeded in doing.

After he came to the palace as a teenager, Ren worked his way up steadily until he became Deputy Chief Superintendent as well as chief eunuch of the Hall of Heavenly Purity. He was an excellent organizer on important occasions such as birthdays, weddings and funerals. For example, he was responsible for planning and overseeing the burial of Empress Dowager Cixi and Emperor Guangxu in the Eastern Imperial Tombs. Many eunuchs believed that if Ren Dexiang had not become paralytic, probably caused by overwork, he would have been promoted to Chief Superintendent.

Ren had five rooms in the palace, two of which he kept for his own use, a drawing room and a bedroom. Sun Yaoting and the other two junior eunuchs had a room to sleep in and another one for leisure activities. There was also a room reserved for Zhu the "White-haired Pig", though he never spent the night there. Most of the time he was away running a business on Ren's behalf, a rickshaw service near the Drum Tower with about a dozen rickshaws for rent. Like most senior eunuchs, he had bought his own house outside the palace.

Long-time confinement to bed made Ren very irritable. Sometimes he flew into a rage for no apparent reason and hurled abuses at others. Of the three junior eunuchs who served Ren, there was a cook, a eunuch attendant, and a menial – which meant Sun Yaoting. It was his job, for example, to take care of the heating stoves in winter. In the morning he had to prepare the stoves in the yard, then move them inside. During the day he nursed the fire by adding coals from time to time. At night he could not enjoy a sound sleep, for he had to get up several times to look at the fire in the stoves. Fortunately he got along well with the other two eunuchs so life was on the whole peaceful and strife-free.

Sun Yaoting came to the palace in winter, a good season for the eunuchs in terms of food. Some of the meat sacrificed to the gods was taken off the altar after a period of time and divided among the eunuchs, who could thus enjoy relatively good dishes until the Lunar New Year. However, daily meals were neither plentiful nor palatable most time of the year. A few smart eunuchs went out to buy meat, which they cooked and sold to other eunuchs in the palace. Business was brisk, and they made good money. They could not turn the Imperial Palace into a marketplace, so they learned to hawk their wares quite discreetly.

Ren Dexiang loved smoked fish and braised pork seasoned with soy sauce. There was a eunuch named Bo who specialized in selling braised pork legs in the palace. When he walked past Ren's room and shouted, "Good Fortune, chief", Ren would tell Sun Yaoting, "Go and get some pork legs! Everyone has a share!" Sun Yaoting ran out happily to get the pork legs, one for Ren and the rest for the junior eunuchs. He did not have to pay Bo on the spot, for Ren would settle accounts with him once every month. In fact, most eunuch-peddlers accepted credit and collected money when their customers received their monthly stipend. They also knew their customers' food preferences and financial status. Ren was an excellent customer who had no difficulty paying his bills. Though he did nothing but drink tea and read newspapers all day, he was paid a hundred taels of silver each month as a special favor from the Emperor. Having rendered meritorious service for many years, he enjoyed an exalted, impregnable position in the palace.

One day Ren Dexiang was lying on the kang in the afternoon when a eunuch walked in. "The Lord of Ten Thousand Years is coming in this direction!" At this, Ren immediately sent for Sun Yaoting. "Don't let anyone see you! Run to the east room and stay there!"

"Yes," Sun Yaoting answered, but he did not go right away. He could not understand why he had to hide himself from the Emperor.

"The Emperor likes young boys," Ren explained. "If he sees you he will probably take you away from me." He failed to mention that the Emperor might get angry with him for keeping an unregistered eunuch.

Sun Yaoting ran into the east room, closed the door, and peeped out through a crack. He found out to his surprise that the Emperor was a boy a few years his junior.

Pu Yi in his court robes

Two eunuchs entered Ren's room and stood on either side of the kang. Then Pu Yi, the thirteen-year-old Emperor, walked in. He was wearing a black fur coat with a sleeveless jacket and a black skullcap. "Are you feeling better these days?" he greeted Ren in a loud voice.

Ren made a failed attempt to straighten up, and his face was all smiles. "Your slave is useless now and gets by with Your Majesty's blessing."

Pu Yi glanced around the room and said a few more words of consolation.

"Take good care of yourself!" Then he went away, followed by the large retinue of eunuchs who followed him everywhere. Ren kept muttering "Thanks for Your Majesty's favor" until Pu Yi was out of sight.

The incident made Sun Yaoting realize that Ren actually liked him and wanted to keep him.

With no salary, Sun Yaoting relied on tips from Ren as the only source of income. At the end of the year he got his first tip: ten silver dollars. Overjoyed, he knelt before the kang and kowtowed. He believed that better time was yet to come and that he had a future to look forward to. All that he had to do was to work hard and bide his time.

Things did take a turn for the better some days later, when Ren Dexiang called him over to give him a name for use in the palace. "Though you are not listed in the files," Ren said, "it would be convenient for you to have a palace name. From now on you'll be called Chunshou."

3. High Consort Duankang

Sun Yaoting was quite happy now that he had finally gained a foothold in the Imperial Palace and acquired a semi-official palace name. He asked for a leave and went back home.

It was a joyous family reunion. "I can die with a contented heart," his mother said, "now that you have a future ahead of you! Being a eunuch and unable to get into the palace – that's what worried me to death!"

"Why do you have to say such unlucky words?" Sun Huaibao said. "Our child has entered the palace and got a name. We should feel happy for him."

"I do feel happy," she said, wiping away her tears.

"Pour out some wine," Sun Huaibao shouted. "Let's celebrate!" The family sat down at the table to enjoy a lunch with wine, dishes, and laughter, something they had not known for years. As the news of Sun Yaoting's return spread quickly, many villagers came to congratulate the family.

At dusk a distant relative brought a middle-aged woman who came to ask for a favor. She had a nephew who had been castrated, and she wanted Sun Yaoting to find him a position in the palace. "Please help us," she pleaded with Sun Huaibao. "Otherwise his life would be ruined."

"How old is he?" Sun Huaibao asked. He had no idea whether his son could be of any help.

"He's twelve already," the woman replied. "What else could he do? The palace is his only hope."

The woman's worries were justified. In the rural area around Tianjin many people had undergone castration in order to enter the palace as eunuchs. The downfall of the Qing Dynasty plunged them into despair. They lived a miserable life, the object of public scorn and ridicule.

"How does he look?"

"He's not at all bad-looking, but his family is very poor. They get by in good years and sometimes starve in bad years. That's why they wanted to send the boy to the palace. Who could have guessed the Emperor would soon abdicate?"

Sun Huaibao told Sun Yaoting to come over, and the woman bowed to him deeply. "You have entered the palace now, so please give us a hand!"

"Where is the boy from?" Sun Yaoting asked.

"Gaozhuang, a village not far from here."

"All right, I'll see what I can do."

On his return, Sun Yaoting met a senior eunuch named Liu near the Palace of Gathering Elegance. "Are you the newcomer with Chief Ren?" Liu asked.

"Yes," Sun Yaoting replied.

"How old are you?"

"Seventeen."

"Where are you from?"

"Jinghai County of Tianjin."

"Which village?"

"Shuangtang."

"Hey, what a coincidence!" Liu looked pleased. "Do you know Kou Zizhen?"

"Yes, of course!" Sun Yaoting had heard of Kou, who used to be the Emperor's head eunuch. "He is from the eastern part of the village, and my family live in the western part. We can even hear cocks crow in their house!"

"He's my mentor, you know."

"Then I can count on your favor," Sun Yaoting said. Eunuchs would feel a close bond with one another if they shared the same mentor or came from the same village.

"If there's any child in your village suitable for the palace," Liu said, "just let me know."

"Believe it or not, I know of such a boy right now!"

"Well, write and tell him to come. I'll take a look at him."

"Yes!" Sun Yaoting was happy to comply.

A few days later Liu came to see him. "Is there a problem? Where is that child?"

Sun Yaoting was shocked, for he had forgotten all about it. Ren was in a nasty mood these days and gave him a very difficult time, making him too preoccupied to think of anything else. Not daring to tell the truth, he said, "The boy's coming. He'll arrive very soon, I think."

"Write again and tell him to hurry up," Liu said.

Sun wrote a letter at once, and the boy came very soon. Sun Yaoting took him to Liu, who turned out to be a head eunuch for High Consort Duankang. He liked the boy and let him stay at the Palace of Eternal Harmony.

The next day Zhao Rongsheng came to see Sun Yaoting. "Did you help find us that boy?" he asked.

"Yes, I did."

"I see." Zhao left without saying anything.

A couple of days later Zhao brought Sun Yaoting some good news. It seemed that High Consort Duankang would like to have him for her theatrical group, but she was aware that Chief Ren might be reluctant to let him go. Though delighted, Sun Yaoting knew he had to be very cautious. A junior eunuch who chose to "jump the manger", or leave his position for a better one, might be regarded by others as a traitor to his ex-mentor. "You must be patient and bide your time," Zhao advised him. "The rehearsals for the New Year celebrations could be a good chance." As Sun Yaoting went on to serve Chief Ren, the boy who had entered the palace with his help became a registered eunuch in the Palace of Eternal Harmony and received a formal name, Chunzhong.

Beijing opera had long been a main course of entertainment in the palace, its growing popularity coinciding with the steady decline of imperial power. On major festivals the palace became a gigantic theatre, with theatricals staged in various parts of the palace in addition to performances by the best troupes in the country. The amateur players were mostly eunuchs but also included princes, nobles, high officials and even the Emperor. The theatricals lasted for half a month during the Spring Festival, probably serving as a reminder for the "little court" of its past glory.

The Spring Festival was drawing near. One day Zhao Rongsheng was combing Duankang's hair when she mentioned that the opera group at the Palace of Eternal Harmony still lacked competent players. "Chunzhong is no good!" she said. "He can't sing with his Tianjin accent, and he can't even turn a somersault! He's so useless!"

Zhao took this chance to remind her of Sun Yaoting. "What about the child your slave mentioned earlier? He's quite smart and sensible. Give him a lesser role, and he'll do fine. Perhaps you'd want to take a look at him?"

"How old is he?" Duankang asked with some interest.

"About sixteen or seventeen."

"Has he played before?"

"No, but he has very supple limbs. He used to work in Prince Zai Tao's house. There he learned to somersault, walk on his hands, and so on."

Knowing Zai Tao's enthusiasm for Beijing opera, Duankang was satisfied. She immediately sent for Zhang Anji, deputy head eunuch of the Palace of Eternal Harmony. "There's a child at Ren Dexiang's place who can do somersaults and everything," she said. "Bring him here. I want to have a look."

Zhang Anji passed on the order to a subordinate, Herald Xia.

"Good Fortune!" Xia went to greet Ren.

"Good Fortune to you," Ren responded. At the sight of Xia, he had an inkling of what was going to happen.

"Madam Duankang has heard you have a very talented child here. She'd like to take a look at him and see if he can play a role in the theatricals."

"No problem!" Ren said without the slightest hesitation. He had not lived in the palace for dozens of years without learning to conceal his true feelings.

Aware of what Ren must have in mind, Xia suggested, "Chief Ren, if this will cause you any inconvenience, I can send someone else to replace him."

"You are being too nice." Ren said. "Chunshou, come over and pay respects to Mr. Xia!"

Sun Yaoting had overheard the conversation in the adjoining room. He trotted in and kowtowed to Xia, who waved him up and said, "You should salute Chief Ren."

Sun Yaoting knelt and kowtowed to Ren, then got up and stood beside the kang.

"Chunshou," Ren straightened up a little and stuck out a finger. "Remember this: You can go wherever you like, but don't ever forget about me!"

"No, I won't! I'll always remember your kindness."

"Get him some money." At Ren's order a eunuch took out ten silver dollars and gave it to Sun Yaoting. "Buy yourself a nice gown and a pair of trousers," Ren said.

Sun Yaoting was delighted to get the unexpectedly handsome tip.

Over half a century later Sun Yaoting described the incident as a turning point in his career. "To be chosen by Duankang to play in her theatricals was like 'reaching heaven at a single stride'. For one thing, I would soon receive a formally registered palace name! I spent three dollars on two sets of new gowns and trousers before I went to pay respects to her."

Xia took Sun Yaoting to the Palace of Eternal Harmony. As they approached the gate Xia suddenly grew a little apprehensive. He turned to ask Sun Yaoting, "You were in Prince Zai Tao's house for some time, weren't you? What did you learn to do?"

"You want me to give a demonstration?"

"By all means."

"Please don't laugh at my incompetence." After making the standard "performer's opening remark", Sun Yaoting slipped out of his long gown. He turned two somersaults, made a handstand, and moved on his hands for two steps.

Xia patted him on the shoulder, looking very pleased. "Excellent! Study hard with Chief Zhang, and you'll be fine!"

Sun Yaoting was taken to Zhang Anji, who was in charge of the theatrical group at the Palace of Eternal Harmony. "Are you Chushou?" Zhang asked.

"Yes."

"You learned to play at Prince Zai Tao's house, didn't you?"

"Just for a few days," Sun Yaoting replied cautiously. He did not want to boast only to be found incompetent afterward. "I can do a couple of somersaults, that's all."

"You have to work hard and keep on learning," Zhang exhorted. "Madam Duankang knows about you. Now that you are here, you must do your best to bring credit to the Palace of Eternal Harmony."

"Yes, I understand."

Sun Yaoting had to get up early each morning to practice the performer's basic skills: bending, stretching, somersaulting, and so on. Only when the sun was high in the sky could he sit down at the table to eat the leftovers from Zhang Anji's morning meal. Then he had to resume training without a break until dusk.

One day Sun Yaoting had just finished his first meal, his face still sweaty from the morning's strenuous exercises, when Zhang Anji told him to get prepared to meet Duankang. Wiping off the sweat from his forehead, he got up and followed Zhang to the hall in which Duankang was sitting.

Sun Yaoting knelt in front of an open window. "Where are you from?" asked a woman's shaky voice inside.

His head lowered, Sun Yaoting recounted his personal background and details, something he had done many times after his entry into the palace.

"Can you read?"

"Yes, your slave has learned to read."

"Name a few books you've studied."

"Your slave was in a private school for four years and studied *A Hundred Family Names*, *The Book of Songs*, and *The Four Confucian Classics*."

"You stayed in Prince Zai Tao's house?"

"Yes, your slave was there for over a year."

"So you can read," Duankang turned to a eunuch in attendance. "Bring the newspaper."

Sun Yaoting was greatly relieved when it turned out to be a copy of Beijing News.

"Read a passage aloud," said Duankang.

Sun Yaoting started to read in a soft but articulate voice. After a while Duankang stopped him. "You know quite a few characters," she said approvingly. "Zhang Anji will put your name on the list."

"Thanks!"

Before leaving, Sun Yaoting stole a glance at the high consort. She was a

High Consort Duankang

rather plump lady in her forties. She wore a gray cheongsam, the typical Manchu-style dress for women. Her face looked wan without any make-up, and there was a conspicuous wart on her neck. But for her fine dress and headwear, she could have been mistaken for a countrywoman. Sun Yaoting could not help wondering why she had been chosen to be a consort for Emperor Guangxu, described by many as a quite romantic person.

At Duankang's order Sun Yaoting was formally recruited into the theatrical group at the Palace of Eternal Harmony. Duankang had a large retinue of 121 registered eunuchs, including 13 head eunuchs. Sun Yaoting had yet to be granted a formal palace name.

4. The Theatrical Troupe

Head eunuch Zhang Anji now had three junior eunuchs to serve him. Sun Yaoting and another eunuch got up before dawn every day to practice with the theatrical troupe. A third eunuch, who was Zhang's personal servant, enjoyed exemption from such drudgery.

The troupe had three tutors: two brothers, Zhang Changbao and Zhang Qishan, who were both martial arts masters, and a eunuch good at turning somersaults. They were the leading members of the group, treated with special favor by Duankang. Under their supervision the junior eunuchs learned and practiced the basic movements and gestures in Beijing opera. For example, they must be able to split their legs wide apart either to the sides or to the front and back respectively. With stone weights fastened to the sides, Sun Yaoting lowered his waist gradually as his legs spread wider. He suffered excruciating pain and broke into a sweat. But the training method proved highly effective. Before long he could do the splits easily.

Compared with the training in Prince Zai Tao's house, the drills at the Palace of Eternal Harmony were tougher and the discipline more rigid. The instructors, club in hand, watched the young eunuchs closely. Whoever showed the slightest sign of laxity would get a sharp poke on the back. The morning exercise lasted a long time, so they seldom ate before nine o'clock. After the meal they practiced martial arts routines with spears and broadswords. In the afternoon the instructors discussed in detail the scenarios of operas they were to be performing.

Despite all the hardships, Sun Yaoting felt happy, for there seemed to be a future ahead. Play-acting was considered the lowliest profession in traditional China, but the situation was somewhat different in the Imperial Palace, where a good performer could attain a high status and win favor from the Emperor or his consorts. It was well known that Li Lianying, one of Empress Dowager Cixi's favorite eunuchs, first attracted her attention by his excellent theatrical performance. Sun Yaoting remembered the words of Xin Hengru, the old eunuch who had helped him enter the palace: "One

The Palace of Eternal Harmony

can never attain wealth and fame without suffering aches and pains." He was prepared to suffer aches and pains to get what he wanted.

On a late spring day Zhang Anji took Sun Yaoting to see Duankang again, this time to receive his formal palace name. No one knew when the practice began, but many eunuchs listed in the palace registry were long dead, with their monthly stipend pocketed by the head eunuchs. Instead of registering in his own name, a newly recruited eunuch often had to purchase one of the names of his dead predecessors. The process must be undertaken with the approval of the person in charge of the specific palace – the Empress Dowager, the Empress, or an Imperial Consort, with whom the head eunuchs had to split the proceeds. Though absurd, it had become normal practice in the palace. Sun Yaoting had to pay Zhang a handsome bribe before the latter agreed to secure a name for him.

"You are granted a name," Duankang's voice was rather amiable. "From now on you will go by the name of Wang Chengxiang in the palace!"

"Your slave is grateful for the great favor!"

"You will get a reward of a hundred dollars," Duankang added.

Sun Yaoting kowtowed repeatedly in obeisance. Walking out, he felt as if a heavy weight had been lifted from his chest. The reward of a hundred dollars did not amount to much, for they were paper money worth only a couple of silver dollars, and he had to give sixty to a registration office. As a listed junior eunuch he should be paid two taels of silver a month plus a daily ration of rice, but he never received it. Nonetheless, he was happy just to get a secure position in the palace.

After a meal one day, Sun Yaoting cleared up the table for Zhang Anji. He put the bowl and dishes into a box and carried it away on a pole with another junior eunuch, Chunxi. Unfortunately they tripped on the steps. The box fell to the ground and the bowl was broken. In a panic he ran back and told Zhang Anji tearfully, "Master, it's too bad! I've broken your rice bowl!"

"What?" Zhang Anji glared at him. "You've broken my rice bowl?" Like all senior eunuchs, he was supersensitive to any inauspicious remark. In everyday language the "rice bowl" referred to one's job, career, or livelihood.

Sun Yaoting did not get the clue. "Yes," he said, "your rice bowl is broken into pieces!"

Zhang Anji banged the table with his hand and barked out an order. "Get the Office of Palace Justice!"

Sun Yaoting knelt and kowtowed to beg for mercy, but it was too late. Soon four eunuchs from the Office of Palace Justice walked in, throwing a yellow cloth bag on the floor. One of them took a few bamboo sticks from the bag. Two came up and pushed Sun Yaoting to the floor, slipping him out of his trousers. "Cross your feet!" they ordered. Sun Yaoiting placed his left foot on the right one and leaned to the right to expose his left buttock. With his hands and feet pinned down by three eunuchs, he stretched out on the floor in the shape of a cross.

Zhang Anji counted out twenty bamboo strips and dropped them to the floor. This meant that Sun Yaoting was to get twenty strokes of the stick.

"Have mercy! Have mercy! I'll never do it again!" As a eunuch brought down a bamboo stick on his buttock with great force and precision, Sun Yaoting kept wailing piteously. Silence, he knew, would be considered a defiant gesture and increase his penalty. After getting twenty strokes, he kowtowed to thank Zhang for the punishment. Then he staggered back to his room with the help of two eunuchs, collapsed into bed, and stayed there for over ten days.

The theatrical troupe at the Palace of Eternal Harmony had a very impressive lineup. Little Seven, a eunuch attendant for Duankang, composed a rhyme enumerating the important members of the group: Xia, Zhou, Cai, Bian, and Ying. Xia Kueixuan was the "backstage manager". He was not only eloquent in speech but could actually write screenplays. Zhou Yuting had enjoyed great favor since the time of Empress Dowager Cixi and Empress Dowager Longyu due to his expertise in martial arts. Cai excelled in beating the big gong, while Bian was good at beating the small gong. Ying Yuchuan, a master drummer, enjoyed the favor of Empress Dowager Cixi and Emperor Guangxu. Listening to the rhyme, Sun Yaoting vowed that he would work hard and make a name for himself.

Liu, a martial arts instructor, was quite a well-known figure in the Imperial Palace. Easygoing and pleasant in nature, he had no equal in the palace when it came to martial arts expertise. One day Sun Yaoting and seven other eunuchs were practicing somersaults in the courtyard when Liu came and told them to line up and bend forward. Then he jumped from the head of the line and landed at its tail. Young eunuchs liked him because he was amiable and tolerant. When exhausted by exercise, some young eunuch would call out, "Please Dad, give your children a break!" Liu would usually laugh and dismiss them.

As a young boy Liu used to play the "flowery face role" in Beijing opera, representing a virile man or rough character such as a warrior, a general, or a brigand. He often played pranks during performance, and most of the time he got away with it. One day Xiaode Zhang found an excuse to give him a heavy beating. That very night he disappeared from the palace, and Zhang had to send people to search for him in his hometown. They found Liu sleeping soundly at home. When asked if he realized what an offence he had committed, he replied with a grin, "I stole His Majesty's gold vase! Didn't I give it to you as a gift?"

"Stop talking nonsense! You will lose your head!"

"Don't try to scare me! If the sky falls, the tallest men will get crushed first, not me!"

They set out for the capital in a carriage. Half way out Liu suddenly disappeared to the great alarm of the runners. They looked for him everywhere but could not find him. At last Liu called out on top of the carriage, where he had been perching all along. Back in the palace, Liu did not get any punishment thanks to Chief Eunuch Li Lianying, who appreciated his talents and spoke in his favor to Empress Dowager Cixi.

Liu was once made a personal attendant for Pu Yi, who disliked the mischievous boy and dismissed him on the same day. He finally became a chief eunuch for Wenxiu, the Sedate Consort.

Sun Yaoting was greatly impressed by the story of Liu, who seemed to have attained a high status in the palace by his outstanding martial arts skills. Taking Liu as his role model, he did the daily exercises most diligently. Thanks to his intelligence and sheer hard work, he soon excelled among the junior eunuchs in the theatrical troupe. Half a year later he began to get important roles in various plays. In *Shi Xiu Scouts out the Village*, he played the title hero, Shi Xiu. In another famous drama *The Leopard*, he played Little Monkey, a supporting role with a lot of action. Though not yet counted as a pillar of the theatrical troupe, Sun Yaoting became a fairly important member.

At the Palace of Eternal Harmony Sun Yaoting saw Zhao Rongsheng frequently. Zhao, an excellent performer, agreed that they could be good partners on stage. At that time operas were staged regularly at the Palace of Eternal Harmony, attended not only by Duankang but also by the Emperor, Pu Yi, who did not seem to have anything better to do.

Pu Yi in a fashionable suit

In one of the plays Zhao Rongsheng was cast as a beautiful imperial consort, enthralling the audience with his melodious singing, amorous glances and alluring postures, with Sun Yaoting playing a supporting role. Duankang was so pleased with the performance that she awarded Zhao eighty silver dollars, of which he gave eight dollars to Sun Yaoting. Little Seven, whose palace name was Chunlai, also made a good pair with Sun Yaoting on stage. Together they could send Duankang and the rest of the audience into boisterous laughter. But Pu Yi's reaction was usually rather lukewarm, with no more than a bland smile on his face.

Apart from watching Beijing operas, Duankang spent much time playing mahjong with her servants. Her regular playmates included an old palace woman, a eunuch attendant, and a head eunuch. They often sat down at a square table and played for a whole day. Though Duankang was generally amiable and easygoing, the others never forgot the distinction between master and slave and let her win most of the time. They watched her expression closely. If she frowned or looked frustrated, they would deliberately commit one blunder after another until she had the combination of blocks she needed in order to win.

Sun Yaoting, who was not yet an attendant, could only watch Duankang and her playmates from a distance. He had many jobs to do, such as opening the door and sweeping the floor. It was also his responsibility to open the numerous windows in the palace at nine in the morning and close them at four in the afternoon. He could be punished for the slightest negligence.

The hot summer days gave the junior eunuchs an especially hard time. An "overhead curtain" was used in place of electric fans, which had not yet been introduced into the palace. Made of a bamboo frame sewn with cloth and paper, the curtain was hung from the rooftop, facing the door. Four young eunuchs took turns pulling at the curtain from both sides. The air currents generated by the curtain were cool and gentle, but the eunuchs soon got sore in the back. The table was placed opposite the door, right under the curtain, so that Duankang could play mahjong unhampered by the summer heat.

"What don't they use fans? Wouldn't it save us a lot of trouble?" Sun Yaoting once asked an old eunuch.

"What a foolish thing for you to say! Can't you see who's playing? It's Madam Duankang! It would be inconceivable for a slave to hold a fan in front of her!"

"But they can simply have someone fanning her, can't they?"

"Where do you get such nutty ideas? Suppose we only have someone fanning Duankang, and the others are left to sweat and stink in front of her, would she feel comfortable? We've been doing things like this since the Ming times, and you think you are smarter than everybody else?"

Thus Sun Yaoting learned that the "overhead curtain" was actually a legacy from the Ming Dynasty.

5. Death of Emperor's Mother

High Consort Duankang residing in the Palace of Eternal Harmony seemed to be a rather mediocre woman, who emulated Cixi and Longyu in her extravagant lifestyle. For instance, she always had more than twenty dishes laid out for each meal. Unlike other imperial consorts, she seldom invited her head eunuchs to eat with her at the same table.

Duankang had two head eunuchs in charge of the Palace of Eternal Harmony: Liu Chengping and Mu Haichen. Starting as a junior eunuch under Empress Dowager Longyu, Liu worked his way up through the years. After Longyu's death he was promoted to head eunuch in the Palace of Eternal Harmony. Mu was an illiterate with an insatiable craving for money. Duankang used to have over a dozen eunuchs waiting on her at the Palace of Eternal Harmony, but now she only had six. In addition to two head eunuchs, she had Xia Kuixuan and Chi Huanqing as heralds and Zhao Rongsheng and Wang Jiu'an as personal servants. Only rarely did she honor her head eunuchs and heralds by inviting them to eat with her, and then they had to remain

Head eunuch Liu Chengping

standing throughout the meal.

Duankang showed a strong desire to control the child Emperor, Pu Yi. Taking Empress Dowager Cixi as her model, she had a trusted eunuch wait on the Emperor and give her daily reports of his every word and action. Cixi had done exactly the same to Emperor Guangxu. Pu Yi did not like it at all, but he was powerless to stop it.

Pu Yi paid a courtesy call to Duankang every morning. Occasionally she invited him to come for a chat. He sometimes asked her eunuchs whether she was in a good mood before he went in to see her. When informed of this she broke into a fit, which only made Pu Yi more afraid of her.

The young Emperor was fond of fashionable dresses. One day a eunuch named Li Chang'an bought him a Western-style suit complete with socks and leather shoes. Pu Yi put it on and paraded it proudly in the palace. When she heard of it, Duankang was furious. "What a disgrace for the Imperial family!"

"Li Chang'an seemed to be behind it," a eunuch told her.

Duankang summoned Li at once. "Did you get those clothes for the Emperor?"

"Yes, it was your slave's idea," Li replied in a trembling voice.

"What impudence!" Duankang ordered Li to be beaten up with a heavy rod and taken away for further punishment. Incidents like this aggravated the young Emperor's dissatisfaction with the High Consort. From people around him he got the idea that Duankang was merely a consort and therefore did not deserve much respect. Zhang Qianhe, the Chief Superintendent, once remarked contemptuously, "She is just a secondary wife of the late Emperor, isn't she? A country bumpkin trying to play grand lady!"

Duankang had several child eunuchs recruited from the countryside, believing that they were more docile and submissive. Among them, Little

Seven enjoyed her special favor. One day it suddenly started to rain heavily, and he was nowhere to be seen in the palace. Just as Duankang was worrying about him, he burst in, shoes in hand and soaked all over. "Where have you been?" she asked.

"I was playing outside."

"Poor boy! You look like a drenched chicken!" Duankang helped him put on the shoes and told a eunuch attendant to bring a towel, with which she wiped away the raindrops on his face.

"Thank you so much, madam!"

Duankang looked immensely pleased. With no child of her own, she liked young boys and almost regarded Little Seven as her own.

"She treats Little Seven better than she treats me!" Pu Yi muttered angrily when a eunuch told him the incident.

Several eunuchs who were jealous of Little Seven decided to teach him a lesson. One day they sent a young eunuch to provoke Little Seven into a fight. They swarmed over, acting as if they wanted to separate them but taking the chance to hit him in the entanglement. Little Seven tried unsuccessfully to dodge their blows and ended up being beaten black and blue. At the sight of his wounds Duankang asked, "Who did this to you, Little Seven?"

"I can't remember," he shook his head.

When the other eunuchs found out that Little Seven dared not report them to Duankang, they became emboldened and bullied him frequently.

One day Pu Yi came to see Duankang in the Palace of Eternal Harmony. They had a big quarrel over a trivial matter. In the heat of the argument he blurted out, "You like Little Seven better than me!" Then he stormed out with a flick of his sleeve, leaving Duankang in uncontrollable fury. Taking the advice of her two head eunuchs, she invited Pu Yi's mother to come over to mediate. At the request of his mother, Pu Yi gave in and came to the Palace of Eternal Harmony to apologize to Duankang. After Pu Yi left, his mother stayed on to chat with Duankang for a while, then went home. The next morning came the shocking news that she had committed suicide by swallowing a fatal dose of opium. Rumors abounded concerning the cause of her death. According to some people, She had a terrible altercation with Duankang after Pu Yi left.

Sun Yaoting heard the story from Feng Leting, a eunuch attendant of Duankang. "After the Emperor left, Duankang started a tearful ranting,

Pu Yi's birth mother, Lady Gua'erjia

and the Emperor's mother wept with her. Then Duankang stopped weeping and began to complain angrily, so they got into a bitter quarrel."

"I see," Sun Yaoting said. "Otherwise she would not have killed herself."

"Do you know she was General Rong Lu's daughter? People at the Northern Mansion describe her as a very headstrong woman."

"But this would not have happened if Duankang had received better advice to handle the matter," Sun Yaoting remarked.

"You are absolutely right," Feng nodded his head. "Take Liu Chengping, for instance. He did a good job combing Duankang's hair, but he can't read a word and doesn't know the right thing to say. His deputy, Mu, is only good at amassing money. What rotten ideas can you expect from the two of them? If they had advised Duankang wisely, there would have been no quarrel and no suicide!"

Actually there might have been other causes for the death of Pu Yi's mother. The imperial family had always been dreaming of a restoration, and Duankang spent a lot of money to this end. It was said that Pu Yi's mother had received some palace treasures, which she was supposed to use to cultivate the friendship of politicians and military strongmen. But all her efforts proved futile. In the heat of the quarrel Duankang accused her of embezzling the restoration funds. She found the humiliation hard to swallow and therefore committed suicide.

The theatrical group of the Palace of Eternal Harmony rehearsed several famous dramas, and Sun Yaoting was eager to display his newly acquired talents. Unfortunately the sudden death of Zhang Anji put everything to a halt. An opium addict, Zhang had a very weak physique. After suffering a minor ailment, he took to bed and died shortly afterward. The theatrical group, deprived of its manager, stopped all activities. Again Sun Yaoting faced a very uncertain future.

4

IN THE RED WALLS

1. Head Eunuch Mu

In autumn Sun Yaoting began to serve Mu Haichen, who replaced Zhang Anji. Mu was a handsome, white-skinned man of medium height. He was a disciple of Xiaode Zhang and used to wait on Empress Dowager Longyu. Zhang was famous for treating his subordinates well and giving big tips. In contrast, Mu Haichen was extremely tightfisted. His salary and bonuses amounted to about ten dollars a day, but he rarely tipped the junior eunuchs.

Having worked his way up from the very bottom, Mu was not only a good servant but a very difficult master as well. One day Mu told Sun Yaoting to prepare tea. Sun Yaoting went away and returned with a cup of tea on a platter. "Here you are."

"Is it hot?"

"Yes, it is."

Mu picked up an olive and threw it into the cup. Looking at the olive, he said coldly, "It's not hot."

"It's not hot because of the olive," Sun Yaoting said.

Mu screamed , "Nonsense! How dare you talk back to me? Slap yourself!"

Under Mu's cold stare, Sun Yaoting slapped himself once on each cheek.

"Prepare the tea again! If it's still not hot, you'll lose your head!"

Head eunuch Mu Haichen

Mu was of course merely making threats. Sun Yaoting went away and returned with another cup of hot tea. Without a word Mu pushed away the floating tea leaves with the cover and took a sip.

As time went by, Sun Yaoting got used to Mu's temper and idiosyncrasies. Unlike Zhang Anji, whose sole hobby was smoking opium, Mu Haichen enjoyed listening to stories. He often lay on the kang with Sun Yaoting reading for him from popular novels such as *Xue Rengui Leads a Westward Expedition, Xue Rengui Leads an Eastward Expedition*, and *The Hero and Two Sisters*. When they came to a part that he really liked, he would have it repeated.

Mu had three eunuchs as his personal servants: Sun Yaoting, An Kuoting, and Blind Chen. Sun Yaoting managed to gain favor thanks to his ability to read and write. Mu even showed him some partiality by assigning him a sinecure, for which he received extra income in addition to the New Year's bonus of ten dollars. An Kuoting was a blunt man with a fiery temper. Blind Chen, as his nickname suggested, had very poor eyesight.

"What a showoff!" Blind Chen muttered to himself from time to time. At first Sun Yaoting did not understand what he meant. Then he learned that the junior eunuchs were quite dissatisfied with Mu Haichen. Mu always wanted eight dishes for each meal, otherwise he would curse and swear angrily. Only after he finished eating could the attending eunuchs clear the table and help themselves to the leftovers.

When in a lighthearted mood, Mu chatted with Sun Yaoting about various affairs in the palace. One day Sun Yaoting asked, "In the entire palace Duankang has the final say on everything, doesn't she? Whatever she says goes."

"It depends," Mu said. "You know about the child from Nanku?"

"Yes. He's quite a handsome boy!" Sun Yaoting remembered playing hide-and-seek with the young eunuch.

"Duankang likes him, you know. But she failed to get him because of the Chief Superintendent's objection!"

"What?" Sun Yaoting responded in disbelief. "You mean the Chief Superintendent dares to say no to her?"

"You are too young to understand such things," Mu said. "The boy somehow learned that the Palace of Eternal Harmony had an opening for a young eunuch. I don't know who gave him the clever idea, but he got all dressed up and waited at the Gate of Moon Essence, where Duankang passes every day. She noticed him and said, 'What a good-looking boy!' On her return she sent for the Chief Superintendent and told him to reassign the child to her. The Chief Superintendent said he had to look up in the files to find out where the boy was from. Several days passed, and Duankang got very impatient. She summoned the Chief Superintendent and asked him why the boy had not come. He explained that the boy had a very bad temper and often got into fights. 'Who can guarantee that he will not cause trouble? You certainly need a more meek and docile child!' This really made her mad. 'I want that child whatever you say,' she told him. She vowed never to eat until the boy was brought to her. At lunchtime, she didn't touch a thing. Well, you would think that the Chief Superintendent would have given in, but he didn't, because he is a very resourceful man. Somehow he persuaded Duankang's favorite, Little Seven, to talk her out of her fast. 'Please have your meal,' he pleaded. 'I'm starving!' She was coaxed into eating, and the matter was dropped."

"How could the Chief Superintendent get away with it?" asked Sun Yaoting.

"Of course he could," Mu said. "He's lived in the palace for dozens of years and knows perfectly well what he's doing. After all, Duankang is not another Cixi! She can be easily taken in by a few words. It was Little Seven who finally made her change her mind. She no longer wanted the child from Nanku after Little Seven told her they didn't get along very well. Little Seven is her favorite, you know. And you know why the Chief Superintendent acted the way he did? He had already sold the vacancy in the Palace of Eternal Harmony to someone else!"

"This is all so complicated!" Sun Yaoting sighed.

Early one morning Mu told Sun Yaoting, "Madam wants me to offer sacrifice on her behalf to the Well of Precious Consort. Get some cake and fruits. We'll leave in just a moment."

Sun Yaoting quickly prepared two boxes of cake and several boxes of fruits, and they set out. "On the anniversary of the Precious Consort's death," Mu said, "Duankang used to go in person to offer sacrifice. They were sisters, you know. In the last few years I've been doing it for her."

They arrived at the well by the Gate of Submission and Virtue behind the Palace of Peaceful Longevity. Mu lit several joss sticks while Sun Yaoting laid out the offerings. Straightening his clothes, Mu knelt before the well, kowtowed three times, and got up without a word.

"Shall I kowtow too?" Sun Yaoting asked tentatively, but Mu dismissed him with a wave of his hand. The simple ceremony was soon over. On their way back, Mu would answer no question. After a short rest he went to the Palace of Eternal Harmony to report briefly to Duankang about the sacrifice.

As Sun Yaoting got to know Mu better, he began to relax a little bit and even dared to talk back occasionally. Then a sad incident took place.

"Let's go to Dongguang Cinema today!" Mu said. "Take the two children along." The "two children" referred to Mu's adopted sons, Dashun and Ershun.

"I'll go and get the rickshaws," Sun Yaoting said.

They got into two rickshaws and set off. When Mu stepped out of the rickshaw in front of the cinema, he suddenly remembered something and turned to Sun Yaoting angrily. "Look what you've done!"

"What's wrong?" Sun Yaoting asked in dismay.

"Where's that padded jacket?"

"Oh!" Sun Yaoting cried out. "I've lost it!" The day before they had gone to see an opera. On their way to the opera house it suddenly started to rain heavily, so they went into a shop to take shelter. The shopkeeper, Wu Huapu, knew Mu well and lent him a lined jacket. After the performance Mu took off the jacket and handed it to Sun Yaoting, who put it away and then forgot all about it.

Since they had already arrived at the cinema, they went in to see the film anyway. Afterward Mu returned to the palace alone, leaving Sun Yaoting behind to look for the lost jacket.

When Sun Yaoting came back empty-handed, Mu had an outburst and hurled abuses at him. Sun Yaoting kept apologizing "Tell me what was on your mind!" Mu roared. "Were you ogling women? You'll never learn to behave yourself without a beating!" He slapped Sun Yaoting twice across the face. Having vented his rage, Mu sank back into the chair to regain his breath. In the end he took Sun Yaoting's advice and gave Wu Huapu a new jacket in compensation.

Life took an unexpected turn for Sun Yaoting when High Consort Duankang heard a young eunuch selling almond tea one day. "I'd like some almond tea!" she said. Her eunuch attendant Chi Huanqing went out and brought in the peddler. "Get the three heads in the backyard to come!" she ordered. "Bring the young boys here too! Let's enjoy tea together!"

The head eunuchs of the "backyard", or the Accounting Office, were

Wang Shunshan, Liu Ziyu and Xin Xiuming. Sipping her almond tea, Duankang remarked, "The three of you are quite advanced in years, so I'll assign some young boys to help you. Each of you can take another disciple!" The three head eunuchs thanked her, finished their tea, and retreated. Sun Yaoting, as one of the "young boys", thus joined the Accounting Office.

2. The Accounting Office

One day in the 8th lunar month Sun Yaoting, along with two other junior eunuchs, was formally transferred to the Accounting Office located in the rear compound of the Palace of Great Benevolence. Early in the morning Liu Chengping took them, together with the three head eunuchs of the Accounting Office, to pay respects to Duankang at the Palace of Eternal Harmony. She was wearing a gray cheongsam and a pair of black satin shoes. Her hair was worn into a bun, decorated by a rather plain-looking hairpin. The three junior eunuchs, Chunshou, Chunzhong and Chunqing, kowtowed their gratitude. "The three boys are now assigned to you, Duankang told the head eunuchs. "Chunshou is a bit older than the other two." She turned to Sun Yaoting. "How much older are you?"

"Your slave is six years their senior," Sun Yaoting replied with his head lowered.

Duankang told Liu Ziyu to take him as a disciple, much to his delight. He kowtowed three times to acknowledge his new mentor, Liu Ziyu, who was quite well known in the palace. He became a eunuch after getting married. His wife, left behind in their hometown, was so attached to him that she refused to get a divorce and marry someone else.

The rear compound of the Palace of Great Benevolence belonged to the Accounting Office, which employed more than a dozen eunuchs. It was responsible for controlling the finances in the palace other than the Imperial Treasury and articles of tribute. Wang Shunshan was the most senior of the three head eunuchs. A fairly accomplished scholar, he devoted most of his time to studying and teaching. His pupils included not only young eunuchs but also noble ladies from outside the palace. He spoke little but was widely respected.

Sun Yaoting's new mentor, Liu Ziyu, was a fellow disciple of Xiaode Zhang. After Zhang was promoted to be Empress Dowager Longyu's chief eunuch, he got Liu a good job: reading books for Longyu. Every evening at bedtime Liu sat on a cushion in front of her bed to read storybooks. Zhang had briefed him about the Empress Dowager's taste and preferences. For example, she seemed to enjoy romantic descriptions that bordered on the obscene, so Liu marked out such parts in the book beforehand and elaborated on them when he read it. He often kept reading until Duankang fell asleep, then retreated quietly. In this way Liu gradually won her favor. With Xiaode Zhang putting in some good words for him, he was eventually promoted to head eunuch.

Xin Xiuming, the third-ranking head eunuch at the Accounting Office, had the nickname "Immortal". He was an accomplished painter and calligrapher, among other things. With the help of his mentor, Xiaode Zhang, he got the lucrative post of supervising the accounts of the imperial kitchen when he was quite young. Before Longyu's death he was promoted to head eunuch at the Accounting Office, again upon Zhang's recommendation. He was good-tempered and kind to his subordinates, and therefore widely liked and respected.

Of the three head eunuchs Sun Yaoting held Xin Xiuming in the highest regard. Well over fifty, he looked much younger than his age. His nickname fit him well, for he could truly be mistaken for an immortal when dressed in a Taoist robe. When it came to palace affairs, few people were more experienced or knowledgeable. In the final years of the Qing dynasty he was the only eunuch to keep a diary about everyday occurrences in the palace.

The three head eunuchs lived in the eastern hall, each with a junior eunuch to do daily chores. The Accounting Office also employed four male servants, three cooks and a menial; these people had to leave the palace at nightfall. The main hall in the rear was a storehouse for Duankang's clothes and accessories. If she needed anything, she would send her maids or female servants to collect it. The western hall held a shrine in honor of Confucius, with a memorial tablet bearing his title, "The Great Perfect Most Holy Former Teacher".

Sun Yaoting and four other eunuchs lived in the southern hall. They slept on a brick kang, which could be heated in winter. From the middle of the 11th lunar month, the eunuchs took turns tending the fire. Like elsewhere in the palace, the kang had an opening underneath to hold a stove, with a flue leading to the back of the house. In winter they lit a four-wheel stove, known as "the little fire cart", outside the house, then pushed it under the kang. The flue could be used for ventilation in summer.

With his name entered into Duankang's Accounting Office, Sun Yaoting received his monthly stipend for the first time before the Mid-Autumn Festival, which fell on the 15th of the eighth lunar month. It was a little over six taels of silver. By comparison, a junior eunuch in the house of a Manchu prince was paid no more than one tael twenty each month. Though a head eunuch earned about ten taels more than he did, Sun Yaoting felt quite satisfied. After all, he was paid much more than ever before. A few days later he received an unexpected tip of twenty dollars, which the head eunuchs doled out from their extra income. Food on the table also improved; there was even butterfish in their everyday meal. Sun Yaoting was feeling quite content.

The three head eunuchs enjoyed certain privileges. For example, they had food allowances in addition to their monthly stipend. It was Sun Yaoting's duty to keep track of their food expenses. After he submitted his monthly report, they would be reimbursed accordingly. They usually ate at the same table, chatting freely.

Sun Yaoting shared the table with a few other eunuchs and two male servants. Most of the time they ate in silence. Anyone who talked too much would get a warning stare from one of the senior eunuchs. If anyone spoke loudly, a head eunuch would come over and give him a dressing-down.

Lunch usually consisted of four dishes and a soup. In winter they often had mutton hotpot, for which each head eunuch would contribute five dollars. That was quite a lot of money because one could get three kilos of mutton for a dollar. By custom it was the job of the most junior eunuch in the Accounting Office to go out to buy mutton as well as stewed pork, meatballs, bean starch noodles, cabbage, and a bottle of liquor. The hotpot was a treat for everyone.

Though his job could be very tiring sometimes, Sun Yaoting remained in high spirits. Getting up in the morning, he brushed his teeth with a bamboo toothbrush and a sort of tooth powder that came in square boxes. Then he went to the western hall to pay homage to Confucius as a daily ritual, lighting three joss sticks and kowtowing to the memorial tablet of the great sage. Afterwards, he offered morning greetings to the three head eunuchs, wishing them good luck for the day. At about eight o'clock they had the morning meal. At nine some of the junior eunuchs went on duty, placing themselves at the beck and call of the head eunuchs. The others were free to go about their own business within the bounds of the Palace of Great Benevolence. Most spent the time earning extra money by making matchboxes, peddling various items of goods, and so on.

About two weeks before the Lunar New Year, the Imperial Palace celebrated the annual Confucius' Day. The eunuchs got up early and kowtowed before the tablet of Confucius, with whole-cooked lamb and pig among the sacrificial offerings. At the end of the ceremony the junior eunuchs saluted their mentors, wishing them "good fortune", and for once the senior eunuchs returned the greeting. It was a time of goodwill and reconciliation.

The emperor and the empress did not have to go outdoors to relieve themselves. According to a popular legend, a martial arts master assassinated Emperor Yongzheng when he was on his way to an outdoor toilet. After that, chamber pots were installed for the imperial couple. The eunuchs, on the other hand, used the same toilet regardless of rank, and had to pay for their own toilet paper. Separate toilets were built for male servants and palace women. The toilet for eunuch use was kept extremely clean, with incense burned all day as a deodorant.

The most dreaded job for junior eunuchs was taking the night shift, known as "night-sitting". The eunuch on duty had to sleep under the eaves to watch for unusual occurrences in the palace. For this purpose every eunuch had to buy a prop-up tent made of cotton, bamboo and cloth. Depending on the season, the tent might be single-layered, double-layered, or padded with cotton. A handful of shops still remained that specialized in manufacturing bedding for the palace. The most popular one, run by a man named Chi, was located on Beichang Street just outside the palace. Because of their long-standing relationship with the palace, the shop assistants got to know the eunuchs quite well. They always delivered the tents on time and even paid commission to the eunuchs who negotiated deals with them. The shop gradually monopolized the production of prop-up tents for the palace and enjoyed a booming business until 1924, when Pu Yi was driven out of the Forbidden City.

A few days after Sun Yaoting got his first monthly stipend, a bookkeeping eunuch came to see him. "Chunshou, you have yet to pay a

Pu Yi in a nondescript civilian dress

debt of seventeen dollars."

"What?" Sun Yaoting exclaimed in disbelief. "I've never borrowed money from anyone! How can I be in debt?" When he looked at the account book, he was filled with rage. "That bastard!" he muttered. The bookkeeper was astonished by this outburst. "It has nothing to do with you," Sun Yaoting hastily explained. He was angry because Mu Haichen had billed him for the lost jacket.

Sun Yaoting found Mu Haichen sitting in his chair sipping tea. "Mr. Mu, you are going too far!" He forgot all his fear.

"What's the matter?" Mu said slowly, as if he had no idea what was going on.

"Don't play the fool with me!"

"How dare you speak to me in this way? You'd better watch your tongue!" Mu's voice grew harsh and stern.

"Why did you bill me for the jacket? Why? You know the palace rules better than I do – 'Pay your penalty either in money or in kind.' Because of the jacket, you not only beat me but you also billed my account without telling me. What a rotten thing to do!"

"Who do you think you are talking to? You little bastard!"

"You old bastard!"

Flying into a rage, Mu got up and tried to slap Sun Yaoting, who fought back. Hearing the racket, a few eunuchs came over and separated them. Sun Yaoting was still panting and fuming when he got back to his room. "Why did you get into a fight with Mu?" said Liu Ziyu, his mentor. "Everybody knows what a skinflint he is! It's only a matter of ten dollars or so. Forget about it!"

"It's not just the money," Sun Yaoting said. "I can't let him bully me like this!"

"You are too young and impatient. Remember this saying: 'Endure for a moment, and the waves will calm down; take one step back, and you will find the way.' Always try to work out a compromise and avoid conflict."

Sun Yaoting took Liu's advice and did not try to get his money back. But he also stopped going to see Mu altogether. A few months later Mu suddenly sent for him. He was surprised to find a smile on Mu's face.

"Why do you want to see me?" asked Sun Yaoting.

"I've heard that you are looking after the storeroom. Is it true?"

"Yes."

"I need you to do something for me."

"Of course, if I can." Sun Yaoting made a silent vow that he would not lift a finger for Mu.

"I'm sure you can do it. I've been rewarded with lots of cloth and silk, but some are a bit old-fashioned in design. I want to exchange them for more recent ones. It will be an easy thing for you to do."

Sun Yaoting realized what Mu had in mind. Mu wanted to sell the cloth and silk outside the palace. At that time a meter of cloth was worth six to seven dollars and a roll of silk some thirty to forty dollars. "Do you really think it is an easy thing for me?" he said. "Can't you see that I'd lose my rice bowl if I do it? You have too much confidence in me. Maybe you should find someone more capable, such as the head of the Accounting Office or the supervisor of the storeroom. They are in a better position to help you, don't you think?"

Mu looked very displeased. "We can talk about it later," he said reluctantly.

When Sun Yaoting got back, Liu Ziyu asked him, "What did Mu want from you?"

"Oh, that miser! He wanted me to change some old silk for new. He was expecting too much!"

"What did you say?"

"I told him to the face that I couldn't do it."

"You did the right thing. Stay away from people like him."

At the Accounting Office Sun Yaoting spent a lot of time learning to use the abacus and practicing calligraphy. After teaching him the abacus for a while, Liu usually went for a stroll outside the palace. Sun Yaoting then sat down to practice with the writing brush. On his return at noon Liu commented on the merits and weaknesses of Sun Yaoting's handwriting and corrected his posture. "Sit up straight. Hold the brush like this, with its end pointing at the tip of your nose..."

Sun Yaoting was making slow progress with the abacus at first. When the other two junior eunuchs, Chunqing and Chunzhong, practiced under the tutelage of old eunuch Wu Shouchen, he often had to attend to people coming to get various articles from the storeroom. He grew so worried over his slow progress that he could not sleep well at night. He doubled his efforts and studied the abacus rhymes over and over until he learned them by heart. When a eunuch named Chen Zhongsan was formerly assigned by the Accounting Office to teach the three junior eunuchs how to use the abacus, he was surprised to find Sun Yaoting well ahead of the other two. "Where did you learn so much?" he asked.

"I was afraid to lag behind, so I taught myself in my spare time."

"And now you are the best," Chen patted him on the forehead. "That's remarkable."

Sun Yaoting was so determined to excel that he spent a lot of time practicing the abacus. Sometimes he asked Chen and Fan Dongyu, who shared the same room with him, to test him before going to bed. Chen was a master of card games and very good with numbers. "Try this simple problem," he said to Sun Yaoting one evening. "If every dan of grain costs nine dollar ninety-nine, how much does it cost to get nine dan ninety-nine?"

"That's easy." Sun Yaoting came up with the answer quickly.

"No, you have to tell me step by step how you reach the answer. That's the only way to prove you can do it on the abacus."

Sun Yaoting took the abacus and began to calculate, but somehow he could not get it straight. "What's wrong?" he asked Chen. "There doesn't seem to be enough beads to work with!"

"Think it over," Chen said with a smile. "I'm going out to play cards."

Sun Yaoting sat at the table working on the problem until he nodded off. Before dawn he was awakened when Chen returned to the room. "Is it daybreak already?" he asked drowsily, rubbing his eyes.

"No, not yet. Have you solved the problem?"

"I still think there aren't enough beads!"

"Why don't you use your brain?"

"Use my brain? But how?"

Chen smiled. "All right, let me show you. When you think there aren't enough beads, you can use the 'bead-suspension method', like this." He moved a few beads on the abacus. "You see?"

"Wow, it's so easy and simple!" Sun Yaoting exclaimed. "Thank you so much!"

"No problem," Chen said. Then he added in jest, "Just remember who taught you that! As the saying goes, the master starves after the disciple learns the trick!"

3. Constant Learning

Sun Yaoting surprised his teacher and fellow pupils with his rapid progress. He continued practicing the abacus diligently until he excelled among all eunuchs of the Accounting Office by his high calculation speed. One day Liu Ziyu praised him in front of several junior eunuchs. "You haven't let me down!" Turning to Chunqing and Chunzhong, he said, "Chunshou has set a good example for you. He had a late start but eventually got ahead of you. That's no easy thing to do! If you want to become somebody, you must work hard. That's how Li Lianying and Xiaode Zhang worked their way up to the top!"

One day Liu Ziyu's good friend Chen Zechuan called over the three young eunuchs at the Accounting Office and handed them ten dollars. "It's holiday tomorrow. You can go outside the palace and have a good time."

The next day Sun Yaoting and his two companions were in high spirits. Chen sent for a male servant to look after the young eunuchs. "You can take them to temple fairs, watch a play, whatever. Make sure they don't get into trouble or get lost." Then he handed the servant three "certificates". "Hold this for them." It was the first time Sun Yaoting had seen a eunuch's certificate, a square piece of paper with the name, age, and birthplace of the bearer. It was kept in a tiny silk bag that could be attached to one's underwear with a thin hemp string.

Accompanied by the male servant, the three young eunuchs went around in the city eating lots of snacks until their stomachs felt funny. Back in the palace, Sun Yaoting went straight to bed, totally exhausted. For Sun Yaoting and his companions, the outing was one of their fondest memories, and they talked about it for many days afterward.

"There is no limit to what one can learn," so goes a popular saying. It actually rang true for Sun Yaoting's life in the palace. After playacting, calligraphy, and calculation with the abacus, his next subject of study became ancient Chinese classics. When Liu Ziyu made the suggestion, Sun Yaoting was delighted. "You'd better have Wang Shunshan teach you," Liu said. "He's very good at it, second only to Xin in the entire palace."

"But will he agree to teach me?"

"No problem. I've talked it over with him. He's an old acquaintance of your former teacher, Mr. Fu Wenpo."

Wang Shunshan also came from Jinghai County of Tianjin. His younger brother had been a classmate of Fu Wenpo in a village school for several years. Wang had a great reputation for erudition. He knew the *Four Books* and *Five Classics* by heart and had even memorized the annotations. He could recite whole passages from any part of these books without missing a word. Many eunuchs had studied under his tutelage. He never turned anyone down, nor did he ask for anything in return.

Wang Shunshan was so wealthy that he owned large tracts of cultivated land in Jinghai County and several estates in Beijing. Like Liu Ziyu, he got married first and became a eunuch afterward. He visited his hometown several times a year to pay respects to his parents and see his wife. After he returned from a homecoming trip, Sun Yaoting asked, "How was this year's harvest for your family?"

"Not good. They told me the total yield was no more than seven hundred dan of wheat."

"That's quite a lot!" Sun Yaoting said. Obviously Wang was not nearly as knowledgeable about farming as about Confucian classics. A *dan*, meaning literally "a load of shoulder pole", was equal to about 80 kilograms.

Under Wang's tutorship, Sun Yaoting studied eight volumes of ancient texts. He not only understood the ideas in the books but could also expound upon them eloquently. Because of this, some eunuchs at the Accounting Office gave him the nickname "Little Scholar".

While talking with other eunuchs, Sun Yaoting heard much gossip and "inside stories" about what had taken place in the imperial palace. One day Xin Xiuming strolled into his room, and Sun Yaoting asked him about Duankang, the former Prudent Consort, and her sister the Precious Consort.

"That's quite a long story, " Xin Xiuming said. "The Prudent Consort was quite attractive, as you can still imagine by looking at her today. But the Precious Consort was prettier and also livelier. Emperor Guangxu liked her better and often sought her company. This resulted in intense hostility between the two sisters. Everybody knows that Empress Dowager Cixi had an extreme dislike for the Precious Consort. To make matters worse, the Precious Consort did something that gave Cixi a handle against her. She made money by selling official posts!"

"Really?"

"Few knew about it, but it was true. At that time many people were willing to pay large sums of money to get official posts, and the Precious Consort made deals with them. After taking their money, she spoke in their favor to Emperor Guangxu, who often gave her what she wanted. She did this more than once. Then a brawl broke out over the distribution of profits, and someone involved in the scheme reported her to Cixi. Cixi flew into a rage and ordered an investigation at once. They found enough evidence to prove that the Precious Consort had been responsible for selling the profitable post of a high-ranking tax officer. Over a dozen of her eunuchs were beaten to death, and she would have suffered severely if Emperor Guangxu had not begged Cixi to have mercy. This incident deepened Cixi's hatred for the consort. When the capital was under siege from the allied forces of eight foreign powers, Cixi ordered the consort to be drowned."

"The story is well known," Sun Yaoting said. "But what really happened?"

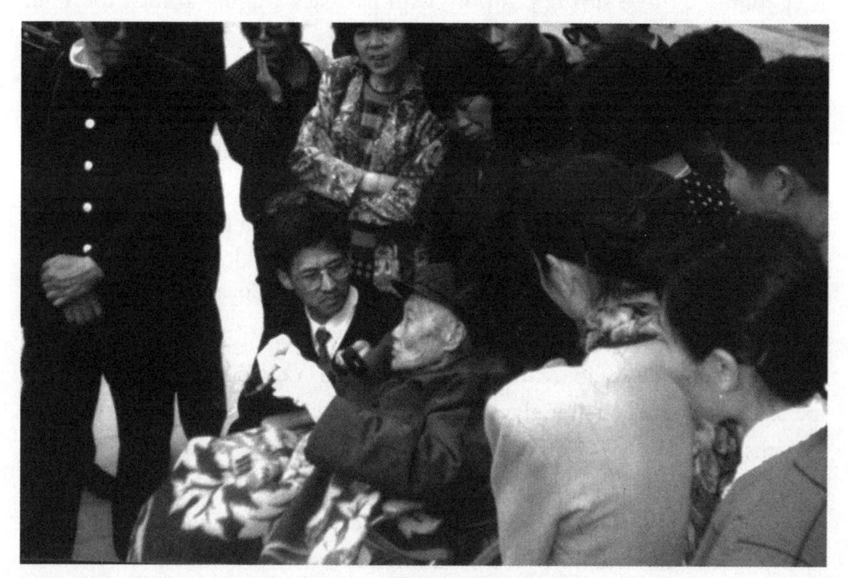

Sun Yaoting recounting the death of the Precious Consort in the Palace of Great Benevolence

"The Precious Consort sided with Emperor Guangxu in the so-called 'Hundred-Day Reform', which made Cixi hate her even more. Before leaving the capital, Cixi called a meeting at the Palace of Peaceful Longevity to discuss the escape route to Xi'an. Emperor Guangxu and several head eunuchs were present. Cixi suddenly turned to the Precious Consort and said, 'What about you? What are we going to do with you?' The Precious Consort immediately realized what Cixi meant. She fell on her knees and kowtowed repeatedly. 'Please take me with you! Treat me as your little kitten or puppy!' But Cixi said as an imperial consort she would stain the reputation of the Great Qing if she were captured and humiliated by enemy troops. Emperor Guangxu heard everything but did not dare say a single word. Cixi then shouted, 'Why are you standing still doing nothing? Cui Yugui, why are you hesitating? Throw her into the western well!' Everyone was stupefied at Cixi's cruelty, but no one dared to object. The Precious Consort kept saying 'have mercy' and even begged Cui Yugui to help her. But Cui wrapped her in a rug and pushed her into the well."

"Some say she was wrapped in a rug, and some say she wasn't," Sun Yaoting remarked.

"I'm not sure about that. Anyway, when Cixi returned from Xi'an, she ordered a few eunuchs to get the Precious Consort's body out of the well. They found her in a sitting position, with her back leaning against the wall. The well was small and narrow, but the water not very deep. They had to use a basket to fetch the body. At Cixi's order, the Precious Consort was buried in the cemetery of eunuchs at Enjizhuang. What a hardhearted woman!"

"During Cixi's rule in the palace, eunuchs were often beaten. It that true?"

"To get beaten was part of the daily routine! If you had been here then, you would have gotten your share!" Xin then added, "Keep away from the Office of Palace Justice! Let me get you a copy of the Rules of Punishment, and you'll know what I am talking about!"

The next day Xin Xiuming handed Sun Yaoting a booklet, which spelled out the exact penalty for several dozen offences committed by eunuchs. But Xin told him there were ways to get around the punishment. If an imperial master or mistress were present, the eunuchs carrying out the punishment would not dare to play any tricks. The only thing the hapless culprit could do was to place a handkerchief in his mouth to prevent severe injury to the mouth and teeth. If the punishment was left entirely to eunuchs, the culprit could bribe the eunuchs in charge beforehand, and they would make a show of heavy beating without inflicting much injury.

From another old eunuch, Liu Xingqiao, Sun Yaoting learned a method of self-protection against corporal punishment. "It's an open secret. But if you don't know it, you'll suffer a lot when they give you a beating!"

"I am grateful to you for telling me this," Sun Yaoting said.

"When Empress Dowager Cixi became angry, she often had dozens of eunuchs kneel in the hall and beaten with the club one by one. That's why everyone wore a 'shield' those days."

"Shield?"

"It's made of two pieces of ox skin, which you tied to your thighs and buttocks before you went on duty. We must always be prepared for a beating!"

"That's horrible!" Sun Yaoting exclaimed. "How did you survive the beatings when they happened so often?"

"To tell you the truth, many eunuchs were beaten to death. One of the cruelest punishments was called 'sealing breath'. First they sealed up the offender's mouth, eyes, nose and ears with seven layers of cotton paper soaked in water, then they beat him to death with clubs. During the hundred-day reform many eunuchs of the Precious Consort passed messages between Emperor Guangxu and the reform leaders. When the reform failed, Cixi had all those eunuchs put to death by the 'sealing breath' method. I heard there were over thirty of them. In the end the hall was scattered with corpses!"

Sun Yaoting turned pale. The heavy beating he had received was still fresh in his memory. His curiosity aroused, he went to the Office of Palace Justice to take a look. He found two kinds of instruments of torture leaning on the wall: solid bamboo poles and bamboo planks, all stained with blood. Some whips were hanging on the wall. At a corner of the room he found ropes and wooden cangues. He went to Xin Xiuming and described what he saw. Xin smiled. "There is more to it than meets the eye. The bamboo planks should have been soaked in water so that they only cause superficial wounds without hurting the bones. But some eunuchs there keep a few untreated planks for beating their enemies. That's why sometimes an offender died before the punishment is over. To protect yourself, never get into any trouble. Be especially careful in front of the emperor; watch every move you make and every word you say. Contempt of the emperor is punishable by death. On the other hand, strange things do happen. Recently someone did something wrong before His Majesty and was promoted to eunuch-in-attendance as a result!"

"How?" Sun Yaoting was incredulous.

"You know Chunxi?"

"Yes."

"I'm talking about him. If you don't believe me, go and ask him."

A few days later Sun Yaoting ran into Chunxi, who showed him a photo. "Isn't it the emperor?" Sun Yaoting asked in surprise.

"Of course it is," Chunxi said with a smug look on his face. "Do you notice the way His Majesty wears his long queue?"

"You are now waiting on His Majesty, aren't you?"

"Yes." Chunxi then described how he had got lucky by accident.

One day Chunxi went to play in the Palace of Eternal Harmony. As he prepared to leave at dusk, a eunuch told him to wait. "You'd better not go at this moment. His Majesty will soon come out to walk the dogs." Ignoring this advice, Chunxi picked up a stick and left. Just then Pu Yi walked out of the Mind Nurture Hall. At the sight of a dark shadow in the distance, he stamped his feet forcefully. At this signal several dogs dashed toward Chunxi, barking fiercely and leaping on him. Chunxi brandished the stick madly to beat off the dogs while cursing loudly. Pu Yi walked up to the scene at a leisurely pace. "Why are you hitting the dogs?"

"Because I don't want to be killed!" Chunxi shouted, still flourishing his stick. It was impossible for him to kneel and salute the emperor properly. Pu Yi whistled softly, and the dogs retreated at once. Chunxi expected an outburst, but Pu Yi smiled. "You may go. Tomorrow you'll get a message." Chunxi was so upset that he spent a sleepless night. The next morning, to everyone's surprise, Pu Yi issued an order making Chunxi his eunuch-in-attendance. The unusual incident was much talked about in the palace.

"A misfortune has turned into a blessing for you," Sun Yaoting said enviously. "How lucky you are!"

"Well, I suppose you could say that. But the dogs won't leave me alone!"

Pu Yi's dogs had long memories. They barked fiercely at Chunxi at the very sight of him. Finally Pu Yi had to reassign Chunxi to wait on Wenxiu, the Sedate Consort.

4. Palace of Great Benevolence

Every evening at dusk, eunuchs on duty at the Gate of Intense Happiness called out, "Draw the bolts, lock up, careful with lanterns!" The same words would be repeated by eunuchs on duty at other corners of the Forbidden City. As the last sound died away, the palace sank into darkness and silence.

The eunuchs were very superstitious and told many stories of ghosts and spirits. For example, it was believed that gods patrolled the palace after dark. According to some old eunuchs, one of them had accidentally run into a palace god, who was of medium height, had large, penetrating eyes, and was wearing a yellow mandarin jacket with a red tassel on his hat. "Be careful when you pour water into the yard at night!" an old eunuch warned Sun Yaoting. One must shout "pouring water" before doing so, otherwise he might come to great harm if he accidentally splashed a palace god. When entering an empty hall, a eunuch would usually shout "opening the hall" for fear of taking a palace god by surprise and getting punished for it.

When talking about palace gods, old eunuchs cited numerous incidents as proof of their existence. A much-quoted story was about the two huge footprints in the northeast corner of the Hall of Imperial Peace, which was said to be devoted to the God of Water. In winter of the 2nd year of Emperor Jiaqing's reign a great fire broke out in the Hall of Heavenly Purity. The God of Water showed his presence in the palace to protect the emperor, leaving the giant footprints on the stone floor.

After nightfall, when the majestic palatial buildings receded into dark shadows, the Accounting Office in the rear compound of the Palace of Great Benevolence lit up with candles, and the eunuchs sat down for a few rounds of mahjong. "Lay out the table!" At Liu Ziyu's order, several servants would move a table and four chairs to the outer room of the main hall and bring tea served on platters and dishes of cooked melon seeds. If they were told to "make the tea strong", it meant that the game would probably last until the next morning. While the head eunuchs played in the main hall, the junior eunuchs enjoyed their own game in the side hall. At midnight the cooks served snacks such as wonton or slices of pork tripe. In summer they had iced watermelon, almond-flavored tofu, sweet-sour plum juice and other delicacies for dispelling heat. When none of the above was available, the eunuchs would get some ice shavings from the kitchen, add a little sugar, and munch them noisily. At the end of the game the servants and cooks would get tips for their extra service.

At the Accounting Office mahjong was played not only at night but also during the daytime. The palace authorities did not intervene as long as the eunuchs went on duty on time. At first Sun Yaoting just watched the others play, but then he was invited to join the game. They were taking a risk, for all his partners happened to be on duty that day. They took turns going out to take a look and see if any head eunuch was coming. Though the bets were small, Sun Yaoting felt extremely nervous, his heart leaping to his throat as he watched the die rolling on the table. At the end of the day he broke even, taking back the strings of coins he had brought to the game. After that he became an enthusiastic player. He was very cautious at first, sitting quietly at the table and not daring to make any rash move. Gradually he realized that given the small bets, no one was going to make a fortune or go bankrupt. Junior eunuchs played mahjong just for fun. As for the head eunuchs, they bet in silver dollars and played for big money, sometimes gaining or losing a hundred dollars in a single night.

After playing all night the head eunuchs went yawning to their rooms to sleep, while some of the junior eunuchs went on duty. They did not get a chance to sleep until the afternoon. During festivals and holidays gambling at the mahjong table was a favorite pastime. Eating and drinking, smoking opium, and playing mahjong constituted the main pleasures in life for most eunuchs.

One day Sun Yaoting walked into Liu Ziyu's room to find him sipping tea from a small teapot. He greeted Liu and was invited to sit down. During their conversation he asked, "Could you tell my fortunes?"

"Let's see." Liu picked up a divination book on the table. "Tell me the exact time of your birth."

"I was born on the thirtieth day of the eleventh month in the twenty-eighth year of Emperor Guangxu's reign."

"Can you be a little more exact?"

"My mother said I was born after three rounds of cockcrow."

Referring to the book, Liu did some calculations on his fingers. "Well, this is your destiny, it seems!"

"What destiny?"

"To be a eunuch!" Liu took another sip from his teapot.

"Can you explain it to me?" Sun Yaoting grew very curious.

"This is not a joke. Everything about your life is spelled out in the book. Listen to what it says here: 'Enough food and clothing, without wife or children'."

"Quite right!" Sun Yaoting said. "It's true that I have no wife or children and will do without them for the rest of my life. As for food and clothing, who knows? Who can guarantee I'll always have money in my pocket?"

"What's so good about having money?" Liu said. There were two silver dollars in his right hand and a few dozen dollars stacked on the table.

"You are in good luck, master, " Sun Yaoting remarked.

"So what?"

"You have money. You can lead a comfortable life."

"Well," Liu sighed deeply and threw the two silver dollars on the table. "No matter how much money you have, you are still an outcast in other people's eyes! This is true for all eunuchs, including Li Lianying and Xiaode Zhang. Zhang has several concubines and spends money like water. But in return he will have no offspring!" Liu put down the teapot and beckoned Sun Yaoting to sit beside him. "I'm your mentor, right?"

"Right," Sun Yaoting replied.

"You know who my mentor was?"

"It was Chief Liu, wasn't it?" Sun Yaoting had heard about Liu Ziyu's late mentor, also named Liu. Nicknamed "Frog Liu", he had a broad face with very big eyes and unusual audacity. He had waited on Emperor Xianfeng before getting promoted to head eunuch of the Accounting Office.

"He was very wealthy for a eunuch," Liu Ziyu said with a sigh. "For all his wealth, he came to a miserable end. After Emperor Xianfeng suddenly died of illness, he went back to his hometown, but the way his family treated him was a real shock. It happened to be springtime, when the chimney of their house had to be swept clean. His younger brother climbed up the roof to do it, but his mother called out, 'Get down, quick! If anything happens to you, our family would have no offspring! Let your elder brother do it. It won't matter so much if he has an accident.' Well, his mother's words made him very angry. 'How can you talk like this? I'm also your son! Do you think I am not human just because I am a eunuch?'"

"Maybe she was not his real mother," Sun Yaoting suggested.

"Well, maybe. Anyway, he left home to work as an apprentice at a money shop in the county. He worked hard and became very good at using the abacus. During Emperor Tongzhi's reign he returned to the palace. With his quick mind and excellent abacus skills, he kept perfect accounts and finally became head of the Accounting Office. He lived very thriftily and saved some money, quite a big sum, you know, but he did not send a single cent back home. Instead, he opened a few shops and donated to several temples around the Haidian area. He also had his wife brought to the capital."

"He had a wife?"

"Yes. It seems that they had some debts to clear from their previous lives. He was engaged to her in childhood, and after he became a eunuch she did not want to leave him. Anyway, his parents got news that he was rich. His mother felt too ashamed to see him, but his father came to the capital. 'Why are you here?' he asked his father. His father said, 'I've come to see you.' And he said, 'Well, look then.' He just stood there, first facing east, then turning west, south and north. 'Have you finished looking?' he asked his father. Then he walked away."

"Why did he treat his father like that?"

"Isn't it obvious? His father came to see him just to ask for money. After all, why did his family want him to be a eunuch in the first place? When he died, no one from his family came to his funeral. Would you call this a good life?"

Staring at the stack of silver dollars on the table, Sun Yaoting did not know what to say.

5. Stories and Anecdotes

One day Sun Yaoting went for a stroll in the Palace of Eternal Harmony, where a few eunuchs from the Administrative Bureau were standing in a corner with their backs to the wall and intoning the sound "chir, chir, chir". "What are you doing?" he asked curiously.

"Don't bother us with your stupid questions, kid!" said a young eunuch impatiently.

"Please spare some time and teach me!"

Delighted with Sun Yaoting's politeness, the eunuch deigned to explain. "All right, listen carefully! This is called 'sound the warning'. When the Emperor, Empress, or Empress Dowager comes out, we make this sound to warn the others to get out of the way at once. This is the responsibility of the Administrative Bureau. Is that clear?"

"Yes, thanks so much!"

Back at the Accounting Office Sun Yaoting learned more about the subject from Liu Ziyu. For eunuchs of the Administrative Bureau, making the warning sounds was a basic skill, and junior eunuchs had to practice it regularly. A skilled eunuch was able to make his voice travel far without causing any discomfort to the imperial master. Different sounds were used to announce people of different ranks. By listening to the sound, one could tell from a distance whether it was an imperial consort or a lower-ranking imperial wife. If unable to get out of the way in time, a eunuch must turn away without looking at the procession. Otherwise he would be charged with "utmost disrespect", a felony punishable by death.

"By stealing a look from behind, you can tell who it might be," Liu Ziyu said. "To do this you must be familiar with the imperial color codes. Only the emperor, empress, and empress dowager can be dressed in bright yellow. The imperial consorts, including High Consort Duankang, have to use a different shade called apricot-yellow."

Liu Ziyu then told Sun Yaoting about a taboo among the eunuchs. "Never eat beef!"

"Why?"

"Don't ask why, just abide by the rule. If you dare eat any, the palace gods would

Stacked Beauty, a rockery where eunuchs paid homage to the Little Palace God

take you to a tree in the Summer Palace and make you rub your lips against its bark!"

There were numerous palace taboos. Even the elderly eunuchs could not explain their origin, but most took them very seriously. Because of the taboo against beef, Sun Yaoting abstained completely from it. The next time he ate beef was many years later, when he was over fifty and had long left the palace.

The eunuchs paid special homage to the Little Palace God believed to specialize in protecting eunuchs and other palace servants and to bring good fortune to devoted worshippers. Regular sacrifices were offered on the 2nd and 16th days each lunar month at a rockery called "Stacked Beauty" just inside the Gate of Divine Prowess. One day Sun Yaoting and another junior eunuch decided to emulate the others by going to pay respects to the Little Palace God at the rockery. Before they left, Liu Ziyu warned, "You must kowtow to the god if you go there, otherwise stay away. Don't offend the god for no cause!"

When they reached the rockery, Sun Yaoting and his companions followed the example of other eunuchs, kowtowing once before they started to climb. Halfway to the top, they kowtowed again. Getting back on their feet, they giggled, but an old eunuch standing nearby silenced them with a glare. On top of the rockery was a small temple holding a statue of the Little Palace God. While going down Sun Yaoting noticed a rock bearing the inscription "Precious Pedestal", on which lay a sword and a sword hilt. It was said that the god used the sword to kill evil animal spirits such as weasels, porcupines, and snakes.

On his return Sun Yaoting found Liu Ziyu chatting with an old eunuch named Yao. Liu was describing an incident in which the palace god had apparently played a role. In the Palace of Heavenly Purity the eunuchs were busily preparing for Empress Dowager Cixi's birthday celebration when one of them noticed a wet patch on the main seat. The head eunuch had the spot ironed dry, then questioned his subordinates. "Did any of you offend the palace god recently?" When no one answered him, he decided it was probably the deed of an evil spirit, so he burned incense and kowtowed before the Stacked Beauty. The next morning a weasel was found dead under the rockery. "You just have to believe it!" Liu concluded.

"I agree," said Yao. A disciple of Li Lianying, Yao had spent his entire life in the palace and knew many tales and anecdotes. "Have you heard about the snake spirits?" he asked Sun Yaoting.

"Not quite."

"Well, I can tell you about them because I've seen them with my own eyes. They are two giant snakes that live near the dock in the Summer Palace. They can change their body size at will, so that sometimes they look like two pythons and sometimes they look like two worms. If you find them lying in the way by the lakeside, just step over, and they won't hurt you. I also had an incredible encounter with some palace gods. One evening I was walking around in the Summer Palace in search of a place to play mahjong when two men stopped me. I wanted to take a close look at them, but they suddenly vanished. Then I was happy to see a house all lit up. I walked in and said, "So you are all here!" But the lights went out at once. When I lit the candles, there was nobody in the room. People told me I had upset the gambling game of some palace gods!"

In front of the Palace of Eternal Harmony was a pool built with cement, where a lot of goldfish were kept. Walking past the pool one day Sun Yaoting got into a conversation with an old eunuch. "Do you know what the pool is called?"

"Does it have a name?" Sun Yaoting asked in surprise.

"Of course it does! This used to be called the Crystal Palace, you know."

"The Crystal Palace of the Dragon King?" Sun Yaoting felt amused.

"Believe me," said the old eunuch. "It was Xiaode Zhang who built it."

"Please tell me about it." Sun Yaoting always had a keen interest in the history of the Imperial Palace.

"All right. You can learn a lot from people like me." And the old eunuch told the following story about Xiaode Zhang.

Xiaode Zhang was famous for a lot of things: his fiery temper, his frequent use of swearwords, and his filial piety. His father died when he was young. At his mother's death he was already a senior eunuch of immense wealth, and he spent six thousand dollars on a grand funeral in his hometown, Tianjin. The splendor and lavishness of the funeral, undertaken by the best funeral parlor in Beijing, remained the talk of the town for a long time.

Zhang had business acumen, too. He was able to propose expensive projects that pleased his superiors while earning him a handsome profit. The construction of the so-called Crystal Palace was a typical example.

The foreground of the Palace of Eternal Harmony used to be a forbidden zone, a burial ground for the afterbirths of empresses, imperial consorts or princesses. One day Zhang was walking past the place when an idea occurred to him. Why not create a scenic attraction there? He submitted his plan to the palace authorities and got their approval. Naturally, he was put in charge of the Crystal Palace project. Hired laborers and craftsmen dug a deep pond in front of the palace, shaped it with cement, and supposedly lined it with waterproof material. Over the pond they also built an awning surrounded by glass walls. Zhang had a variety of goldfish, including some rare breeds, purchased from different places and hired experienced people to look after them. It became such a delightful spot that Empress Dowager Longyu visited it every day on her morning walk. In addition to winning the Empress Dowager's favor, Zhang also made a huge fortune by falsifying accounts and pocketing the better part of the construction budget.

"Xiaode Zhang was not the only one in the palace good at making money," the old eunuch said at the end of his story. "Let's take the Accounting Office as an example. There used to be four famous eunuchs who shared the character "Zi" in their names: Xu Zicai, Zhang Ziyu, Tian Zijiu, and Wei Zidan. They left the palace after the founding of the Republic, and all of them are very successful now. Tian is chairman of the Beijing Association of Taoism. Xin Xiuming is its vice-chairman. Xu has opened a bank and is now a quite respectable 'businessman'. Zhang owns a pharmacy called the 'Eternal Youth Parlor'; he has made a fortune selling 'plague-dispelling pills'. As for Wei Zidan, he is running several businesses in the capital: a salt shop, a flour company, you name it. As eunuchs we should feel proud of them!"

Cixi's name often emerged in the gossip of eunuchs. One day a eunuch said to Sun Yaoting, "You can't imagine how extravagant the 'Old Buddha' was! When she stayed in the Summer Palace, she spent ten thousand taels of silver a day!"

"That sounds impossible!" Sun Yaoting said.

"If you don't believe me, you can go and ask Chief Xin."

Sun Yaoting went to Xin Xiuming with the question. "Do you happen to know Cixi's full title?" Xin asked.

Leafing through the account books, Sun Yaoting found the title that consisted of sixteen characters beginning with "Cixi". "Why is it so long?" he asked.

"The longer the title, the higher the salary," Xin explained. "When she first became Empress Dowager, there were only four characters in her title. Afterward, whenever there was a big celebration in the palace, she took the chance to add two more words to her title. Let me see: there were the ascensions of Emperor Tongzhi and Emperor Guangxu, Guangxu's wedding, her fortieth, fiftieth, and sixtieth birthdays. So finally she had sixteen characters in her title. According to established rules, each character entitled her to a salary of ten thousand taels of silver a month."

"Wow! The amount she earned every year must be enormous!"

"You don't have to look into the account books to know that," Xin said. "She received a hundred and sixty thousand tales a month!"

Out of curiosity, Sun Yaoting looked through the old account books later and was able to verify Xin's words.

One day Sun Yaoting asked Xin Xiuming to explain Emperor Guangxu's posthumous title, "Dezongjing", literally "Virtuous Ancestor of Display".

"After the emperor's demise the court officials got together to choose a posthumous title for him," explained Xin. "The title usually has three auspicious-sounding characters that sum up the late emperor's life experience and merits. For Guangxu, the key word here is of course 'jing', which implies that his rule was just for display. Everyone knows it was Empress Dowager Cixi who presided over the imperial court during all that time."

"But things would have been different if Guangxu had given birth to a son to be his successor," Sun Yaoting said. "Why didn't he have a son?"

Just then Chen Zechuan walked into the room. "This is the right person to answer your question," Xin said. "He used to wait on Emperor Guangxu."

"Surely you know the story well, " Chen said.

"Not as well as you do," Xin said. "From what I've heard, Cixi kept giving Guangxu a hard time until he became sick and sterile. But I don't know what actually happened to him."

"It was nothing very serious," Chen said in a hushed voice. "He suffered from 'involuntary emission', you know."

"That's not even considered an illness." Xin happened to know quite a lot about medicine. "Many young men have it, and it's not difficult to cure."

"You are right. Just about any doctor knows how to treat the problem, let alone the imperial physicians. But Cixi did not want the emperor to be cured. She did not want him to give birth to an heir to the throne. She often asked the imperial physicians about Guangxu's illness. She knew everything and controlled everything."

"What about Empress Dowager Longyu?" asked Sun Yaoting. "Did she resemble Cixi in some way?"

"There is no comparison between them," Chen replied. "Despite her exalted status, Longyu had no real influence in the palace and no say in anything that mattered."

"That's why her posthumous title also contains the character 'jing'," Xin said. "As Guangxu's empress she never did anything of importance. Her days were spent drinking tea and watching Beijing opera."

As familiarity breeds contempt, eunuchs who lived together in close proximity rarely had nice things to say about one another. However, Kou Liancai was a name that won widespread respect among eunuchs of the Accounting Office. Even Chen spoke of him with admiration. "He was a truly remarkable person!"

"Yes, he was!" Xin Xiuming agreed.

When Sun Yaoting asked why they held Kou in such high esteem, Chen gave him a detailed explanation. "Kou Liancai was born in a village in southern Changping County north of Beijing. After entering the palace he was first assigned to the Accounting Office. He did such an excellent job that Cixi made him her personal attendant. When Guangxu took the throne, Kou became his eunuch-in-attendance. Cixi wanted Kou to spy on the emperor and report back to her. After a period of time Kou discovered that Guangxu really cared for his people and was acting in the best interests of the empire. So he assisted the emperor in his reform efforts and carried messages for him. When the Hundred-Day Reform was crushed, Cixi decided to dethrone Guangxu. This caused a furor in the imperial court. A minister named Wu Kefa submitted a memorial and committed suicide to attract Cixi's attention. In his memorial Wu warned her against 'making the same mistake twice'. Of course she ignored his advice, and he died in vain."

"But what did Kou Liancai have to do with all that?" Sun Yaoting asked.

"After Wu's death, Kou wrote a memorial and handed it to Cixi. Well, she was quite pleased to read the first part that put forward ten strategies for strengthening the empire. But it went on to criticize her for the way she treated Emperor Guangxu and advised her to 'read Minister Wu's words every day.' She burst into fury and had Kou brought to her at once."

"What happened then?"

"Cixi asked him if he knew he was guilty. He said it all depended on her opinion. If she considered him guilty, then he had to be. Cixi ordered him to be arrested by the Household Department. Two days later he was beheaded in the public execution ground at Caishikou. And you know why Cixi got so angry? It's because Kou dared to speak in favor of Emperor Guangxu. You could say he was deliberately courting death by doing so."

When the topic of their conversation moved to Empress Dowager Longyu, Chen actually had something nice to say about her. "Though she did not have much practical ability, she was better than Duankang in many ways. At least she knew how to foster loyalty and treated some of her eunuchs well."

"Could you give me an example?" asked Sun Yaoting.

"In Longyu's palace, Xiaode Zhang was the chief eunuch and Yao Mengshan the deputy. Their names still remain on the payroll after their retirement. That's something almost unheard of for eunuchs, and it could not have happened without Longyu's arrangement."

"Really?" Sun Yaoting found it hard to believe. Afterwards, he was able to verify the truth of Chen's words with records from an old account book.

6. The Emperor's Wedding

Sun Yaoting had learned to read and write in childhood. In the Imperial Palace his attention was attracted not only to its numerous treasures but also to the couplets, calligraphic inscriptions and paintings on display everywhere. For difficult words and phrases he could always count on Chen Zechuan or Xin Xiuming for thorough explanations. He especially enjoyed looking at the screens with their colored paintings, maxims and famous sayings. An essay on a screen in the Palace of Great Benevolence impressed him so much that he memorized it thoroughly and could still repeat it word for word in old age. It advised two brothers engaged in a lawsuit over family

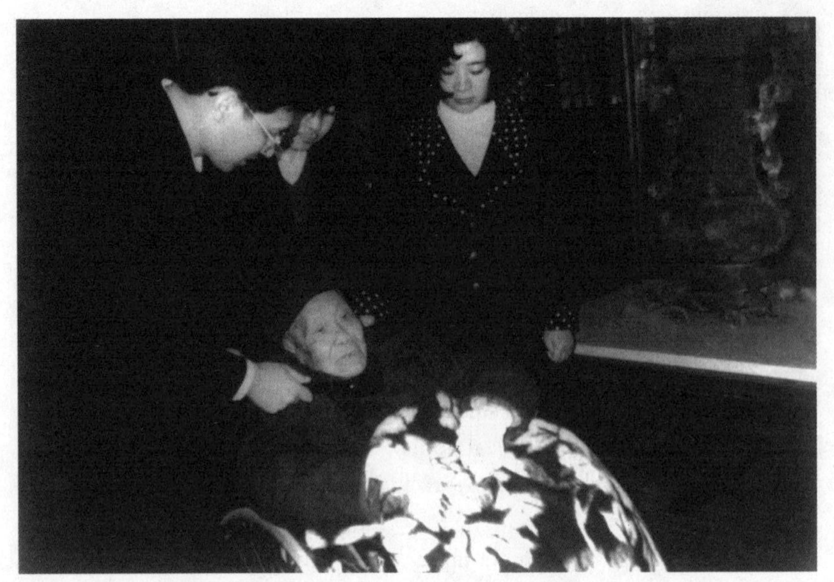

Sun Yaoting tells the story of two brothers fighting over family property in the Palace of Great Benevolence.

property to place brotherly love above material interests. Sun Yaoting asked a friend with beautiful handwriting to copy the essay and compose a painting to go with it. He had the work mounted and made into a four-piece screen, which he sent back home. At that time his brothers were all married with their own children, and he wanted to use this screen to help maintain peace and harmony in the Sun family.

In the winter of 1922 the palace became alive with noise and bustle in preparation for the emperor's "grand nuptials". Many eunuchs in the Accounting Office had to work extra hours. As a junior eunuch Sun Yaoting was not given much to do. "I don't want to miss the ceremony," he told Chen. "Is there a chance for me to take a look?"

"You really enjoy fanfare, don't you? What do you want to look at?"

"I don't know. I'll do as you tell me as long as I can watch what's going on."

"All right. The wedding will take place in the evening. First you must dress up properly, and I will tell you what to do."

The day before the wedding Sun Yaoting put on his best clothes. Chen looked him up and down. "Not too bad," he finally said. "I don't think they will throw you out."

At his grand nuptials Pu Yi was actually marrying two wives: Wanrong as his empress and Wenxiu as his consort. On the wedding day Wenxiu was ushered into the palace early in the morning, but the would-be empress did not arrive until midnight. Chen told Sun Yaoting what to do. "You can follow the others to the Gate of Heavenly Purity and kneel there. Don't stand up or make any noise. Don't walk away until the procession has passed. Do you understand?"

"Yes," Sun Yaoting replied. "I won't cause any trouble, I promise."

In the afternoon the trousseau arrived. At twilight eight ministers set out from the palace to receive the empress at her residence on Mao'er Alley in northern Beijing. When the procession arrived in the palace, another eight ministers were waiting at the Eastern Flowery Gate to conduct the empress's sedan chair to the Gate of Heavenly Purity. It was not until two o'clock in the morning that Sun Yaoting saw the phoenix-pattern "nuptial chair" of the empress, escorted by two imperial princes on either side, move slowly through the gate. By established rules the empress must be carried on a sedan chair into the palace at night. She entered the palace from the south by the Meridian Gate, going all the way to the Gate of Heavenly Purity. An imperial consort, on the other hand, entered the palace in a carriage through the rear gates during daytime.

The wedding procession moved to the Hall of Union and Peace, where Pu Yi and Wanrong completed the ceremony by "paying respects to heaven and earth". Afterward Sun Yaoting saw many people head north for the Palace of Earthly Peace. "Where are they going?" Sun Yaoting asked an elder eunuch by his side.

Wanrong, Pu Yi's Empress

"Of course you wouldn't know! The emperor and the empress are going to their nuptial chamber!"

Sun Yaoting followed the procession to the nuptial chamber and saw many old women kneeling on the ground chanting in Manchu. "What are they doing?" he asked an old eunuch.

"They are singing a wedding song."

Wanrong(middle), Wenxiu(left) and Tang Shixia in the Imperial Garden

After a while a resplendently dressed woman arrived and entered the room. "Look, here comes the treasure-finder!" a eunuch said.

"What's a treasure-finder?" Sun Yaoting asked.

"Who is this ignorant brat with such silly questions?" a eunuch complained.

An old eunuch acquainted with Sun Yaoting explained to him in a low voice, "The lady's job is to look for the 'happy sign' after the emperor and the empress have spent their wedding night together."

"What's the 'happy sign'?" Sun Yaoting asked.

"How can you be so ignorant? I'll explain it to you later."

The eunuchs waited a long time outside the nuptial chamber without catching a glimpse of the emperor. The next morning word got around that Pu Yi did not spend the night with his bride-empress. Some eunuchs said he did not even like her in the first place. According to another rumor, the emperor had little interest in women.

Sun Yaoting learned from Chen Zechuan that the "happy sign" referred to the empress's virgin blood on her first wedding night. For many eunuchs, the absence of the "happy sign" following the emperor's wedding was a good joke. But several senior eunuchs looked very worried, regarding it as a bad omen.

After the hustle and bustle of the emperor's wedding died down, life in the palace went back to normal. One day Sun Yaoting was walking in the palace when he heard the sound of music coming from a room. He went over to find an old eunuch sitting on the kang playing xiao, a vertical bamboo flute. "Who are you?" the old eunuch asked.

"I am from the Accounting Office."

"Are you new here?"

"Yes."

"Who is your mentor?"

"Chen Zechuan."

"Oh!" The old eunuch's expression softened. "We know each other very well. Come in."

Sun Yaoting learned that the old eunuch, Wang, used to work at the Court Theatrical Office and could play various instruments.

"Do you want to learn?" Wang seemed to read Sun Yaoting's mind.

"Yes, I'd like to."

"All right. I don't have much to do from day to day, so I'll take a pupil. Let's begin with xiao, shall we?"

Delighted, Sun Yaoting bowed deeply to Wang. At that time many eunuchs were trying to learn a practical skill or two so that they would be able to make a living after leaving the palace. Sun Yaoting got into the habit of visiting Wang at nightfall to practice xiao every day.

7. Dispersal of Eunuchs

On the 26th of the 6th lunar month in 1923 a big fire broke out in the Forbidden City. That evening Pu Yi had watched a movie in the Palace of Established Happiness and left around eight o'clock. Shortly afterward a fire broke out there.

Sun Yaoting had just gone to bed when another eunuch woke him up. "Did you hear that? Something's going on outside."

"What?" Sun Yaoting got up and opened his eyes. A loud noise was coming from outside the Palace of Great Benevolence. Lots of people seemed to be running and shouting. "The Palace of Established Happiness is leaking water!"

In traditional language "leaking water" was euphemism for "catching fire".

Sun Yaoting went out to see almost all the eunuchs of the Accounting Office in the courtyard. Outside the Palace of Great Benevolence a eunuch on duty shouted, "The Palace of Established Happiness is leaking water! Bring water pails! Hurry!" Sun Yaoting saw the conflagration in the northwest. Black smoke curled up to the sky, and there were intermittent sounds of explosion. Sun Yaoting also heard what he took for police sirens, but which later turned out to be fire engines coming from the Foreign Legation Quarters.

In front of the Palace of Great Benevolence people were coming and going hither and thither, carrying cases, boxes, or water pails. "Stay where you are and don't go running around," Xin Xiuming told Sun Yaoting and other eunuchs of the Accounting Office. "Otherwise something bad might happen." Therefore Sun Yaoting did not leave to join the firefighters.

In the meantime Pu Yi was having an outburst in the Mind Nurture Hall. "Those eunuchs are no good!" he bellowed. "They started this fire because they want to kill me!"

"We must investigate this thoroughly," said Zai Tao, who had been summoned to the palace.

Site of the Palace of Established Happiness after the fire in 1923

Just then Wang Huaiqing, the officer in charge of palace security, came in. "All the fire engines in the city have arrived."

Pu Yi made no comment to this but kept muttering to himself, "The damned eunuchs! I'll get rid of them all!"

"His Majesty thinks the eunuchs are responsible for the fire?" Wang asked Zai Tao in a whisper.

"That's impossible," Zai Tao said. "Eunuchs would never start a fire in the palace."

"How can you be so sure?" Pu Yi demanded.

"Such things are unheard of," Zai Tao said. "Why should anyone want to do it?"

"You never know," Wang said. "From what I've heard, some eunuchs have stolen treasures from the palace, and they may have started the fire to cover their tracks."

"Eunuchs wouldn't dare steal things from the palace!" Zai Tao said.

Nothing came of their discussion. After Zai Tao and Wang Huaiqing left, Pu Yi continued to stare at the conflagration and swear at the eunuchs. The eunuchs-in-attendance heard his loud curses and spread the news quickly.

The fire engines came first from the Italian Legation, then from the city's Fire Department. Many eunuchs and palace women and a few male servants who had not yet left the palace joined in fighting the fire. Though Pu Yi was convinced that some guilty eunuchs had started it, Sun Yaoting heard another story. The man in charge of electricity had forgotten to turn off the power after showing the movie. As the wires were worn, fire broke out due to an electrical shortage.

The following day Sun Yaoting learned that everything around the Palace of Established Happiness had burned to ashes. According to *Beijing Daily*, the fire destroyed a total of 132 rooms, along with the numerous treasures stored in them. "What a pity!" Sun Yaoting said. "All those priceless treasures lost forever!"

"It is a pity that these things are lost," responded Fan, a senior eunuch of the Accounting Office. "It is also a pity that our days in the palace are numbered."

"What?" Sun Yaoting could hardly believe his ears.

Though the cause of the fire remained a mystery, Pu Yi made up his mind to get rid of the eunuchs once and for all. When he informed his tutors of his intention, they raised vigorous objections, saying it would be a violation of the practice dictated by previous emperors. But Pu Yi remained adamant. "The eunuchs are all treacherous! They started the fire on purpose! Who knows what they'll do next to murder me?" Even the high consorts could not dissuade him.

While heated arguments went back and forth between Pu Yi and his tutors and the high consorts, all the eunuchs in the palace were put on notice. Rumors circulated at lightning speed.

"The emperor wants to punish the eunuchs! Some may lose their heads!"

"The emperor's uncle, Prince Zai Tao, has come to the palace to discuss the matter."

"The emperor will probably not have his way. The high consorts and the regents are all against the plan!"

Then news came that Pu Yi had left the palace for his father's house, the Northern Mansion. "If you do not agree to send away the eunuchs," he declared to his father, "I will never return to the palace!" Finally the regents gave in. Except for a few to wait on the high consorts, all the eunuchs would be expulsed. When Pu Yi returned to the palace, the eunuchs realized they were doomed.

At the Accounting Office the eunuchs received orders to take stock and return all keys to the storerooms. The man who came to take over the Accounting Office was Zhi Danxi, elder brother of the late Precious Consort. His daughter was engaged to Pu Jie, the emperor's younger brother. Zhi was a frequent visitor to the palace, and Sun Yaoting knew him quite well.

"Mr. Sun!" Zhi Danxi walked into the room. He was good-tempered and looked especially amiable on that day.

"Please accept my respects, Mr. Zhi." Sun Yaoting was about to kneel on one knee when Zhi Danxi stopped him. "Don't be so polite."

Zhi, a man of medium height, was wearing a gray gown and a pair of cloth-soled shoes. His plain features did not remind one of his pretty sister. "Thanks for the trouble," he said to Sun Yaoting.

"Chief Wang told us to make an inventory of all things and give you the keys." Sun Yaoting described the accounts and stock in his charge, locked up all the storerooms, and handed the keys to Zhi.

Afterward Wang summoned all the eunuchs of the Accounting Office to the courtyard. "The emperor has issued an edict to reduce the number of eunuchs in the palace. Most of you must leave!"

Though this was exactly what they had expected, the eunuchs raised a clamor of complaints. Some began to weep and wail, which caused a chain reaction. Most eunuchs burst into tears.

"Heavens! How are we going to live?"

"I have no place to go in the world!"

"His Majesty must have mercy on us! Otherwise we are going to starve!"

Along with a few other eunuchs, Sun Yaoting did not weep aloud though he felt totally at a loss. By Pu Yi's order, about 170 eunuchs were allowed to stay to attend to the high consorts. The rest of the 900-plus eunuchs must all leave the palace. Each eunuch would receive two months' pay as compensation and one month's pay as "imperial bounty". Those with no place to go could stay temporarily in the Goose-Wing Tower by the Gate of Divine Prowess, where they would have a bed to sleep in and porridge to eat but must leave within a month.

"Let it be," Sun Yaoting told himself. "If other people can live outside the palace, I will also survive."

It had been raining heavily since early morning. "Time to leave the palace! Time to leave the palace!" shouted a loud voice. Shao Ying, head of the Household Department, was leading a squad of palace guards to round up the eunuchs and escort them out of the Gate of Divine Prowess. The palace guards frisked all eunuchs to prevent them from stealing any palace treasure. The moment they stepped out the gate some eunuchs began to curse angrily: "We have served the emperor all our lives, and in the end they treat us like thieves! Damn them!"

"Help! Help!" The humdrum of protests and complaints was suddenly interrupted by shrill cries. Overcome with despair, a couple of eunuchs had jumped into the moat.

Walking out of the palace, Sun Yaoting did not know where to go. The muddy road under his feet seemed to signify a life of uncertainties and hardships ahead. The rain stopped. He was still pacing up and down the moat when someone called his name. It was his mentor, Liu Ziyu. Sun Yaoting put his hands on Liu's shoulders and broke into tears. Liu comforted him by patting him gently on the back.

They could see the dimly lit Gate of Divine Prowess in the distance. A quarrel seemed to be going on, with some eunuchs uttering loud complaints.

"You don't have a place to go, do you?" Liu asked.

Sun Yaoting shook his head.

"Come with me. I have a home of sorts."

Though also expelled from the palace, a senior eunuch like Liu Ziyu was in a much better position than Sun Yaoting. Some years before he had secured a home outside the palace, spending all his money on about twenty rooms on Cuihua Alley. Sun Yaoting followed Liu to his residence, and they sat under the oil-lamp chatting late into the night. "Some things are destined to happen," Liu said. "If I had not seen you, you would have no place to sleep tonight!"

"You saved my life," Sun Yaoting said gratefully. "Without you I might have jumped into the moat!"

"Life is difficult. You know the old saying, 'One may meet numerous people under heaven, but few are close to one's heart.' It's no easy thing to find a faithful friend!"

"I will never forget your kindness," Sun Yaoting said. "If I live to see better days, I will pay you back!"

The following morning Sun Yaoting went back to the Gate of Divine Prowess, where he learned that he could go in to collect his belongings. Afterwards, he would never be allowed to step into the palace again. At the emperor's order a new kind of identification cards complete with the bearer's photograph would be issued to the remaining eunuchs in the palace.

In the Accounting Office Sun Yaoting met Xin Xiuming. "I'd like to come back," he said. "Could you find a way to make me stay?"

"I'm afraid it can't be done," Xin replied. "The number of people allowed to stay in each place has been fixed." In the Accounting Office, only Xin Xiuming and Fan Dongyu were left.

In disappointment Sun Yaoting returned to Liu Ziyu's house, where he stayed for over a month. Unable to make a living and unwilling to be a nuisance at Liu's house, he went back to his home village in Jinghai County.

He did not stay home for long. To his astonishment, two eunuchs suddenly showed up. "What has brought you here?" he asked.

"Good news! Madame Duankang wants you to come back!"

As it happened, many palace maids were also sent away after the dispersal of eunuchs. This resulted in a shortage of servants in the palace. Duankang, who had a favorable impression of Sun Yaoting, sent the two eunuchs to bring him back to the palace. Sun Yaoting was overjoyed.

"You must find Chunzhong, Chunqing and Chunlai, and bring them along with you," the two eunuchs told him.

Sun Yaoting immediately sent a message to Chunqing, who had already found a job in the house of a Manchu prince in Beijing. Then, together with Chunzhong and Chunlai, Sun Yaoting left for the imperial palace again.

5

SERVING THE IMPERIAL COUPLE

1. The Empress

With his two companions, Chunlai and Chunzhong, Sun Yaoting returned to Beijing and stood once again before the Gate of Divine Prowess. The palace guards stopped them. "Step aside and wait there!"

At that time Pu Yi's chief eunuch was Shao Xiangqing, nicknamed "White Deer". Pleased to learn that several eunuchs had returned, he ordered them to be taken to Pu Yi at the Mind Nurture Hall. Pu Yi looked at them one by one and decided he liked Chunlai the best. "I'll take this one," he said. "The other two can also stay."

Sun Yaoting hastily told Shao in a whisper that it was High Consort Duankang who had summoned them.

"Your Majesty, please pardon them," Shao said to Pu Yi.

"What's wrong?" Pu Yi looked displeased.

"Your slave just learned that they have been called back by the Empress and High Consort Duankang."

"All right, take these two to the Empress."

After kowtowing to Pu Yi, Sun Yaoting was taken to the Palace of Gathering Elegance, the residence of Wanrong, the Empress. He was assigned menial duties such as cleaning the rooms and sweeping the hall.

Chunqing, who had received Sun Yaoting's message and come to the palace before the other three eunuchs, was made Wanrong's personal attendant. Unfortunately he failed to win her favor. "The boy is so dumb and stupid!" Wanrong complained to Fu, an elderly female attendant.

"Yes, he is a bit too slow," Fu agreed. "Sometimes he just doesn't seem to know what he's doing." Fu was one of Wanrong's most trusted servants, having waited her since her childhood.

"Let Chunshou have a try," Wanrong said. Sun Yaoting thus got promoted to be a personal attendant of the Empress.

In the meantime Chunqing did not show any improvement. He was honest but so slow-witted that he could not make head or tail of the palace rules. For one thing, he never learned the proper way to salute people of different ranks. A little hard of hearing, he sometimes failed to understand Wanrong's order. It would be unthinkable to ask the Empress to repeat her words, so he always responded with a loud "Yes".

One day a jewelry dealer from the Dong'an Market was ushered into the palace. When Wanrong told Chunqing to go to the eastern hall to look for the jeweler, he did not catch her words. As it happened to be around mealtime, he called out, "Serve the meal!" Furious, Wanrong drove him away at once. Chunqing went back to his home village, where he meted out a living by doing farm work.

The Palace of Gathering Elegance, located in the western part of the Forbidden City, was known as one of the six "western palaces". After he became a eunuch-in-attendance for the Empress, Sun Yaoting moved to the western hall of the Palace of Universal Happiness west of the Palace of Gathering Elegance. He shared a room with a herald named Zhao Xingzhen. The head eunuch, Wang, lived in the main room to the north.

Wanrong seemed kind and amiable, but she had a quick temper and occasionally lashed out at the eunuchs when she was in a bad mood. One day she got angry because her room had not been cleaned properly. "Chunshou!" she called out. "Look at this! How did they do their job? They are really insupportable!"

Sun Yaoting walked over to take a close look. The room was indeed not very clean.

"Look over there! There's dust on the screen! You must go and teach them a lesson!"

Sun Yaoting ran out to scold the eunuchs responsible for cleaning the room. "Clean up the room again! If you don't do it properly this time, the Empress will have you punished severely!" He hit his right palm several times with his left hand, producing a slapping sound.

Pu Yi and Wanrong

Chen Zechuan was pleased to hear of this incident. "Well done!" he said appreciatively when he met Sun Yaoting. "Very well done!"

"Though I am waiting on the Empress now, I can't bring myself to hit others!" Sun Yaoting said.

"Quite right. Always be tolerant toward others. In this way you will accumulate merits for your own benefit!"

"I will always follow your instructions," Sun Yaoting pledged.

The menu for eunuchs remained more or less the same from day to day. Most of the time they only had a single dish, stir-fried tofu. In winter they ate Chinese cabbage for a change. Occasionally they had sweet pepper, eggplants, or potato, but there was always just one dish. Only on holidays or the Empress's birthday did they enjoy a three-dish meal.

As Pu Yi seldom visited her, Wanrong usually ate alone with a dozen dishes laid out on the table. During her meal she sometimes chatted with the eunuchs.

"Have you eaten, Chunshou? Come, let's eat together."

"Your slave thanks the Empress."

"Save your thanks." She did not seem to be concerned about etiquette.

"Your slave has just eaten."

"What did you have?"

"Pies."

"How many did you eat?"

"Seven," Sun Yaoting gestured with his hands. "They were about this big, the size of a palm."

"Go to the kitchen and tell them I'll have meat pies tomorrow."

The next day the Imperial kitchen made meat pies for Wanrong. "Come and have some," she told Sun Yaoting. He went over and stood eating by the table.

"Come on, have some more," she urged.

"I'm full already."

"How many did you eat?"

"Four."

"Didn't you say you could eat seven?"

Sun Yaoting hesitated for a few seconds, groping for the right answer. "Your slave cannot eat so many because these pies have thin wrappings and plenty of meat."

Wanrong giggled.

Actually Sun Yaoting felt uneasy eating with the Empress. Wanrong was usually genial and amiable but sometimes burst into sudden fits of temper. Other eunuchs had warned Sun Yaoting against her volatile character. Moreover, he must remain standing throughout the meal, which made him feel uncomfortable.

The Empress's throne stood in the middle of the front hall of the Palace of Gathering Elegance. When uncovered, it represented the authority of the Empress, and eunuchs passing by had to walk quickly in a bowing position. To make things easy for everyone, Sun Yaoting kept the seat covered on ordinary days.

Wanrong usually slept in the room on the eastside accompanied by a palace maid. Sun Yaoting and three other eunuchs took turns keeping night watch in the room on the west. Both the maid and the eunuch on duty were allowed to go to sleep after the Empress took to bed. She often kept the door open at night and merely drew the door curtain. When Pu Yi came to spend the night with her, the maid would be sent away and the door closed. But that rarely happened. Most of the time the Empress had only her maids and eunuchs for company, which partly accounted for her friendly attitude toward these lowly servants. As Sun Yaoting found out, he could even joke with her from time to time.

One day Wanrong was eating alone in the front hall attended by Sun Yaoting and Zhao Xingzhen. When the "ox-tail soup" was served, Sun Yaoting peeped into the bowl, saying, "I can see nothing in there. Where are the ox-tails?"

After a while a dish was served with four "small chickens" the size of a child's fist. "Do you know what they are?" Sun Yaoting asked Zhao.

Zhao strained his neck to take a better look. "I don't know. Never seen such things before. Have you?"

"They look like sparrows, don't they?"

Wanrong overheard their conversation. "Sparrows? What kind of sparrows can be so big? You've never eaten them before?"

"No," Sun Yaoting said. "You are eating so fast that I can hardly see what they look like!"

"All right, you can have one each." Wanrong pushed over the dish.

"Please take pity on your slave," Sun Yaoting said with a big smile. "I'd like some bread."

"Here you are," Wanrong handed a bun to him.

"And where's the jam?"

"You really know how to enjoy yourself, don't you?" Wanrong laughed.

A Western-style kitchen staffed with foreign cooks had just been installed in the palace at Pu Yi's order. It prepared one of Wanrong's favorite dishes, "crawling dog-meat", which was simply dog's meat and bones cooked together. The imperial couple seldom ate at the same table, but their daily menu was more or less the same.

After the meal it was Sun Yaoting's duty to prepare a big fruit plate. One day Zhao Xingzhen said to Wanrong, "Chunshou has stolen some apples! There aren't enough fruits on the plate!"

"A few apples were rotten and I picked them out," Sun Yaoting explained. "Do you call this stealing?"

"Whatever you call it, some apples are missing!"

Wanrong burst out laughing. She took the plate and emptied the fruits on the floor. "Come and eat them all!"

Assured that the Empress was in a good mood, Sun Yaoting picked up an apple, wiped it with his sleeve and took a big bite. At the noise a few other eunuchs came over to grab the fruits. Wanrong found the scene extremely amusing and nearly split her sides with laughter.

Though electric light bulbs were first installed in Beijing in 1888, the palace still relied mainly on candles for lighting in the early 1920s. Only the residences of the Emperor and Empress and a few other places had electric lights, which did not always work. In the western hall where Sun Yaoting lived, there was a twenty-five-watt pendent lamp. One day Zhao Xingzhen came in from the rain and reached for the switch to turn on the lamp. An electric shock sent him reeling, and he turned pale with fright. Afterward the eunuchs were afraid to touch the switch on rainy days. They would rather stay in the dark or use candles. However, electricity shocks were not limited to the switch of the lamp. Coming in from the rain one day, Sun Yaoting put his hand on the doorframe, and the electric shock made him scream.

At the suggestion of Wang, the head eunuch, Sun Yaoting went to find "Lord Ning", a court official of the third rank responsible for electrical maintenance in the palace, who had a dozen workers under his command. Ning came and solved the problem quickly. When it rained again a few days later the problem came back, and Sun Yaoting had to get Ning again. "There's very little I can do," Ning said with a sigh. "The electric wires and switches are all old and worn."

One day the Palace of Gathering Elegance had an electric blackout, and Ning came without being asked. "It must be the wire somewhere," he told the eunuchs. "Anyway, the electric lights are not very dependable. If I were you I would keep candles ready all the time."

At the age of eighteen or nineteen, Wanrong behaved like a child in many ways. She enjoyed games, often with eunuchs and maids as her playmates. Sometimes she would summon a eunuch who was on duty elsewhere for no other reason than to keep her company and play with her.

The Palace of Gathering Elegance was very beautiful in autumn, with sweet-scented flowers like osmanthus and hops blooming in the courtyard. Wanrong stayed outdoors longer and had more frequent visits from Pu Yi's three sisters.

"Chunshou, come and play 'drop the handkerchief'!" Wanrong called out.

Wanrong and three Imperial princesses joined together with some palace maids and two eunuchs to play the game in the courtyard. Wanrong was so absorbed in the game that they played until nine o'clock in the evening, with electric lamps turned on. Wanrong must be extremely bored to be so interested in "drop the handkerchief", a game fit for small children under the age of ten.

Wanrong was always glad to have visitors and reluctant to let them go. She would make them play games with her until everyone was utterly exhausted. Only then would she tell Sun Yaoting to escort the princesses to leave the palace.

Due to their upbringing the three princesses did not talk much and responded to just about anything with a bland smile. They were treated with great respect by the eunuchs. When meeting one of them, Sun Yaoting bent both knees, saying, "Your slave salutes the princess!" The princess would lower her head slightly, touch her left knee with both hands, and hold out her hands in a lifting gesture. Only then would Sun Yaoting get to his feet.

There was a swing in the veranda of the Palace of Universal Happiness. Suspended on two ropes fixed with screws, the swing did not look very secure. According to an old saying, the three most dangerous things to do were "riding a horse, sailing a boat, and going on the swing". Unfortunate for the eunuchs, Wanrong enjoyed the dangerous game very much. She not only liked to get on the swing herself but also wanted her maids and eunuchs to join her.

One day she made Sun Yaoting get on the swing, with two other eunuchs pushing vigorously. She laughed heartily to see Sun Yaoting turn pale with fright as the swing rose higher and higher. "All right, come down," she finally said. "You are as timid as a mouse. Let me show you." She sat down on the swing. As it gathered momentum, she suddenly stood up on the seat. "Be careful!" Sun Yaoting cried out.

"I'm all right!" Wanrong was having a good time and giggling with excitement. She got down after a while and picked out a young maid named Ruixia. "Go and have a try. Don't be as timid as Chunshou."

Ruixia, a pretty girl fourteen or fifteen years old, sat down daintily on the swing. As it began to move faster, her skirt was blown up in the wind and she cried out in alarm. The eunuchs and maids cheered and clapped their hands, and Wanrong found it very amusing. "Don't laugh at her," she said to Sun Yaoting. "You were just as scared a moment ago."

"No, I was not."

"So you are the brave one! Why don't you join her to give her some courage? How about that?"

The swing was brought to a halt, and Sun Yaoting was made to sit side by side with Ruixia. She calmed down and even began to smile. "Stand up! Stand up!" the others shouted in unison. "That's no big deal!" Sun Yaoting whispered to Ruixia, and they slowly got to their feet. Though a bit nervous, they kept on smiling. Wanrong had a good time that day and did not return to her chamber until nightfall.

As it grew cold, the imperial princesses spent less time outdoors during their visit to the palace. They would play with Wanrong for a while, then retreated to the rear hall. As the Empress, Wanrong could not follow them around, and she went back to her own room in desolation.

Dinner was usually served at four o'clock in the afternoon, but Wanrong ate little, if at all. Those who had the best appetites were eunuchs who would go on duty that night. The cooks and other non-eunuch kitchen servants left the palace at around seven, carrying away two large boxes of leftover food. In one of boxes were two big pots of porridge made of rice, millet, corn flour, or green beans. The other box held steamed rolls, cookies, and small dishes such as fish and pork tripe.

Sun Yaoting in front of the Palace of Gathering Elegance

2. Palace of Gathering Elegance

Apart from the three princesses Wanrong had very few visitors. She was always happy to see a new face in her house. One of her welcome visitors was Mr. Zhuang Shidun, or Reginald Johnson. Johnson, a graduate of Oxford University, had been personal secretary of the Viceroy of Hong Kong and Commissioner of the British-leased territory of Weihaiwei before coming to the palace in 1919 to be Pu Yi's English tutor. He described his dealings with the last Emperor of China in his famous work, *Twilight in the Forbidden City.*

One day an unexpected visit from Johnson gave Wanrong a pleasant surprise. He was wearing a Chinese long gown and a dark hat, and spoke Chinese with a strong accent. Instead of kowtowing like the Chinese subjects, he paid his respects to Wanrong by bowing with clasped hands, a very bizarre gesture in the eyes of the eunuchs. "How are you, Empress?"

"Fine, fine. Please sit down." Wanrong found his Chinese pronunciation very funny.

"It is a perfect day today. Shall I take some photos for you?"

"That'll be great!" Wanrong was elated. "Excuse me for a minute. I'll have to change clothes."

While Johnson sat there waiting, Sun Yaoting served him a cup of jasmine tea. After a while Wanrong returned in a cheongsam, the Empress's crown of the "nine-dragon-and-four-phoenix" design, and a pair of high-heeled "flower-pot" shoes. They went out to the courtyard, and she had some pictures taken in front of the flowers. Then she returned to her room and emerged in her favorite dark green cheongsam. Johnson took many pictures of her posing in the room, before the hall, and under a tree. His visit kept her in high spirits for several days as she waited impatiently for the photos to be developed. When she finally got the photos, she looked at them together with her maids and eunuchs, laughing happily.

In the evening Wanrong retired to the bedchamber, where she had her head adornments removed by a lady-in-waiting, Liu. Then she went to the main hall and sent for all her servants. Sun Yaoting was told to bring out

Reginald Johnson (back row, first from the right), Pu Yi (front row, right) and Wanrong (front row, left)

some imported sweets and scattered them on the floor. "This is all for you!" Wanrong said. She sat there watching quietly as the servants tripped over one another to get the sweets. "These foreign sweets are very expensive, at least six or seven silver dollars a jin," she remarked. Bought at a local shop dealing in imported goods, the sweets were actually much less expensive than she thought. Wanrong had no idea how the Accounting Office falsified accounts and cheated the imperial house of its money. Pu Yi seemed hardly to know better. According to a story widely circulated among the eunuchs, the Emperor actually believed that an egg cost several taels of silver on the market.

One of the most eye-catching items in Wanrong's dressing room was a large porcelain bath. She wanted it to be kept immaculately clean and would chastise her maids if she spotted the slightest stain there. When taking her bath, Wanrong usually had two elderly female attendants to wait on her. They undressed her, bathed her, scrubbed her back, massaged her feet, manicured her toes, dried her up and dressed her, without her having to lift a finger. She just sat there and let them do everything. After the bath she sometimes sat on the side of the basin to examine her own naked body. In the words of her maids, the Empress acted like "a solitary flower admiring its own beauty and fragrance". In the Palace of Gathering Elegance everyone knew that Pu Yi seldom came to see his Empress and usually stayed only for a short while on his rare visits. He almost never spent the night with her.

The strained relationship between the imperial couple, as well as Wanrong's bathing habit, became a topic of endless gossip among palace maids. "The Empress is a real beauty! She has such creamy white skin!" A maid remarked.

"Her figure is also superb," said another. "I just can't help staring at her when I am rubbing her back!"

"I wish I had a chance to attend to the Empress when she takes her bath," a young maid said wistfully. For some reason Wanrong preferred to be bathed by elderly maids.

With nothing better to do, eunuchs and maids often gossiped about the Empress. Sun Yaoting even overheard a eunuch and a maid arguing whether the Empress would look better with nothing on than fully clothed.

Eunuchs and maids who worked as attendants of the Emperor, Empress or imperial consorts had to pay special attention to personal hygiene. For example, they must trim their nails regularly and took frequent baths. Bedwetting was a common problem for eunuchs due to their castration, and they had to take extra care to avoid giving off any offensive smell. Apart from taking a bath every five or six days, Sun Yaoting got into the habit of wearing toilet water. He even bought a small bottle of vanishing cream for a silver dollar. That was why he always smelt of perfume from a distance.

There was no bathhouse for eunuchs on palace grounds. Lu, head eunuch of High Consort Jingyi, ran a eunuch-only bathhouse at the north end of Beichang Street. Every customer had a bed, a small table, and a bathtub to himself, and was served a pot of tea before taking the bath. The eunuchs felt at home at the bathhouse because many of its employees, including the back-rubbers and pedicurists, were eunuchs. However, Sun Yaoting found something sinister about the place. Several old eunuchs there showed a perverted interest in young eunuchs. If a young eunuch acknowledged an old eunuch as his "master" at the bathhouse, they might be having a sexual relationship. Sun Yaoting therefore often went to a public bathhouse north of Shatan Street. It had a large bathing pool, but he usually paid extra to get a small bathtub to himself to avoid being ridiculed because of his mutilation.

Castration did not always deprive the eunuchs completely of sexual desires. Quite a few eunuchs had an obsession with anything related to sex and would go to extreme lengths to find substitute outlets. They enjoyed looking at pornographic paintings, had endless gossip about sex, and sometimes engaged in homosexual relationship. Sun Yaoting found himself attracted to pretty women. When first shown some pornographic paintings in Prince Zai Tao's house, he remained sleepless all night with excitement.

In the Palace of Gathering Elegance the Empress's menstruation aroused great interest among the maids and eunuchs. When Wanrong started to have her period, an Imperial physician would come to feel her pulse. Then she would have to go to the Mind Nurture Hall to ask the Emperor for a leave. As her relationship with Pu Yi became strained, she stopped going to see him in person and had Sun Yaoting run the errand for her.

Sometime during the month Wanrong's female attendant Fu would whisper to Sun Yaoting, "Today you have to ask His Majesty for a leave."

Thereupon Sun Yaoting went to the Mind Nurture Hall to see Pu Yi. "Your slave has come to ask for a leave for the Empress." He had to kneel to say these words, but sometimes he got away with a bow if Pu Yi appeared to be in a good mood. "All right," Pu Yi would say, and dismissed Sun Yaoting with a sweep of his hand.

At the end of Wanrong's period Sun Yaoting had to go to the Mind Nurture Hall again to "cancel the leave" for her. This became a standing joke among the eunuchs and maids.

"Chunshou, here comes your monthly business again!"

"It's your job to do everything for the Empress, isn't it?"

"I can only ask for a leave for her," Sun Yaoting laughed. "She has to do the rest herself."

A couple of days before her period Wanrong usually showed an aversion to cold dishes, and by close observation Sun Yaoting could anticipate his "monthly errand". Many maids and eunuchs found this very mysterious, and even Fu was impressed with his precision. Several eunuchs kept asking him for an explanation until he finally disclosed his "secret technique".

3. Languishing in Seclusion

Every now and then Wanrong took to bed for an unknown illness. When this happened, Pu Yi showed his concern by sending over a trusted Imperial physician, Dong Chenghai.

Dong Chenghai came from a family of physicians. His father, Dong Wenbin was the Commissioner of the Imperial Academy of Medicine. Dong Wenbin got the nickname "Plaster Dong" because of his unconventional prescriptions. "Give plaster to the poor and antelope's horn to the rich," was his medical motto. He once prescribed 100 grams of plaster for a sick eunuch. "Trust me," Dong reassured his startled patient. "The remedy is exactly suited to your illness. It will reduce fire in your system." After taking the medicine, the eunuch fully recovered.

In contrast to his father, Dong Chenghai was cautious with his prescriptions and recommended very moderate doses. Knowing him, Pu Yi trusted his prescriptions but always had the dosage doubled. A simple, honest man, he was especially good at treating women's illnesses. Pu Yi relied on him greatly. He later became an "Imperial physician" in Manchukuo, the puppet regime set up by Japan in Northeast China.

At the news of the Empress's illness Dong Chenghai would hurry over from the Academy of Imperial Physicians. Otherwise Pu Yi would telephone him at home. He was always very formally dressed when he arrived. Walking into Wanrong's bedchamber, he knelt to salute her, saying, "Your slave has come

Wanrong fully dressed up

to feel your pulse." Still on his knees, he moved to her bedside, where her hand was already placed on a small pillow. After feeling her pulse, he moved to the other side of the bed to feel her pulse again by the other hand. During all this time she must keep her face turned away from him, with Sun Yaoting standing in attendance by her side. Still on his knees, Dong announced his diagnosis: "Your slave has finished feeling the pulse. The left-hand pulse feels a little bit slippery, and the right-hand pulse is taut. Therefore..."

After hearing him out, Pu Yi sent him away to write the prescription. A moment later Dong submitted a report describing the cause of the illness and the proposed treatment, together with the price for all the ingredients in the recipe. Pu Yi looked it over and usually sent Dong away to fill the prescription. Occasionally he consulted other Imperial physicians, who might suggest a few changes to Dong's prescription.

Pu Yi personally supervised the preparation of the medicine together with several eunuchs of the Empress, including her head eunuch and Sun Yaoting. After the medicinal herbs were brewed and filtered, Sun Yaoting and another junior eunuch tasted the liquid. If they developed no unusual symptoms after a while, the medicine would be locked up in a casket. Only then would Pu Yi leave. At bedtime Sun Yaoting came to Wanrong, saying, "It's time to take the medicine."

"It must be very bitter," she would complain.

The medicine, heated to lukewarm, was brought over in the casket and opened in front of her eyes by a eunuch. After drinking the medicine, she rinsed her mouth and went to sleep.

During the treatment of Wanrong's illness, the status and prestige enjoyed by the Imperial physician left a deep impression on Sun Yaoting. He decided to teach himself medicine, hoping to become a master physician someday. He managed to get hold of a copy of *The Nature of Medicinal Drugs* and began to memorize it by heart. After much difficulty he succeeded, but there was of course never an opportunity for him to put to use what he had learned.

"The Emperor and the commoner have different things to worry about," so goes a popular saying. Seclusion and boredom was perhaps Wanrong's biggest problem. After supper she had precious little to do, sitting alone under the lamp. To kill time she developed a hobby of braiding her hair every evening before going to bed, then undid it when she got up in the morning.

The Imperial Consort Wenxiu was not as pretty as Wanrong. She appeared to be a bit shorter and spoke in a softer voice. But she enjoyed reading and practicing calligraphy. Like Wanrong, she was also tolerant toward her servants.

Wanrong and Wenxiu had been rival candidates to be Pu Yi's Empress, supported by different high consorts. Pu Yi first picked out Wenxiu, but she became a mere consort due to Duankang's objection, and Wanrong was made Empress instead. Such a beginning was naturally not conducive to a congenial relationship between the two girls. They rarely saw each other except on holidays, and Pu Yi almost never ate at the same table with both his Empress and Consort.

Pu Yi seemed to be treating Wenxiu quite well. For one thing, he sent a trusted eunuch-in-attendance named Liu Xingqiao to wait on her. Liu had served Pu Yi's family for a long time, with his palace name, Deshou, given by Pu Yi's father.

One day Wenxiu came unannounced to the Palace of Gathering Elegance. Sun Yaoting caught sight of Liu Xingqiao and greeted him respectfully, then Wenxiu emerged. He hastily offered to prepare tea for her, but she stopped him. "Do you have a small pail?"

"Yes."

"Fetch me some water from the well!"

Sun Yaoting went away and returned with a small pail, with which he drew some water from a deep well in the courtyard. Wenxiu told him to pour the water to the ground and draw another pail. He filled a tea bowl from the second pail of water and handed it to Wenxiu, who drank it at a gulp and went away. Afterward Sun Yaoting asked Liu Xingqiao, "Did anything ever go wrong after she drank water like that?"

"No. She is quite strong and almost never gets ill."

"She does not seem to get along with the Emperor."

"Well, you would not believe it if I tell you what happens between them."

"Do tell me about it!"

"I don't know how anyone could treat His Majesty the way she does. When we announce the Emperor's arrival, she does not even bother to come out to greet him. Sometimes the Emperor tries to attract her attention by standing outside her room and tapping the window, but she acts as if she heard nothing. Only when the Emperor walks into her room does she get up from her seat. If she happens to be writing something when the Emperor leaves, she will finish whatever she is writing before she stands up to see him off. Do you consider it proper behavior for a consort?"

"But they had exchanged birth charts before the marriage was settled," Sun Yaoting said. "They couldn't be restricting each other by fate."

"And their birth signs are said to be compatible. Well, such things are hard to tell."

"But she treats us servants quite well, doesn't she?"

"I would say so. But please remember: what I said just now is only between you and me!"

On the whole Sun Yaoting was having a good time in the Palace of Gathering Elegance. As an attendant of the Empress he earned much more than before even though the regular stipends of eunuchs had been slashed after their massive expulsion in 1921.

In her loneliness Wanrong longed for someone to come and bring her some kind of amusement. Occasionally her wish was fulfilled. One day Pu Yi arrived with a eunuch wheeling a brand-new German-made bicycle. "Come, let the Empress learn to ride the bike!"

Wanrong began to practice with several eunuchs supporting the bike for her. After a few days she could circle the courtyard on her own. During this time Pu Yi came to see her every day. One day she felt a bit tired after riding for a while. "Who wants to have a try?" she asked the eunuchs.

Perhaps due to Pu Yi's presence, none of the eunuchs volunteered.

"Can any of you show a little bit of courage?" Pu Yi said. When no one responded, his eyes fell on Sun Yaoting. "Chunshou, can you ride it?"

"No, Your Majesty. I don't have the slightest idea how to ride a bike." Sun Yaoting stood back, waving both hands.

"Come on. Have a try. I'll hold the bike for you, so you won't fall to the ground. Don't be such a coward!"

"Your Majesty, I really can't ride!"

"You'll learn to in no time!" Pu Yi practically dragged him onto the bike.

With Pu Yi and several eunuchs holding the bike, and Wanrong stood by watching with a smile, Sun Yaoting took the first bicycle ride in his life. After a few seconds Pu Yi suddenly let go. Sun Yaoting staggered on for a few seconds before collapsing on the ground, causing the onlookers to laugh and clap their hands.

4. The Capricious Emperor

A telephone line between the Mind Nurture Palace and Wanrong's bedchamber was installed after Pu Yi's wedding. Occasionally he made a phone call to tell her he was coming or just to say hello.

Shortly after he came to the Palace of Gathering Elegance, Sun Yaoting sensed that something was wrong between the Imperial couple even though he could not put his finger on it.

One day Pu Yi suddenly emerged, going straight into Wanrong's bedchamber. Without bothering about formalities, he threw himself on the bed. "Come over," he said to Wanrong. After a short moment he called out, "Somebody come here!"

Sun Yaoting, who had been waiting outside, hurriedly entered the room, only to find the imperial couple lying in bed together. Pu Yi had Wanrong in his arms and seemed to be feeling her up. Sun Yaoting stepped back hastily, but Pu Yi threw him a glance and ordered, "Come in."

"Your Majesty, what do you need?" Sun Yaoting felt embarrassed, with one foot in the door and the other outside.

"Nothing. Just stand over there." Pu Yi sat up and pointed to a corner of the room. Then he lay down again.

Wanrong blushed and turned her face to the wall. Pu Yi continued to hold her and talk to her, but their conversation sounded rather clumsy.

"What did you eat today?"

"Nothing special. Just the same old dishes."

"If there's anything you want to eat, tell them to buy it for you."

"I can't think of anything special, really." Wanrong had apparently lost interest in the subject.

Sun Yaoting stood in the corner, feeling very awkward, with Pu Yi fondling his Empress without passion and trying to strike up a conversation. He feigned a fit of severe cough and slipped out of the room. A moment later Pu Yi left.

From time to time Pu Yi came to have lunch with Wanrong, but he usually left as soon as he finished eating. One day he burst into fury over a small incident. They were about to have their meal when Wanrong mentioned that a new dish, "cucumber slices stir-fried with pepper", had been prepared with fresh vegetables sent by her family. "Chunshou," she turned to Sun Yaoting. "Tell them to bring the dish here. I want His Majesty to taste it."

Sun Yaoting, together with two other eunuchs, Zhao Xingzhen and Yang Deshou, left for the kitchen at once.

After a while Pu Yi grew impatient. "What's the matter? Why does it take so long? What are they up to?" He left the room and headed straight for the kitchen. In the front courtyard he saw Yang Deshou holding a dish in his hands. The dish was not properly covered, nor was it placed in a food box.

"You dirty slave!" Pu Yi turned livid with anger. "Where is the cover? How do you know the lizards in the trees have not pissed into the dish?"

"Your Majesty, please have mercy on me!" Yang dropped on his knees.

Without a word Pu Yi picked up the dish and smashed it on Yang's head. Blood oozed out and trickled down Yang's cheeks. Yang felt his face with his hand and swooned at the sight of so much blood.

Pu Yi grew a little worried, for he had no intention to kill the eunuch. After all, the days of Imperial China when the Emperor wielded supreme power over his subjects were long gone. The violent death of a eunuch on palace grounds would surely cause a lot of trouble. Feeling both angry and flustered, Pu Yi left without eating anything.

Yang Deshou came to after a while, and Wanrong telephoned Pu Yi to tell him the news. Still feeling uncertain, Pu Yi ordered a German hospital to be contacted. When the German doctors pronounced Yang to be out of danger, Pu Yi heaved a sigh of relief and sent for Zhang Qianhe. "Give Yang Deshou a hundred dollars. He can take some time off to rest and recuperate."

Yang was grateful to get the hundred dollars, but he felt apprehensive about his future. Even if Pu Yi did not mind letting him stay, Wanrong was unlikely to agree. She attached great importance to maintaining good relations with Pu Yi and would not forgive Yang for what he had done.

After his recovery Yang came to see Wanrong. Ignoring him, she turned to Sun Yaoting. "I don't want him anymore! Tell Qianhe to come here!"

Entering the room, Zhang Qianhe realized at a glance what was happening. "I'll teach him a lesson for what he did," he said to Wanrong, trying to mollify her. "Maybe he could come back later?" He happened to be Yang's mentor.

"No, I don't need him here." Wanrong remained adamant.

Thus Yang Deshou was expelled from the palace for incurring the wrath of his Imperial Master. It seemed that Pu Yi had many things on his mind and often gave vent to his anger by abusing his servants.

The Imperial Palace had many taboo subjects, and gossiping about the Emperor was considered the utmost sacrilege. Sun Yaoting knew he must watch what he said, but for lack of better things to do he often chatted with other eunuchs. Such careless talk nearly cost him his life.

One day he was chatting with a few old eunuchs in a room near the Gate of Intense Happiness. "Now you are attending to the Empress," said an old eunuch. "How does it go?"

"Not bad. She is still a child and enjoys playing games."

"Who does she play with?"

"The Emperor's younger sisters. Few people can mingle with the Empress; you certainly know the palace rules better than I do."

"I've heard that the Emperor does not get along with her. Is it true?"

Sun Yaoting hesitated, knowing it would be dangerous to speak too much. As the old eunuchs looked at him expectantly, he finally said, "If the Empress happens to have the three princesses with her when the Emperor comes to the Palace of Gathering Elegance, she will often ask, 'Has His Majesty left?'"

At this moment Pu Yi suddenly pushed the door open and walked into the room. Flabbergasted, all the eunuchs fell on their knees. Looking at Sun Yaoting, Pu Yi ordered, "Come with me, Chunshou."

Sun Yaoting followed Pu Yi out of the room, while the old eunuchs remained on their knees, not daring to look up. This is too bad, Sun Yaoting thought. Apparently Pu Yi had overheard the conversation.

Pu Yi entered the Mind Nurture Hall. "Close the door!" he ordered.

Sun Yaoting closed the door and prostrated himself.

Pu Yi sat down on the throne. "Come over!"

"Yes!" Sun Yaoting moved forward on his knees.

Pu Yi suddenly grabbed him by the ear. "You dirty slave! How dare you speak ill of me behind my back!"

"Your slave dares not!" Sun Yaoting was too scared to speak fluently.

"What did you say about me? Tell the truth!" Pu Yi did not loosen his grip on Sun Yaoting's ear. "Tell the truth, or I'll make you pay for it. Is that clear?"

"Yes! But your slave never said anything disrespectful about Your

Majesty!"

"You brazen slave!" Pu Yi banged on the table angrily. "How dare you play games with me?"

"Your slave dares not!"

Pu Yi got up abruptly, took a revolver from the drawer, and slammed it on the table. "I'll shoot you if you don't confess!"

Terrified, Sun Yaoting burst into tears. "Your Majesty, your slave really didn't say anything!"

"Liar! I heard you say something about 'His Majesty'! How dare you deny it?"

"Your slave just said that the Empress once asked if 'His Majesty' had left. Nothing else! Please look into the matter! Shoot me if I had said anything else!"

"Hmm!" Pu Yi sank back into the chair.

"I would deserve to be shot if I had said anything bad about Your Majesty, but I really didn't!" As Pu Yi seemed a bit mollified, Sun Yaoting kowtowed repeatedly and kept pleading for mercy, though his words were not always coherent. "I became a eunuch in order to honor my father! My family was so poor! If Your Majesty has mercy on me, I'll burn incense at home to thank Your Majesty's bounty!"

"I'll let you off this time," Pu Yi finally said. Sun Yaoting kowtowed a few more times and retreated. He returned to find the old eunuchs still waiting for him in the room. They were greatly relieved to find him safe and learn that the Emperor would not look further into the matter.

Back in his own room, Sun Yaoting was shaking after his narrow escape. He washed his face and changed out of his gray gown, which had gathered a lot of dirt from all his kneeling and kowtowing. Then he collapsed into his bed.

About an hour later the eunuchs outside suddenly announced the arrival of the Emperor. Sun Yaoting jumped out of bed, wondering if Pu Yi had come to settle accounts with him. The door curtain was lifted, and Pu Yi walked in, followed by Li Tiyu, a male attendant.

"Your Majesty..." Sun Yaoting kowtowed hastily, turning pale.

"Get up!" Pu Yi said, and Li Tiyu pulled Sun Yaoting to his feet. Pu Yi took a close look at him, then left the room without a word.

The moment Pu Yi left, Sun Yaoting caught Li Tiyu by the hem of his dress. "Brother, do you think I'm still in trouble?" he whispered.

"No, not at all," Li Tiyu whispered back. "Were you scared?"

"Yes! I was lying in bed a minute ago!"

"His Majesty said he just wanted to test you. He was only teasing, you know."

"Oh really? He scared me out of my senses!"

Afterward Sun Yaoting talked about the incident with the old eunuchs at the Gate of Intense Happiness. "I was lucky. If the Emperor had been real angry, I would have lost my head!"

"You seem to have a sturdy life," said an old eunuch. "As they say, 'He who survives a big disaster will have good fortune!'"

"Thank you for your auspicious words." Sun Yaoting was feeling much better now.

5. The Emperor's Secrets

The lack of conjugal bliss between the Emperor and the Empress was an open secret in the palace. In the first days of their marriage they might have shared a few amorous moments, but their relationship soon turned sour. On the rare occasions when Pu Yi came to spend the night with Wanrong, he always left early in the morning as if he did not want to stay with her one more minute than necessary. One day a big quarrel occurred between them at the Palace of Gathering Elegance and Pu Yi left in a huff.

Rumors abounded about what had gone wrong between the Imperial couple. One day an old eunuch-in-attendance in the Mind Nurture Hall complained to Sun Yaoting, "Why the hell does he behave like that? Taking the land-way instead of the water-way!"

"What do you mean by 'water-way' and 'land-way'?" Sun Yaoting asked.

"You've been in the palace for some time now, and you still don't know? His Majesty prefers the 'land-way' of eunuchs to the 'water-way' of the Empress!"

Sun Yaoting felt trepidation that such vicious gossip about the Emperor was circulating in the palace. At the same time he began to understand why Pu Yi had hit the ceiling to overhear his conversation with the old eunuchs at the Gate of Intense Happiness. Obviously Pu Yi was not entirely ignorant of the unfavorable gossip about him among eunuchs and palace maids.

"Though I know little about ancient times," the old eunuch went on, "I know this for a fact: In over two hundred years of the Great Qing, no other Emperor ever behaved in this way. What a shame!"

Sun Yaoting listened in dismay but said nothing. He dared not mention what he learned from the old eunuch to anyone for fear of bringing catastrophe on himself.

Pu Yi had a rather bumpy career as an Emperor. He ascended the throne at three, abdicated at seven, and was temporarily "restored" at twelve. It would be reasonable to assume that he often felt overwhelmed and needed to find some solace. According to ancient precepts an Emperor should have about a hundred concubines. As the last Emperor of China, Pu Yi did not get to enjoy such privileges, but numerous palace maids were still available to him. In his article "After the Emperor Got His Special Pardon", published in Da Gong Bao in March 1981, Shen Zui recounted something he claimed to have learned from Pu Yi personally. When Pu Yi was only ten, his eunuch attendants thought up a way to keep him in the room after nightfall so they could go home to rest. They handed him over to a few palace maids, who took him to bed and played naughty games with him until he was utterly exhausted. He got up in the morning feeling dizzy, saying the sun appeared to be yellow. When he complained to the eunuchs, they gave him some pills to restore his energy so that he could better "serve" the sex-starved palace maids. But gradually the pills lost their effect, and Pu Yi all but lost interest in women.

From what Sun Yaoting heard, eunuchs were directly responsible for ruining Pu Yi's health and virility. Without normal sexual outlets some eunuchs developed perverted relationships with palace maids or other eunuchs. A young eunuch named Wang was a case in point. A native of Dongguang County, he looked like a pretty girl with his tall, slim figure, handsome face, and creamy white skin. He entered the palace as a small child and soon became the victim of sexual abuse by some old eunuchs. By his late teens he began to molest younger eunuchs. Later he became a eunuch-in-attendance of the Emperor, who granted him a formal palace name, Wang Fengchi. Pu Yi treated him with great favor, and they were always seen together, "inseparable as body and shadow".

With Pu Yi driven out of the Forbidden City in 1924, Wang left the

Wang Fengchi, Pu Yi's personal attendant

palace and settled down somewhere in the capital. He stayed away from his fellow eunuchs. According to some people, he was still alive when the People's Republic of China was founded in 1949.

Under the circumstances it would be impossible for Pu Yi to develop a normal relationship with his Empress. How Wanrong felt about the awkward situation was anybody's guess. In Sun Yaoting's opinion, Wanrong must have suspected something. After all, it was strange for any man to lose his potency at such a young age. But it would be unthinkable for her to take up the topic with him. Resigned to her fate, she tried to find solace elsewhere.

Unlike Wenxiu, Wanrong rarely practiced calligraphy. She read leisure books from time to time, but it seemed that they only added to her gloom. She was often seen sitting alone quietly, doing nothing. After her entry into the palace, she seldom went back to her parents' house at the east end of Mao'er Alley. To kill her severe abdominal pain she took opium and grew addicted to it. Thus smoking opium became one of her few pastimes.

Perhaps to ease the tension between them, Pu Yi occasionally took Wanrong for an excursion to the Summer Palace. This always made great social news and enjoyed wide coverage in Beijing's newspapers.

Although Pu Yi was merely the "abdicated Emperor", his excursion still reminded one of the Imperial pomp and grandeur in the old days. From the Forbidden City all the way to the Longevity Hill of the Summer Palace, the palace gates and city gates were flung wide open, and sentries from the Imperial Guards in gray uniform were planted at regular intervals. The Imperial Guards usually treated the eunuchs with disdain. When Sun

Yaoting met them in the palace he always saluted them politely, but they never bothered to return the greeting. Now, as part of Pu Yi's retinue, Sun Yaoting felt a great sense of satisfaction looking at the Imperial Guards along the way bowing respectfully to him, or in his direction anyway.

At the vanguard of the excursion party Pu Yi rode in his limousine, followed by about a dozen cars the palace hired from a car rental in Beijing. Wanrong sat with a palace maid in the back seat of the second car, with Sun Yaoting in the front seat beside the driver. The following cars carried a lot of Qing veterans, including officials from the Household Department. Unable to dissuade Pu Yi from such excursions, they chose to accompany him as chaperones to forestall his inappropriate behavior.

An excursion to the Summer Palace took the better part of a day. They usually set out in the morning and returned to the Forbidden City before nightfall. No formal lunch was provided during the trip. Instead, Pu Yi liked to stop at the Hall of Joyful Longevity or the Stone Boat for a snack, drinking tea and soda water and eating Western cookies. Qing veterans unused to such food had to go hungry until their return to the palace.

The itinerary remained more or less the same. First they climbed the Longevity Hill and took a rest at the Pagoda of Buddhist Fragrance. Going down the hill, they visited the Hall of Joyful Longevity, walked down the Long Corridor, and strolled at random for some time. Pu Yi never failed to visit the Hall of Joyful Longevity and the Palace of Nourishing Clouds. In the Hall of Joyful Longevity Pu Yi often lingered in front of the portrait of Emperor Guangxu, who had been placed under house arrest by Empress Dowager Cixi after his Hundred-Day Reform failed. Perhaps his luckless uncle reminded Pu Yi of his own predicament. The Palace of Parting Clouds contained a portrait of Empress Dowager Cixi, painted in 1903 by an American woman, Katherine A. Carl. Pu Yi once remarked, pointing at the portrait, "This is the work of Carl, that 'beauty-painter'. Cixi paid her no less than ten thousand taels of silver for it. That was quite a sum!"

Most of the time Pu Yi remained silent and rarely spoke to Wanrong. The attending eunuchs chatted in a hushed voice from time to time. "Cixi was really remarkable!" Sun Yaoting once said to another eunuch when they walked out of the Summer Palace. "Just think: a mere woman ruling China for forty-eight years!"

"But she also made lots of blunders!"

"Well, one of her blunders was the Summer Palace."

"I see what you mean. But for her, we would have no place to go for a walk like this with His Majesty!"

During one of the excursions Pu Yi gave Wanrong a pleasant surprise. Leaving the Summer Palace, Pu Yi paid a visit to her home on Mao'er Alley. Both her parents happened to be out, so they just strolled around in the courtyard and left in disappointment. Though Pu Yi had done it on a whim, Wanrong was very pleased, for it showed her that despite his habitual coldness Pu Yi seemed to care for her in some way.

6

SUNSET IN THE FORBIDDEN CITY

1. The Empress's Birthday

It took several days to prepare the celebration of the Empress's birthday, called the "Thousand-Autumn Festival" in the palace. After getting up in the morning Wanrong ate some cookies and began to dress up with the help of her attendant Fu. She put on a dragon-designed gown and her phoenix crown. After a while Pu Yi arrived, dressed casually in a Western suit. He chatted with her until the eunuchs announced the "birthday dinner" at eleven o'clock.

The food would have been rather customary but for four big bowls of bird's nest spelling out the Chinese characters "Wan Shou Wu Jiang", meaning "boundless longevity". A rare smile of satisfaction came to Wanrong's face as she studied the four-character saying, which was normally reserved for the Emperor only. The eunuchs serving the dishes were all smiles and kept offering congratulations to her.

After the meal several eunuchs from the Court Theatrical Office came into the main hall to play court music with flutes and clarinets. Wanrong walked to the center of the hall and sat down in her chair to accept congratulations, with Pu Yi standing by her side.

Chief Superintendent Zhang Qianhe was the first to offer birthday greetings to the Empress. Next came Pu Yi's sisters, eunuchs from other parts of the palace, and the Empress's own eunuchs. Next came Pu Yi's attendants led by Chief Eunuch Shao Xiangqing and his deputy, Feng Junchen. They

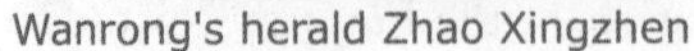

Wanrong's herald Zhao Xingzhen

Zhang Qianhe, one of Pu Yi's most trusted eunuchs

were followed by the "heralds" of the various palaces, with Zhao Xingzhen at the head of them. Attendants of the three high consorts came last. Everyone who offered congratulations to the Empress had to perform the formal salute by "kneeling for three times and kowtowing nine times". In accordance with established rules Wanrong acknowledged their greeting with a nod of her head, saying nothing.

Pu Yi stayed until the evening to have supper with Wanrong. Eunuchs from the imperial kitchen brought the dishes to the gate and passed them to Wanrong's attendants. Sun Yaoting waited on the imperial couple at the table to make sure that the dishes were laid out properly. After the meal Pu Yi took his departure, thus bringing an end to the "thousand-autumn festival" celebrations.

A few days before her birthday Wanrong had ordered the customary reward to be granted to every eunuch in the Palace of Gathering Elegance: a piece of silk to make a long gown. It would have been a piece of light silk gauze in summer or an unlined garment in winter. "If only her birthday were in winter!" a eunuch said. "That would have saved us the trouble of going to the dressmaker!"

"What nonsense!" another eunuch said. "Do you think it's up to you to decide when the Empress should celebrate her birthday?"

With the birthday celebrations going on in the main hall of the Palace of Gathering Elegance, an old female shaman sat cross-legged in a separate room chanting incantations for the benefit of the Empress. She belonged to the Yellow Sect of Tibetan Buddhism, the official religion of Qing, and was the "substitute nun" for Wanrong. A few days after her birthday Sun Yaoting accompanied Wanrong to the Palace of Earthly Peace, where he saw the shaman for the first time. Contrary to his expectations she was neither young nor pretty.

The Palace of Earthly Peace, the Empress's residence in the Ming Dynasty, was used mainly for sacrificial purposes in Qing Dynasty. Three rooms on the east, as Sun Yaoting remembered, had served as the bridal chamber on Pu Yi's wedding day. In the courtyard Wanrong was greeted by her shaman, a woman fifty to sixty years old neatly dressed in a hat, an embroidered gown, and thick-heeled shoes. "It's sacrificial day today, isn't it?" Wanrong remarked casually. Instead of going for the main rooms facing south, she went into a side room on the west, with the old shaman following her closely.

Tidying her hair and straightening up her clothes, Wanrong stood quietly before a wall draped with a curtain. The shaman went up and drew the curtain to reveal a brightly colored painting of an elderly couple, the "Royal Father" and "Royal Mother". According to a Manchu legend they adopted an abandoned baby whose son, Nurhachi, founded Late Jin Dynasty, predecessor of the Qing Dynasty. Wanrong burned incense and kowtowed to the "Royal Father" and "Royal Mother".

Going out of the room, Sun Yaoting noticed a long table with three big woks at the northeastern corner of the courtyard. There was meat cooking in the woks and fresh meat hanging from a long pole. "What's that for?" he asked the shaman.

"How ignorant you are! That's for feeding ravens. It's a way to pay respects to the imperial ancestors!"

Sun Yaoting wanted to take a closer look, but the shaman stopped him, pointing to a rope ring around the pole. "Don't walk in there! It's forbidden!" Obviously she did not want him to offend the imperial ancestors by disturbing the ravens.

For lack of interest in sacrificial ceremonies, Wanrong gladly relegated most of her duties to her shaman. The old woman lived outside the palace and came in only on special occasions. She never called on Wanrong at the Palace of Gathering Elegance. Sun Yaoting saw her in the palace from time to time, but she never acknowledged him though she knew him by sight.

Out of curiosity Sun Yaoting went to watch the process of sacrificing to the gods in the Palace of Earthly Peace. A few runners from the Office of Divine Sacrifice carried in a tied-up pig. Several female shamans, including Wanrong's "substitute nun", chanted scriptures before the pig's head was cut off and put on the altar. The pig, cleared of its tripe and chitterlings, was chopped into large pieces and cooked in a big wok. After a while an inviting smell came out. Eunuchs who happened to pass by the palace could not help but stop to take a look.

Pu Yi also had a "substitute monk", Sun Hu, a square-faced man of medium height. He apparently enjoyed a higher salary and prestige than the old shaman woman. He was often seen strolling in the palace, a caged bird in hand. One day Sun Yaoting ran into him at the Gate of Divine Prowess and greeted him respectfully, but he walked away without bothering to look up. Though annoyed by his arrogance, the eunuchs all agreed that Sun Hu was somebody important. From what Sun Yaoting heard, after Pu Yi was driven out of the Forbidden City, Sun Hu took shelter in a temple in Beijing and eventually died in poverty.

2. The Expulsion

It was November 5, 1924. Early in the morning Sun Yaoting was standing on duty outside Wanrong's bedchamber when Pu Yi arrived. He was wearing a Western suit, a pair of glasses, and shiny leather shoes. "Your Majesty," Sun Yaoting said, "the Empress has not got up."

"Never mind." With a sweep of his hand Pu Yi walked into the room to wake Wanrong up. Then he came out. "Come over, Chunshou. Let's play the shuttlecock!"

Sun Yaoting took a shuttlecock from the room and followed Pu Yi into the open court. After kicking the shuttlecock a few times, Pu Yi passed it over to Sun Yaoting. "Take it!" Sun Yaoting caught the shuttlecock with his foot and sent it high into the sky.

Considering the grievous situation at the time, kicking the shuttlecock seemed a rather frivolous thing for Pu Yi to do. High Consort Duankang had suddenly died of illness not long before. Her coffin was placed in the Palace of Benevolent Peace and all Manchu officials were made to wear mourning affire. It seemed as if they were bemoaning the demise of the Great Qing.

Eunuchs also gathered to mourn the high consort. When the chief eunuch of the Palace of Heavenly Purity signaled by clapping his hands, all the eunuchs began to cry in unison. After a short while the chief eunuch clapped his hands again, and the crying stopped abruptly. Though most eunuchs cried aloud without tears, Sun Yaoting did shed a few tears as he had waited on Duankang.

In the meantime civil war had been raging on in the country. Two powerful military factions, the Fengtian army led by Zhang Zuolin and the Zhili army under Wu Peifu's command, were fighting their second war. At a crucial juncture Wu's subordinate Feng Yuxiang suddenly defected, leading his troops into Beijing and issuing a peace telegram. The Zhili army collapsed. Feng's "National Army" occupied Beijing and put Cao Kun, President of the Republic who had bought the votes for his election, under house arrest. The newly established provisional cabinet decided to revise the Articles of Favorable Treatment.

While playing the shuttlecock with Pu Yi, Sun Yaoting kept an eye on Wanrong's room. "The Empress is up now," he told Pu Yi.

"Let's go in." Pu Yi said, so they entered the room. While Wanrong went away to do her toilet, Sun Yaoting took out a piece of cloth. "Your Majesty, let me polish your shoes."

"All right," Pu Yi said. "Don't use too much cream."

"Yes." Sun Yaoting chatted with Pu Yi ingratiatingly while polishing his shoes. After that, Pu Yi sat down in front of the piano and began to play a merry tune. It then occurred to him that he had not enjoyed his morning tea, so he told Sun Yaoting to bring his "tea box".

"The tea box has not arrived, Your Majesty."

"Never mind, I can use the tea set here."

Sun Yaoting went away and came back with a pot of jasmine tea. After finishing his cup of morning tea, Pu Yi returned to the piano. Just then a eunuch came in to report that Household Department officials Shao Ying, Qi Ling and Bao Xi, as well as Pu Yi's father-in-law, Rong Yuan, requested

General Feng Yuxiang, whose National Army drove Pu Yi out of the Forbidden City in 1924

an urgent audience with the Emperor. Aware that it must be an emergency, Pu Yi received them in Wanrong's studio.

"Is it something urgent?" Sun Yaoting asked the eunuch who had brought in the officials.

"You haven't heard the news?" the eunuch said in a whisper. "Feng Yuxiang has sent Lu Zhonglin and Zhang Bi to the palace! They have a team of soldiers armed with pistols!"

"Good heavens!" Sun Yaoting was dumbstruck. He knew the names quite well. Lu was garrison commander of the metropolitan area and Zhang the chief of police. "What shall we do?" he muttered to himself.

The other eunuch pulled him to a corner. "You know what? Soldiers of the National Army have already entered the palace. They have pistols and broadswords! They have blocked all the gates so no one can either get in or get out!"

"We seem to be in big trouble!"

"Of course we are! Does His Majesty know about it?"

"Not really. He was playing the shuttlecock with me only a minute ago."

In fact, grim rumors had been circulating among the eunuchs for a few days. Some said Feng Yuxiang would send his men to seize Pu Yi. Some of the eunuchs expulsed from the palace after the big fire had reportedly gone to Feng Yuxiang to accuse Pu Yi of secretly removing and selling palace treasures. But few eunuchs had expected the rumors to materialize so soon.

Pu Yi's meeting with the news bearers was very brief. He returned to Wanrong's room devoid of all his composure and self-assurance. "Feng Yuxiang wants to force me out of the Forbidden City!" he muttered in an agitated voice. Wanrong retained her outward calm and even tried to comfort him.

"They want us to move out at once, otherwise they will open fire with artillery from the Coal Hill! Rebels! Rebels!" Pu Yi was working himself into a fit. Suddenly he turned to Sun Yaoting. "Chunshou, hurry to the Palace of Eternal Spring and tell the Sedate Consort to pack up the valuables and come here as soon as possible!"

Sun Yaoting ran into the Palace of Eternal Spring. "His Majesty wants you to pack up and leave for the Palace of Gathering Elegance," he panted. Wenxiu apparently knew what was happening and did not look startled. "Where is His Majesty?" she asked.

"He has returned to the Mind Nurture Hall."

"All right, you may go back to the Empress." Wenxiu then told her eunuchs to pack up at once.

"His Majesty was looking for you," Wanrong said to Sun Yaoting the moment he walked in. He turned and ran toward the Mind Nurture Hall. The entire palace was plunged into chaos, with the eunuchs scurrying here and there. When he got to the Mind Nurture Hall, Pu Yi told him to find Rong Yuan. Sun Yaoting went out and searched around, but in vain. A eunuch told him that Rong Yuan and the officials of the Household Department had probably run for cover. Pu Yi looked very grim when he heard Sun Yaoting's report. He swept his hand but said nothing.

Actually Shao Ying had been negotiating with Lu Zhonglin for more time. Getting impatient, Lu turned to his soldiers and shouted an order:
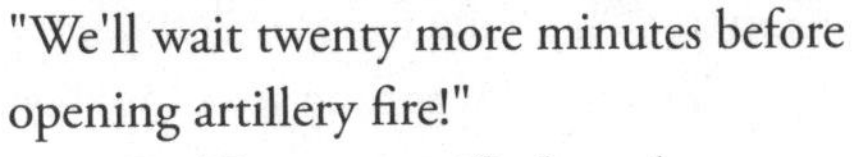
"We'll wait twenty more minutes before opening artillery fire!"

Pu Yi was terrified at the news. "Tell them I will move out! Just give me a little more time to pack up!" His words spread quickly in the palace, adding to the general panic and confusion as people exchanged horrifying rumors.

"The Emperor has agreed to leave the palace! We must pack up quickly before the troops charge in!"

"His Majesty has already handed over the Imperial Seal to Lu Zhonglin!"

Sun Yaoting returned to the Palace

Shao Ying, head of the Imperial Household Department

of Gathering Elegance and told Wanrong what was happening. Wanrong looked despondent and lost, but what she said to Sun Yaoting moved him deeply. "Don't risk your life for the stuff here! If the soldiers come, tell them everything belongs to the Empress. If they want anything, just give it to them. The most important thing is to stay alive!" Her words touched all the eunuchs and palace maids present. The Empress clearly cared for her servants even though she appeared cool and indifferent to them most of the time.

Wanrong sat in silence, with tears rolling down her cheeks. Her maids and eunuchs also began to weep. When lunch was ready, no one had any appetite. They stared at one another, thinking of the dark future ahead. Just then someone shouted outside, "Get ready to leave! Hurry up or calamities will come!" Though no one knew for sure what the "calamities" might be, they all got up and began to pack. A eunuch came in to deliver what was probably the last imperial edict. Pu Yi wanted them to get packed and meet him at the rear gate of the imperial garden.

Sun Yaoting heaved a sigh of relief on hearing this. At least the situation seemed to be under control, and they were not going to lose their lives. Wanrong suggested that for safety's sake they take only a few pieces of clothing with them and leave everything else behind. All nodded their agreement.

At around two o'clock in the afternoon they heard a loud voice. "Time to leave the palace! Time to leave the palace!" Sun Yaoting turned to Wanrong. "It's time for us to leave."

"Let's go," Wanrong said, looking completely drained.

They came to the east end of the imperial garden. After a while Pu Yi walked briskly toward them, followed by Wenxiu, Rong Yuan, several Household Department officials including Shao Ying, and a few male attendants. Sun Yaoting also saw Pu Yi's father, Zai Feng. He was wearing a court gown and his official hat with a peacock feather. As they walked past the rockery Zai Feng looked up at the Coal Hill, muttering, "The Great Qing is over!" and threw his hat to the ground. No one spoke a single a word.

Lu Zhonglin and Zhang Bi met Pu Yi at the Gate of Divine Prowess. "You will be taken to the Northern Mansion," Lu said in a firm and unequivocal voice. Several cars were waiting there.

Without a word Zhang Bi got into the first car. Pu Yi was assigned to the second one. Wanrong, escorted by Sun Yaotin and a palace maid, took the third, and Wenxiu followed in the fourth. Lu Zhonglin got into the fifth car, with Household Department officials tailing behind. As the cars drove out of the gate, Sun Yaoting stole a glance outside and broke into a cold sweat at the sight of the National Army soldiers armed with pistols and broadswords. Wanrong looked taut and nervous.

Soldiers were posted all along the road, and large, clamoring crowds gathered to watch the convoy. "The Emperor is moving out of the palace!" "Let's take a look at the Empress!"

Wanrong lowered her head lest people would recognize her. The palace maid turned pale with fright. Sun Yaoting also felt tense as beads of perspiration formed on his forehead. The cars kept honking to thread their way through the onlookers.

When they finally arrived at the main gate of the Northern Mansion, Sun Yaoting found the place heavily guarded by soldiers of the National Army. "It doesn't look good," he whispered to another eunuch. "We are going into a prison!" Getting out of the car, Lu Zhonglin told Pu Yi that he would stay in the Northern Mansion for his protection and that he was not to leave at will.

As Sun Yaoting learned later, the palace was in utter chaos after they left. Lu Zhonglin ordered all the eunuchs and palace maids to leave immediately. Those who had saved a little money after many years' service

Wenxiu and Wanrong

The exodus of palace maids

packed up their belongings in silence and left the palace. Others went into utter despair as they had no money, no place to go, and no skill to make a living. Among them, a eunuch committed suicide by jumping into the moat. News of Pu Yi's eviction made headlines in Beijing's newspapers, drawing more public attention than his dispersal of eunuchs in the previous year.

Several dozen years later the author Pan Jitong interviewed Pu Yi and Lu Zhonglin separately about the incident and recorded their accounts in his book *Legend of the Last Emperor*. Pu Yi's narration was very brief. He said he was with Wanrong at the Palace of Gathering Elegance when Shao Ying and Qi Ling brought him the news. He also mentioned that he shook hands with Lu Zhonglin at the main gate of the Northern Mansion. Lu Zhonglin, on the other hand, gave a vivid, detailed description. As Pan Jitong writes:

In Tianjin I called on Lu Zhonglin, former garrison commander of the metropolitan area. From him I learned the details of that dramatic day in history. Mr. Lu was already seventy-four years old.

We listened to Mr. Lu pouring out his memories in Zhou's Canteen, a famous restaurant in Tianjin. Mr. Hu Ruoyu and a friend of mine were also present.

After a sip of Shaoxin liquor, Mr. Lu began to speak in a soft voice. He had a strong accent of Hebei's Ding County. "There was a long-term cause as well as an immediate cause for Pu Yi's expulsion from the Forbidden City. The long-term cause was the incompleteness of the 1911 Revolution. The immediate cause was the restoration staged by Zhang Xun. Many of us agreed that the Xuantong Emperor was not behaving himself."

"I know what you mean," Mr. Hu said with a smile. "As I remembered, some shops in Beijing suddenly began to sell queues, and imperial dragon-banners appeared in many places. Even President Cao Kun was looking for people who could write memorials."

"That's right. ...We were carrying out Mr. Feng's order. The night before, I talked with Prime Minister Huang Fu and Police Chief Zhang Bi. They wanted me to lead the operation. I told them we must avoid 'startling the snake by beating the grass'. If fighting should break out in the palace, the foreign powers would surely intervene, and that would abort our plan. We must act with lightning speed, I said. They asked me how many men I needed. I thought for a moment and put up two fingers. Huang asked, 'Twenty thousand?' I shook my head. 'Two thousand?' I shook my head. 'At least two hundred.' Again I shook my head. 'I only need twenty soldiers armed with pistols.' They trusted me and did not object. The following day I tucked two hand grenades under my clothes and went into the Forbidden City with my men. Whenever I saw a palace guard, I ordered him to freeze. I did the same with everyone we met, including servants who were carrying food or water. I found Shao Ying of the Household Department and told him Pu Yi must leave in twenty minutes. I also said our troops would open fire with artillery from the top of Coal Hill. 'As for me, I won't be killed by my own men,' I declared, bringing out the two grenades and throwing them on the table. Shao Ying was scared out of his wits and said he would report to Pu Yi at once. He begged me to extend the time limit for them to pack up, and I agreed to give them another twenty minutes. 'Tell our brothers outside to wait twenty more minutes,' I shouted the order to my men."

"What happened after that?"

"After that? Pu Yi left the palace within forty minutes. We drove him by car to his father's house at Shichahai. ...At the gate I shook hands with Pu Yi and asked him whether he would continue to regard himself as Emperor or become an ordinary citizen. When he replied he wanted to be an ordinary citizen, I said he would have our protection."

3. The Northern Mansion

As soon as they entered the Northern Mansion, Sun Yaoting presented Wanrong with a big gold ingot and ten small ones that he had brought

The Northern Mansion, now a cultural site under state protection

secretly from the palace. "Oh!" Wanrong was touched. "I didn't know you were carrying all these!"

"Your slave did it out of loyalty!" Sun Yaoting said in earnest.

What he did was quite remarkable considering that most eunuchs who moved into the Northern Mansion did not hand in anything. Some of them, especially those who rode in the cars, had the chance to take various things with them, but they claimed to have left the palace empty-handed in the general panic and confusion.

Just before they left the Palace of Gathering Elegance, Sun Yaoting noticed that Wanrong's betrothal gift was still displayed on the table: two palm-size gold ingots and twenty finger-size ones. He and another eunuch named Shi Laixiang decided to take the gold with them. They agreed that each would take half of the ingots and hand them over when they got to the Northern Mansion. Shi used to be a eunuch-in-attendance of Pu Yi, who transferred him to wait on Wanrong only two months before. After leaving the palace, Shi showed up once in the Northern Mansion but did not hand in the gold. Then he slipped away quietly and returned to his hometown, Nanyuan, with whatever fortune he had made.

Wanrong had no idea what had happened to all her servants. "Where is Shi Laixiang?" she asked Sun Yaoting, who could only give her an evasive answer. "And where is Zhou Fu?" She asked about another eunuch given to her by Pu Yi. Sun Yaoting told her that Zhou had not shown up in the Northern Mansion. Then she asked about some of her female attendants. "They have all disappeared," Sun Yaoting said. "None of them has come to the Northern Mansion." He did not tell her that they had left with stolen goods from the palace, including her personal belongings. Wanrong did not pursue the topic; she was content enough to have survived.

"Your slave has to ask for a leave," Sun Yaoting said to Wanrong.

"Where are you going?"

"I haven't brought my bedding here."

Sun Yaoting went back to the palace all by himself. Watched closely by the soldiers, he took his clothes and bedroll together with four hundred silver dollars he had tucked away. Then he returned to the Northern Mansion to wait on Wanrong.

A few days later he heard some interesting news from a junior eunuch. "Chunshou, Zhang Zongchang has come here for a visit!"

"What for?" Sun Yaoting asked. A powerful warlord who had joined Zhang Xun's aborted restoration, Zhang Zongchang appeared almost like a savior in the eyes of the Qing veterans.

"I don't know." The young eunuch shook his head.

Hearing the news, Wanrong seemed to be very interested and told Sun Yaoting to find out why General Zhang had come. She was undoubtedly aware that her personal destiny relied on such maneuvers. Sun Yaoting went out several times but failed to learn anything.

In the Northern Mansion Wanrong took up the eastern compound, with Wenxiu on the opposite side. Pu Yi, who stayed in the front courtyard, never came to see his Empress. Nor did he ever sit down to dinner with Wanrong or Wenxiu. Sun Yaoting only remembered a courtesy call one early morning from a pretty woman named Tang Yiying, who had just got married with Pu Jie. But she left almost at once after an exchange of greetings with Wanrong.

In the Northern Mansion life was hard for Wanrong as far as food was concerned. The meal usually consisted of cooked rice and two or three dishes. She always preferred steamed bread to rice, but it didn't look as if she had a choice. After she had finished eating, Sun Yaoting cleared the table and helped himself to the leftovers in the kitchen.

"Duankang's coffin is still lying in the Palace of Benevolent Peace," Sun Yaoting said to Zhao Rongsheng. "No one seems to bother, but it can't be left there indefinitely."

"Yes," Zhao agreed. "Fortunately it is cool these days, otherwise there would be a terrible smell." He felt anxious because he had waited on Duankang for quite a few years.

The other two high consorts, Jingyi and Ronghui had refused to move out on the day of Pu Yi's expulsion. They finally left the palace on November 21 for the house of Princess Rongshougulun. Only a couple of devoted eunuchs went to see them for old time's sake.

Though Pu Yi had too many things on his mind to bother about the high consorts, whether dead or alive, some other members of the imperial family began to worry over the burial of Duankang. When Zai Tao volunteered to handle the matter, Pu Yi readily consented. By Zai Tao's arrangement a team of eunuchs and male servants led by Zhao Rongsheng and Cai Yachen moved Duankang's coffin out of the Forbidden City. After a temporary placement in Guanghuasi, the Temple of Great Deliverance, it was buried in the Western Tombs.

With the help of Johnson and others, Pu Yi worked out a plan to escape and take refuge in the Legation Quarter. One day he left the Northern Mansion accompanied by a eunuch-in-attendance. At the gate battalion commander Ding of the National Army stood at attention when Pu Yi approached him. "Where are you going?"

"I am going to visit my aunt," Pu Yi said. "Don't worry, I'll come back soon."

Ding hesitated for a moment. Unable to find an excuse to stop Pu Yi, he said, "Return as soon as possible! It's my duty to protect your safety!"

Pu Yi left and slipped into the Japanese Legation Quarter. The next day Wanrong and Wenxiu appeared at the main gate of the Northern Mansion, explaining to the guards that they wanted to find Pu Yi. The guards reported to Ding, who went up to stop them. "You cannot leave here," he said. "Pu Yi is gone to visit his aunt and has not yet come back."

At this moment Zhang Bingfang, chief steward of the Northern Mansion, walked over. "Mr. Ding, there is no reason for you to stop them. As you know, Pu Yi is now an ordinary citizen. Why can't he visit relatives?"

Ding was at a loss how to answer him. "Wait a minute. I'll ask for instructions."

"Is that necessary?" Zhang said. "Pu Yi is an ordinary citizen, so are his family members. They can go wherever they wish, can't they?"

Before Ding could decide what to do, Zhang Bingfang walked out of the gate with Wanrong and Wenxiu. They went straight to the Japanese Legation.

The eunuchs all marveled at Zhang's feat of taking the Empress and consort out of the Northern Mansion under the very nose of National Army soldiers.

"The chief steward is really somebody. He was not even afraid of armed soldiers!"

"Zhang is no ordinary man. He is Admiral Zhang Zuolin's sworn brother!"

"Oh! That's why he's so capable!"

However, the escape of Pu Yi along with his Empress and consort left the eunuchs in the Northern Mansion jobless. After Wanrong left, the kitchen stopped serving meals to the eunuchs. Sun Yaoting and a few others went to see Zai Feng, who received them in his studio. "What...what is the matter?" he asked. He spoke in a soft voice and stammered whenever he got a bit nervous.

"We have nothing to eat!"

"Please take pity on us, Your Highness!"

"What's going on? Whose idea is it?" Zai Feng told a servant to bring the steward. Instead of coming in person, Zhang Bingfang sent a subordinate to make an explanation. "We don't know what to do. His Majesty did not leave any edict before he left."

"You ...you can stay and help in the house. Things will remain as usual, as usual." Zai Feng's stammer got worse. After saying this, he disappeared into the inner room. The eunuchs felt downcast. Though they would not starve, there seemed to be no place for them in the Northern Mansion. As they were talking about it, a steward came. "His Highness will see you again."

The eunuchs followed the steward to the studio. After a while Zai Feng walked out of the inner room. "You will receive fifty dollars each and return home for the time being," he told the eunuchs. "I'll send for you as soon as your service is needed!"

The steward doled out the money. Unlike the eunuchs, some palace maids had followed Wanrong and Wenxiu to the Japanese Legation.

The eunuchs were thus discharged from the Northern Mansion. With nowhere else to go, Sun Yaoting returned to his hometown, Jinghai County.

4. Back at Home

Coming back to his home village, Sun Yaoting went immediately to see Zhang Suocheng, the old man who had taken care of him for two months after his castration. "At least you are safe and sound," Zhang said. "Nothing else really matters." Sun Yaoting then went to the house of Granny Sang, the midwife who had delivered him, only to learn from her sons that she had already passed away.

At the age of 23, Sun Yaoting came home with several hundred silver dollars. It was an impressive sum at the time, but no compensation for what he had gone through, and certainly no guarantee against the hard life that lay ahead. He wanted to tuck away the money for rainy days, but the circumstances of the family made it impossible for him to remain tightfisted. His family was planning to buy a house when he returned, and naturally he had to contribute a large share. After buying the house, they could not afford any new furniture. Sun Yaoting did not even know where to put his bedroll at first. Accustomed to the immaculate cleanliness in the palace, he found his own house unbearably dirty wherever he looked. Then his sixteen-year-old younger brother was getting married, but due to crop failure caused by flood, the bride's family could not afford a dowry. Therefore Sun Yaoting's family had to sustain all the expenses of the wedding. It looked as though his precious savings would not last long.

"How is Mr. Kou doing?" he asked. The today of the old eunuch might be his tomorrow.

"What can you expect?" his father said with a sigh. "He has four brothers, but they don't live together. The old man is going on sixty and all alone, with no child of his own."

"He used to live in such grandeur!" Sun Yaoting had learned the story of the old eunuch in early childhood. Kou Zizhen had been a herald of Cixi and won her favor with his outstanding dramatic talents. Later he wielded great clout as a head eunuch of Empress Dowager Longyu. After Longyu's death he returned to Jinghai County, settled down and purchased a lot of land. Though he already had a wife, he took another woman. High Consort Duankang once sent Xin Xiuming to Jinghai County, asking Kou to return to the palace, but he declined.

Kou lived in a large tile-roofed house in western Shuangtang. His three elder brothers lived separately from him, but the fifth brother shared his house, occupying the side rooms on the west. His adopted daughter, a young girl chosen from his own clan, died prematurely, the funeral costing him several thousand dollars. By the reckoning of his fellow villagers Kou had saved enough money to live comfortably into a ripe old age. But in 1924, the year when Pu Yi was driven out of the Forbidden City, the canal burst its banks, flooding the entire Jinghai County. The Kou family suffered heavy losses in the flood. The second brother, Kou Wanrong, was forced to sell his own house for four hundred dollars.

One day Sun Yaoting was walking on the road when he saw Kou Zizhen in a distance. He walked over to greet the old eunuch. Kou had a hunchback and deeply wrinkled face. There was nothing about him to suggest his past glory.

"Why do you come back?" Kou asked. "You are still so young!"

"Haven't you heard the news, uncle? His Majesty has left the palace. I just don't have a choice."

"Well, I suppose so," Kou sighed deeply. As Sun Yaoting watched the old eunuch walk away sluggishly, a feeling of gloom and hopelessness filled his heart.

He soon found out how destitute the family was. One day he was made to eat before the rest of the family. Going out for a walk, he returned to overhear a conversation between his two younger brothers.

"If we don't think of something soon, we'll starve."

"Whatever we do, let's breathe no word to Yaoting. It would only upset him. He has such a quick temper!"

Sun Yaoting pushed the door open and walked in. "Don't try to keep it from me anymore! I heard everything you said. It's not fair for you to take up the burden of the family. From now on I will work along with you."

Early in the morning Sun Yaoting went with his two brothers to carry water from the river. Walking to a flat rock jutting out into the river, he filled the pails with water and put his shoulder to the pole, but he did not have the strength to stand up. He tried a couple of times but to no avail. His father, Sun Huaibao, saw everything from a distance and came running. "You lazybones!" he yelled at the other two brothers angrily. "How dare you make your elder brother carry water?"

"They didn't make me do it," Sun Yaoting explained. "I wanted to have a try myself."

His father continued to scold the two brothers. "Don't you know what Liujin has done for the family? How can you treat him like this?" The two brothers were stupefied by their father's outburst. Sun Yaoting stood there torn by conflicting emotions, and tears trickled down his cheeks. He came to the chilling realization that as a eunuch he was merely half a man, a cripple.

Determined to make himself useful, Sun Yaoting started to do less strenuous work, such as collecting manure. He usually set out at dawn wearing a large straw hat to avoid being recognized, but it was inevitable that he ran into his fellow villagers from time to time. Some were friendly, but others ridiculed him. "Why are you picking manure here? You've made a fortune in the capital, haven't you?" He lowered his head and said nothing.

The family had a small vegetable garden, where Sun Yaoting planted eggplants, potatoes, pumpkins, and chives. Instead of eating the vegetables, the family sold them at the temple fair to earn a little extra money. Sun Yaoting then went to join his elder brother at a small cart shop. Together they worked hard to attract customers. After they saw a kind of carts at the temple fair that sold for seventy to eighty dollars, they learned to make exactly the same model. When the area suffered a drought, there was a big demand for water carts, which sold for over a hundred dollars apiece. Sun Yaoting and his brother began to make water carts as fast as they could. For all their efforts business remained slack, as most customers chose to buy from large shops.

One day a visitor to the cart shop, while chatting with Sun Yaoting, reminded him of an acquaintance of his in eastern Shuangtang. It was an old eunuch with an extra finger on his left hand, which earned him the nickname "Six-Fingers". "Six-Fingers" had worked in the Imperial Kitchen for quite a few years. After leaving the palace, he became the steward of Protect-the-Nation Temple west of Beijing by Xin Xiuming's recommendation. As Sun Yaoting often went to the temple to see Xin Xiuming, he got well acquainted with "Six-Fingers". Though quick-tempered, the old eunuch was kind at heart. Sun Yaoting decided to visit him at home.

"People like us should never come back home!" the old eunuch said bitterly. "Life is too difficult. I would rather starve to death than come home to be a laughing stock for others!"

"Exactly!" agreed Sun Yaoting. "I came back because I could not make a living, but I didn't expect things to be so difficult at home!"

"Well, be patient. You can always leave home again when the opportunity comes."

The old eunuch's words struck a chord in Sun Yaoting's heart.

"On the other hand, eunuchs have made big names in history. Do you remember the stone tablet in Protect-the-Nation Temple?"

"Yes, of course. I remember it quite well." Sun Yaoting knew he had to listen to the same old story again but decided not to offend the old eunuch by cutting him short.

"Why did they erect a stone tablet for a eunuch? I had no idea until Mr. Xin explained it to me in detail. A eunuch named Gao Bing achieved great exploits in founding the Ming Dynasty. So when he died the Imperial Court put up this tablet in his honor, to remind people of the contribution of eunuchs to Great Ming! You are still young. Make something of your life, show them that not all eunuchs are losers!"

"I'll bear your words in mind!"

Sun Yaoting got up to leave, and "Six-Fingers" walked him to the village entrance. "If there is a chance, go back to serve the Emperor, because only the Emperor can make a eunuch useful!"

Sun Yaoting returned home deep in thought. The words of the old eunuch certainly made sense. Why should he have been castrated in vain? As a eunuch he was only good for serving the Emperor and the Empress.

By that time Pu Yi had left Beijing and moved into the Zhang Garden in the Japanese Concession in Tianjin. Taking all the money he had left, Sun Yaoting went to Tianjin. Getting off the train, he bought two baskets of cookies and fruits. He arrived at the Zhang Garden to find it guarded by policemen in black uniforms. At his fawning smile and obsequious words, a policeman went in and came back with Dong Shouxiang, a eunuch-in-attendance of Wanrong. "What are you doing here?" Dong asked with a sneer.

"I've come to wait on the Empress."

"Well, nowadays things are not so easy as before..."

Sun Yaoting handed over the two baskets. "Please take this little gift."

"You don't have to," Dong said. He took the baskets and went in.

After waiting for a long time, Sun Yaoting begged the policeman to go and find Dong. Finally Dong came out, spreading out his hands and shrugging his shoulders. "I am just too busy to keep you company."

"But can I come back to wait on the Empress?"

"I'll have to ask about it. Just wait here." Dong went in and never showed up again. Sun Yaoting left in bitter disappointment.

He was strolling aimlessly in a rundown area of the city when three ragged young men stopped him, calling "Brother! Brother!" Sun Yaoting could hardly recognize them. They were his eunuch friends: Big Baldhead, Second Baldhead and Little Cheng. They used to earn good money and smoke opium in the palace. "What has happened to you?" he asked, looking at their disheveled hair and dirty faces. They wore unlined clothes though it was already winter.

"Brother," Big Baldhead began to speak but choked on his words. "Brother, take pity on us!" said Second Baldhead in a sobbing voice.

"Where do you live?"

"We are homeless," Little Cheng cut in. "The three of us sleep near the pier and beg people for some food and coins to get by."

Sun Yaoting shook his head sadly. He took out several strings of coins and put them in Big Baldhead's hands. "I don't have much money, but you can take this to buy a little food."

"Thanks, brother! See you later!" At the sight of the coins the three eunuchs smiled broadly and bowed. Sun Yaoting watched them disappear into a nearby opium parlor, and a cold shiver ran down his spine. Would all eunuchs end up like this? Would he join the ranks of beggars someday?

Sun Yaoting went back to the Zhang Garden and requested to see Pu Yi, but this time the policemen refused to announce him. He left Tianjin but did not return home. Instead, he came to Beijing to try his luck with the two high consorts. He found out that they had left Princess Rongshougulun's residence and moved into a house on Qilingbei Alley. To cut expenses they had sent away most of their eunuchs. Left with no choice, Sun Yaoting decided to go to Xinglongsi, the Temple of Prosperity, which served as a sanctuary for eunuchs.

On the terrace in front of the gate Sun Yaoting met several old eunuchs basking in the sun. "Chunshou!" One of them greeted him. "Didn't you go back home? Why are you here?"

"I have nowhere else to go," Sun Yaoting replied sadly. "I don't have a choice!"

"You are kidding me!" said an old eunuch named Zhang. "Everyone who left the palace with the Emperor got quite a bundle! They can lie in bed all day doing nothing for the rest of their lives!" He mentioned the names of several eunuchs. "Surely you know them. Didn't they all run away with palace treasures?"

"You can't lump all of us together. I did not take anything from the palace!"

"Oh, really? You were waiting on the Empress at the time, and you were not dumb. How could you have been so foolish as to leave the palace empty-handed?"

"I am telling the truth! I turned in everything when we got to the Northern Mansion. Well, maybe there is no wealth in my stars!"

"I don't think you are foolish," said Chen Zechuan walking out the gate. "A man must be honest and true to himself. I still believe the old saying, 'Never seek after ill-gotten gains'!"

"Nonsense!" an old eunuch named Li sneered. "Money won't bite!"

"Think twice before you say something like that!" Chen Zechuan retorted. "You must remember Zhou Fu. He was said to be very smart, and he grabbed a huge hoard when he left the palace. But what happened to him afterward? He had a young wife, but his adopted son took to smoking heroin. He was building a very big mansion but breathed his last before its completion. His wife and son didn't lift a finger. It was his mentor, Lu, who took care of his funeral affairs. Doesn't this example tell you anything?" Chen glanced at Li, then turned to Sun Yaoting. "You were acquainted with Shi Laixiang, weren't you?"

"Yes. We left the palace at the same time."

"Do you know what happened to him?"

"No. I haven't seen him since."

"He was kidnapped!"

"What? That's incredible!"

"The kidnappers finally killed him. Well, I believe in doing good deeds and expecting no return. Accumulate merits by doing good deeds is the best choice!"

"Yes!" Sun Yaoting agreed. "If I am not destined to get rich, what's the use of hoarding treasures? Say, if I had taken gold ingots from the palace to become a big landlord, what would have happened to me next? Maybe my long-time enemy, the Shang family, would have sued me on a trumped-up charge. Maybe I would have become a victim of kidnapping. Who knows? It's not too bad to live in poverty peacefully!"

"Well said!" Chen looked pleased. "If you are capable, you can get what you want by hard work. If you are not capable, you can still get by without having to steal or rob. Never do anything dishonest!"

"I'll abide by your words," Sun Yaoting promised. At this Chen broke into a happy smile.

7

TEMPLE OF PROSPERITY

1. Eunuch Sanctuary

The Temple of Prosperity on Beichang Street adjacent to the Forbidden City was first built in the Ming Dynasty. It had served as the household temple of a high-ranking eunuch named Wang Zhen, who wielded great power in the court of Ming Emperor Yingzong.

As a sanctuary of eunuchs the temple used to have very strict entry rules. To get permission to stay in the temple after leaving the palace, a eunuch had to pay at least a hundred dollars in advance. Then he had

The Temple of Prosperity

to labor for four years without doing any misdeed before being formally accepted. As a full member, he could do whatever he wanted outside the temple. The person in charge of the temple was called supervisor instead of abbot.

In the beginning most eunuchs who settled down in the temple were quite wealthy. In 1924 the expulsion of Pu Yi from the palace suddenly made many eunuchs homeless. Those who had not made any advance payment to the temple were allowed to stay as long as they could afford to rent a room. Thus the Temple of Prosperity became inhabited by a motley assortment of characters. Wealthy eunuchs took their wives into the temple. Some even moved in with a large family of three generations, turning the temple into a hotel. They hired their own cooks, with fresh meat and fish on their dinner table every day. The poor eunuchs, on the other hand, got their free daily meals from the temple mess.

At the gate Sun Yaoting met Ma Deqing. "I haven't seen you for a long time. How have you been?"

"Not too bad." Ma spread out his hands in a gesture of resignation. "I went back home but could not make a living, so here I am." He was a native of Yaozikou, a village in Qing County of Tianjin. Like most eunuchs he was fairly good-looking, with large eyes and a square nose, and stood a head over Sun Yaoting. Entering the palace at thirteen, he finally became an attendant of the Emperor, but left the palace three years later. He had difficulty controlling his temper and got into frequent quarrels with other eunuchs. He was also very stubborn. When he had a chance to purchase a formal name from some old eunuch about to retire, he refused to do it. "I won't pay for it! I don't have the money! Name or no name, I still live on as I am!" Therefore he remained an unregistered eunuch to the very end.

"If you were not so headstrong, you might have done better," Sun Yaoting remarked.

"Well, a man's nature can never change. Anyway I don't ask for much. I'll just stay in the temple for the rest of my life."

"What did you do at home? Someone told me you got a job at a foreign firm. How did you get so lucky?"

"It was a total disaster, and I hate to talk about it! The so-called firm was run by some Russians, who paid me next to nothing for a month's hard work! A bunch of crooks!"

In the afternoon the same day Sun Yaoting met his fellow villager Chi

Huanqing. "Haven't seen you for a long time," Chi greeted him warmly.

"I've just come back from home," Sun Yaoting explained. They went to Chi's room and sat down for a chat. "You don't look your age after all these years," Sun Yaoting said.

"I am getting old," Chi sighed. "An old man is useless nowadays." He was in fact only six or seven years older than Sun Yaoting. "Looking back on it, I've been quite lucky. I entered the palace and went to work for Empress Dowager Longyu right away."

"By the time I entered the palace you were already a herald. In the eyes of our fellow villagers, you certainly have made it."

"Well, all of us have ended up here!" Chi said sadly. In the palace he had earned a lot and spent liberally on housing property for his family. But his father, a spendthrift given to opium smoking and gambling, blew the entire family fortune he had taken pains to accumulate. Embittered, Chi began to smoke opium. By the time he left the palace he was almost penniless and had to take shelter at the Temple of Prosperity.

Chi looked rather calm and placid talking about the past. He had already quit opium smoking, a luxury he could no longer afford. He also grew quite amiable and submissive, greeting everyone with a smile. He had obviously come to terms with life.

In the evening Sun Yaoting went to see the temple's supervisor, Wang Yuezheng. A native of Qing County, Wang was plump and white-skinned, looking more or less like an official. Regarded as a smart fellow among the eunuchs, he could read, write and do accounts. After leaving the palace he opened a sedan-chair shop in Tianjin, which enjoyed a period of booming business. Some people disliked him for his unctuous manners.

"Has Mr. Xin come?" Sun Yaoting asked.

"I don't know for sure. I don't get informed every time he comes." There was a tinge of annoyance in Wang's voice. Xin Xiuming had always showed a partiality for Sun Yaoting, and as Xin's disciple, Wang could not help feeling a bit jealous. A few days later Xin Xiuming came to the temple. Sun Yaoting hurried over, only to be sent away by Wang on a shopping errand. By the time he returned, Xin had already left. Seeing the disappointed look on his face, Wang smiled in satisfaction. "Mr. Xin is gone!" he said triumphantly.

With Chen Zechuan's help Sun Yaoting secured a room and settled down. One day Sun Yaoting ran into Zhang Xiuyue, who happened to drop by the temple. As a eunuch Zhang belonged to the same peer group as Xin Xiuming, as indicated by the common character in their names, "Xiu". He had always been on good terms with Sun Yaoting, and they exchanged greetings like old friends.

"Thanks to the Temple of Prosperity, I am doing a prosperous business!" Zhang joked. His pastry shop in Dong'an Market in downtown Beijing was doing very well.

"Don't make fun of us!" Sun Yaoting said. "Thank your own lucky star. Those of us who live in the Temple of Prosperity have no prosperity to speak of !" In their conversation Sun Yaoting learned a lot about Xin Xiuming, with whom Zhang was in close contact.

Life at the temple was far from idyllic. Infighting among the eunuchs, rampant on palace grounds, grew to new proportions in the absence of a central authority. Sun Yaoting had to watch his steps carefully to keep himself out of trouble.

At the temple Sun Yaoting found many eunuchs to be in dire circumstances. Tian Bichen, a native of Zhuozhou, was ten years his senior. Strongly built and illiterate, Tian had worked as an attendant in the residences of Prince Zai Tao and Prince Yu Lang, but had never set foot in the Imperial Palace. According to him, Yu Lang was rather mean toward the servants. He gave them three meals a day but did not spend a cent on their clothes. "He was rich but extremely tightfisted," Tian said. "With my stipend I could hardly afford a pair of boots." He had come to the Temple of Prosperity almost penniless, wearing the same faded blue gown all year round. His story was well known among the eunuchs.

The situation of many other eunuchs was scarcely better. Feng Leting, who used to wait on Pu Jie's grandmother in the Northern Mansion, entered the temple with very little money in his pocket. Liu Xingqiao, Sun Yaoting's old acquaintance, had squandered all his savings so that he had to paste cartons every day to mete out a hand-to-mouth existence. Most of the eunuchs at the temple lived in poverty, but at least they did not suffer from starvation. "Have you eaten?" they greeted each other first thing in the morning.

At the temple Sun Yaoting made a good friend named Sun Shangxian, a native of Nanpi County who had waited on a concubine of General Zhang Zongchang for many years before entering the palace to be Pu Yi's eunuch-in-attendance. From him Sun Yaoting learned that the temple had accumulated a "secret fund" by charging coffin storage fees.

Some eunuchs with a glorious past in the Imperial Palace came to a miserable end. Shi Junfeng, for example, boasted an impressive career record for a eunuch: he had waited on Empress Dowager Cixi, Empress Dowager Longyu and Pu Yi in succession. His great singing voice enabled him to compete with the best professional performers of Beijing opera. In a few years after leaving the palace, he squandered all his money and had no choice but to take shelter at the Temple of Prosperity. When he wanted to go home some years later, he could not even afford a train ticket. He finally bought the ticket with money pooled by some eunuchs and a fellow villager who happened to be a merchant. Shi returned to his home village, where he died in utter poverty. He was generally considered to have been lucky, as poor eunuchs like him often died in a strange land far away from home.

"Mr. Kou was gone!" A fellow villager brought Sun Yaoting the news.

"Really?" Sun Yaoting was astonished. "He looked quite well the last time I went home!"

"Well, it's a very sad story. Mr. Kou seemed to be running out of money, so he sold his big house for eight hundred dollars and moved into a smaller one with four rooms on the edge of the village. But then the flood destroyed all the rooms, and he had to take shelter in the house of Xiao, his neighbor. He soon died of bitterness and exhaustion. The Xiaos refused to let a eunuch's coffin go through the gate of their house because they believed it would bring misfortune to the family. So they tore down the wall in the backyard to let the coffin through."

"How could they act like that?" Sun Yaoting said indignantly. He remained in a sad mood for several days. Kou's miserable end reminded him how despicable a eunuch must appear to other people, including his own fellow villagers.

2. Myriad Fates of Eunuchs

"Eight horses! Five champions! ..."

The noise of half-drunk eunuchs playing the finger-guessing game at the table could be heard late into the night. The Temple of Prosperity served as an important social venue for eunuchs. Many non-resident eunuchs came here for companionship. Occasionally a eunuch on the verge of starvation came to get free meals. A few simply came to gamble, sometimes staying for days on end until they had lost their last penny.

Zhang Xiude, an old wobbly eunuch, was a frequent gambler. He lived in a dilapidated temple called Jade Emperor's Land on Xixie Street, but he spent much of his time gambling at the Temple of Prosperity. One day Sun Yaoting was leaving the temple when he met Zhang at the gate.

"Where are you going, Chunshou?"

"I am taking a walk," Sun Yaoting said. "What business has brought you here, Mr. Zhang?"

"Don't poke fun at me," Zhang patted him on the shoulder. "You know why I am here. I come to engage in my little hobby."

"Well, have a good time. See you later."

Zhang was a decent, good-tempered person who never picked fights with others, but Sun Yaoting kept a distance from compulsive gamblers like him. Having seen people win fortunes and gamble away their land and houses, Sun Yaoting had long decided to have no part in such a dangerous game.

Just then Liu Xingqiao walked into the temple. "Where have you been all these days?" Sun Yaoting asked, taking him by the arm.

"I've just got back from home," Liu replied. "My wife, you know, used to stay here with me. A few years ago she insisted on going back home, but she died there half a year later. I just went to offer sacrifices at her grave."

"Did you kowtow to her gravestone?" Sun Yaoting asked in jest. "After all, you must have knelt before her countless times when she was alive!" Liu smiled wryly but said nothing.

Liu Xingqiao was a disciple of Feng Junchen, one of Pu Yi's chief eunuchs. He had served as an attendant for Pu Yi and his consort Wenxiu. When he was on night duty, Pu Yi happened to walk by, apparently in a jolly mood. Finding him awake, Pu Yi threw over a bundle of money. "This is for you!" Liu could hardly believe his good luck when he counted the money: two thousand dollars! For fear of getting into trouble he did not breathe a word to anyone in the palace. When he finally told others of this long-buried secret at the Temple of Prosperity, most of the money had already been spent on his wife.

Liu Xingqiao seemed to have got lucky again. "I just received a message

Pu Yi and Wanrong, a nominal couple

from the Regent," he told Sun Yaoting. "He wanted me back. I'll pack up and leave for the Northern Mansion soon." Sun Yaoting watched him disappear into the room. "A eunuch should not have a wife!" he said to himself with a sigh. "It seems that one of them is bound to die young!"

At noon Ma Deqing came to Sun Yaoting's room to have a chat over lunch. "Have you heard the news? Ren Futian just came to the temple."

"Yes, I've heard about it. Well, Ren treated me quite well in the palace. Let's go and visit him!"

"Yes, why not? He has a very nice wife, and I'd really like to take a look at her!"

After supper they went to Ren Futian's house east of the Coal Hill. It consisted of three rooms facing south, which he had purchased before leaving the palace. They exchanged greetings and sat down. Just then a middle-aged woman came out of the inner room. "This is my wife," Ren said.

"Hi, sister-in-law!" Sun Yaoting stood up to greet her. Judging by her comely features, she must have been a real beauty when young. Looking bashful, she muttered a few words before retreating into the inner room again.

"You lucky fellow!" Ma Deqing said. "You live like a king, 'keeping a beauty in a house of gold'!"

"Well, you know me well. I didn't become a eunuch until I was grown up. Don't blame me for having such earthly desires!"

Ren Futian had stayed in the Northern Mansion for many years before entering the palace. There was a well-known anecdote about him. Once he went to a toilet outside the palace, where some people insulted him gratuitously. "Hey, let's see what he's got in his pants?" He stormed out of the toilet and vowed that someday he would buy a house with a toilet for his own use.

The "toilet incident" occurred to Sun Yaoting when he was sipping his cup of tea. "By the way, where is the toilet?" he asked. "I mean, the toilet for your own use?"

"I'll let you take a look. Go out the door and turn left."

Returning from his "ground check", Sun Yaoting held up his thumb to the old eunuch. "It surely deserves its reputation!"

"What do you mean?" Ren asked.

"Everyone has heard of Mr. Ren's toilet. I am truly impressed!"

Ren Futian smiled broadly. Like most eunuchs he desperately needed something to be proud of.

As Sun Yaoting and Ma Deqing stood up to leave, Ren's wife came out again to bid them goodbye.

It was not unusual for a eunuch to have a wife. In late Qing Dynasty it became rather fashionable for a eunuch to establish a romantic relationship with a palace maid. Wealthy eunuchs would be considered abnormal if they spent no money on women. "Easy circumstances breed lewd thoughts," so goes a popular saying. After leaving the palace, Xiaode Zhang settled down in Tianjin to a life of great luxury with several young wives. Castration, it seems, seldom extinguished sexual desires once and for all. A few eunuchs retained a strong craving for sex into old age. When interviewed at eighty-nine, Sun Yaoting admitted to having sexual yearnings that could nevertheless find no outlet.

Some eunuchs had an obsessive need to accumulate personal possessions. Though unable to enjoy a fulfilled marriage, they derived satisfaction from the mere fact that they had a wife who completely belonged to them. Such eunuchs made possessive husbands. When Xiaode Zhang found out that one of his wives had committed adultery, he killed her and had her body chopped into pieces. On the other hand, most eunuchs who got married hankered after a peaceful family life to make up for the hardships and humiliations they had endured in the palace. A eunuch could do a lot of things with his hard-earned money: buying a house outside the palace, securing a wife or concubine, and adopting a son to "continue the family line". Even eunuchs could not ignore the ancient teaching, "Of the three unfilial things to do, to have no son is the worst."

Quite a few people, including Wang Yuezheng, became eunuchs when they were already married with children. After many years in the palace, they saved enough money to buy a house in the capital. On leaving the palace, they usually fetched their wife and children to the capital to live together as a reunited family. In some rare cases, a eunuch might get married while pretending to be a "normal" person. Generally speaking, one had to be good-looking to enter the palace as a eunuch. After obtaining a well-paid position in the palace, he could afford to get fashionably dressed and adorned, and an inexperienced girl might take a fancy to what she regarded as a handsome, elegant young man. When that happened, the eunuch left the palace to find another job and get married. The girl usually did not find out about her mistake until it was too late. However, marriages attained by fraud often had an unhappy ending.

Some of the worst marriages belonged to wealthy old eunuchs. They spent the better part of their life in the palace, working hard and enduring all forms of maltreatment from their superiors. When they eventually left the palace with considerable savings, they often chose a young woman for a wife or concubine. Marital happiness was out of the question and horrific sadistic behavior far from rare. The hapless young woman might be stripped naked and scorched with lit cigarettes, pierced with needles, or ruthlessly whipped. The old eunuch might want to inflict on her whatever torment he had suffered in the palace; he might even take a perverted pleasure in torturing her private parts. According to an old saying in Beijing, "You only have to marry a eunuch to suffer the worst afflictions in the world!"

Among the frequent visitors to the Temple of Prosperity, Shang Yanyin was quite a prominent figure. A successful candidate in the metropolitan examination, Shang had been a member of the Hanlin Academy. He had even taught Pu Yi, though he was not among the formal imperial tutors. One day Sun Yaoting was chatting with Xin Xiuming when Shang came. Tall and fair-skinned, he had the graceful manners of a true Confucian scholar. Seeing that the two old friends had plenty of things to talk about, Sun Yaoting quickly excused himself.

"Do you know why I often invite Mr. Shang to come over?" Xin Xiuming asked Sun Yaoting after Shang left. "You won't believe it. Look!" He took out a manuscript in several volumes. "I've put down what I have seen and heard in the palace for future generations."

"I never heard you mention it before!" Sun Yaoting said. "This is the real treasure!" They both laughed at the word "treasure", for eunuchs habitually used it to refer to their severed genitals. "But you haven't told me why Mr. Shang comes here."

"I want him to go over my manuscript and tell me what he thinks. Well, he read it very carefully and made some corrections and supplementary notes. He knows many things better than I do!"

"You are both very knowledgeable," Sun Yaoting said. "I'd like to read the book after you finish it."

Xin Xiuming, who had lived through many ups and downs in life, enjoyed high esteem among the eunuchs. In the Babaoshan area west of Beijing, he had a temple built with his own money. On his birthday in the 3rd lunar month, most eunuchs at the Temple of Prosperity went there to join in the celebration, which consisted solely of mahjong gambling. The game often went on nonstop for two days and two nights. "Mr. Xin is invincible in his own temple!" complained some eunuchs who kept losing. Xin had been a very good gambler in the Imperial Palace. He could lose several hundred silver dollars without turning a hair; eventually he would turn lucky again and finish the game with flying colors. In old age he quit gambling abruptly and never played again.

Xin Xiuming was especially famous for his tenacious fight to protect the "eunuch preserve" in western Beijing. When rebel troops captured Beijing in 1644 the last Emperor of Ming Dynasty, Chongzhen, hanged himself at the foot of Coal Hill. Lin, a eunuch over sixty, did not run away in time, so he hid himself in the palace. Later, Manchu troops discovered him and brought him to the Qing Emperor Shunzhi. As Lin had spent all his life in the palace, Shunzhi questioned him in detail about the various rules and practices in the Ming court. On learning that Lin had been earning two taels of silver a month, Shunzhi agreed to pay him the same amount. At Lin's death the Qing Emperor ordered a grave to be built for him in western Beijing and named the area Enjizhuang, or "Bounties-Bestowed Village". Afterward eunuchs of the Qing Dynasty used the place as their cemetery. In addition, they developed the region by building houses, planting fruit trees, and growing crops. Occupying a total area of four hundred mu, it became a major source of income for the Old People's Relief Society, a charity for eunuchs in Beijing of which Xin Xiuming was a leader.

A fierce fight broke out over the land at Enjizhuang that pitted the eunuchs against Beijing's Social Bureau, which suddenly retrieved ownership of the land and sold it. Xin Xiuming decided to raise money to redeem what he considered to be eunuchs' property. He called on all eunuchs in Beijing to donate two dollars each and borrowed twelve thousand dollars from Xiaode Zhang. When money was still short, he hit upon a brilliant idea: they could fell the trees in the cemetery and sold them. But first they had to get a license from the municipal government. Fortunately Chen Zechuan was well acquainted with a brigade commander named Dong Zuobing. Through another connection he got to know Chu Xichun, garrison commander of Beijing. Urged by these two officers, the municipal government agreed to issue the license.

The eunuchs finally got enough money to redeem the land, but the Social Bureau refused to give it back. Instead, it published an official announcement condemning eunuchs as "a great scourge of modern society". This enraged all the eunuchs in the capital. With their support Xin Xiuming sued the Social Bureau. To pay for legal expenses many eunuchs donated money, including those well known for being miserly. Wang Shunshan gave eight hundred dollars and Yao Mengshan, three hundred. Even the adopted son of the late Chief Eunuch Li Lianying gave three hundred. Sun Yaoting also contributed his share. Backed by the Beijing garrison command, the eunuchs won the case and got back their land. Then Xin Xiuming had some fruit trees planted around the cemetery.

For all his learning and talents, Xin Xiuming failed to manage his own finances well. He liked to make friends and spent money freely, only to find himself in straightened circumstances in old age. When he heard that Shi Junfeng, a former eunuch-in-attendance of the Emperor, bought a house for a thousand dollars and sold it later for three thousand, he spent all his money on a house on Beichang Street. Unfortunately the timing was wrong, and no one would buy the house from him even at a bargain price. In spite of his financial difficulty Xin did not change his lifestyle but continued to spend most of his time meeting friends and engaging in various literary activities.

3. White-Cloud Temple

"Do you want to join the All-True Sect of Taoism?" Chen Zechuan asked Sun Yaoting. They were taking a walk outside the Temple of Prosperity.

"Is there an entry fee?" Sun Yaoting had no extra money to spare these days.

"No need to worry about that," Chen said. "They won't force you to pay anything."

Sun Yaoting did not object to joining a sect that cost him nothing.

Baiyunguan, or White-Cloud Temple, had been the headquarters of the Dragon Gate Order of the All-True Sect of Taoism since the 13th century in early Yuan Dynasty, when the Emperor Kublai Khan appointed a renowned Taoist priest named Qiu Chuji the "National Teacher". After various ups and downs in history, the temple enjoyed a revival in late Qing Dynasty thanks to Empress Dowager Cixi.

At her mother's death Cixi sent a chief eunuch Liu Chengyin to place the coffin in a temple for some days before burial. Liu visited several temples but got lukewarm responses. Annoyed, Cixi told Liu to try the White-Cloud Temple. The abbot of the White-Cloud Temple, Liu Zongxuan, received the imperial envoy most enthusiastically. The coffin was moved into the temple

The Temple of Azure Clouds

in a formal ceremony. Every seven days the temple offered a sacrifice attended by various members of the Imperial family, with Liu Chengyin overseeing everything from ceremonial procedures to the reception of guests. By the time the coffin was moved away for burial at the end of forty-nine days, the chief eunuch and the abbot had become good friends. Liu Chengyin had the western garden of the temple completely renovated, and soon afterward he took the order and became a Taoist. At the abbot's invitation, Cixi visited the temple to enjoy an "All-True style" vegetarian feast. Almost overnight the White-Cloud Temple began to wield considerable clout in the Imperial capital.

Liu Chengyin acknowledged Liu Zongxuan as his mentor and became the "honorary abbot" of the temple. He showed true enthusiasm in promoting the interests of the sect and propagating Taoism in general. As many eunuchs joined the All-True Sect after him, though mainly out of practical considerations rather than religious faith, he became the founder of a Taoist sub-school consisting solely of eunuchs. Thanks to his efforts many Taoist and Buddhist temples were built or renovated in Beijing. For example, he raised enough money to build the Temple of Bountiful Grace behind the Drum Tower. "I want it to look like the Imperial Palace!" he remarked to another eunuch. The temple boasted elegant design and superb workmanship. He purchased large pieces of cultivated land and opened many shops, using the proceeds to "sustain the temples", and announced that any eunuch who had no place to go after retiring from the palace could take shelter in one of these temples for the rest of his life. Such generosity and goodwill attracted more and more followers to the sect. After joining the All-True Sect Sun Yaoting acquired a Taoist name, Shanfu, meaning "benevolent and happy".

"Take a look at this if you don't have better things to do," Feng Leting said to Sun Yaoting, handing him an old almanac.

"What's in it for me?"

"Profound wisdom! If you know your birth-characters, you can look up your lifelong fortune."

Sun Yaoting borrowed the almanac. Alone that evening he looked up the prediction according to the eight characters indicating the exact time of his birth. It read, "Enough food and clothing. Without wife or children." He exclaimed in astonishment, for he had read the same words in a divination book many years before in the Accounting Office. He mentioned it to Xin Xiuming, who responded, "Well, it seems that we share the same fate." They looked at each other and broke into a rueful smile.

4. Tales about Cixi

Apart from eating three meals a day, eunuchs in the Temple of Prosperity had precious little to do. Many played mahjong or smoked opium to while away the time. Sun Yaoting, however, enjoyed chatting with Chen Zechuan over a cup of tea in the evening. Their conversation often revolved around palace incidents in late Qing Dynasty. Chen had waited on both Empress Dowager Cixi and Emperor Guangxu. Though sometimes at odds with official history, his narrative offered a peculiar perspective and sounded quite plausible.

On a moonlit night Chen Zechuan sat down for a long chat with Sun Yaoting, sipping his favorite jasmine tea from a small pottery teapot. Chen liked to talk about his exploits in the palace theatricals. "Xiaode Zhang and I performed on stage side by side. I usually took a black-clothed female role, and Zhang played an unbearded young man. Though he did not have a nice singing voice, he was quick-witted and versatile and knew how to make the best of his talents. We also had Yao Lanrong, whose sonorous voice made him an ideal actor for the black-face role. You may think I am boasting, but the three of us alone could pull off an excellent performance! Cixi often came to watch us play. She was a real connoisseur of Beijing opera, you know.

"I waited on Cixi for a long time until a few years before her death, when I left to serve Emperor Guangxu. She was a cruel woman, believe me! Any old eunuch could tell you that. She must have beaten countless eunuchs in her lifetime. Her history is of course pretty well known. She entered the palace at seventeen and soon got the title Worthy Lady. She was very good at currying favor with Emperor Xianfeng. But she once got herself into big trouble."

"What happened?"

"Well, this is known as the incident of the 'Buddha-hand' princess. On the Mid-Autumn Festival Emperor Xianfeng and her younger sister went to the Summer Palace at night to watch the moon, accompanied by Ci'an and Cixi. They climbed up a two-storied pavilion, where they sat down to a few cups of wine. When Xianfeng stood up to go downstairs, Cixi came over and bumped against him playfully. Xianfeng was tipsy and had difficulty keeping balance. He staggered and would have fallen down the stairs if his sister had not caught hold of him. 'You are a Buddha-hand princess!' he said gratefully. Then he turned to Cixi, and you can imagine how angry he was. She quickly knelt and begged for mercy. 'Your slave deserves ten thousand deaths for bumping into Your Majesty. I was too careless!' The Emperor did not believe her excuse. 'You did it on purpose! You tried to push me downstairs!'"

"It was a capital offense!" Sun Yaoting said. "A murder attempt against the Emperor!"

"It certainly was! But Ci'an took pity on Cixi and came to her rescue. Cixi happened to be pregnant at the time, so Ci'an asked the Emperor to put off any punishment until she had given birth. 'If she bears you a daughter, she will get whatever punishment she deserves. If she gives birth to a son, that will atone for her crime.' Xianfeng agreed. Well, Cixi gave birth to a son, the future Emperor Tongzhi. She not only got away with her previous offense but received one promotion after another."

Chen paused to sip at his jasmine tea, then went on.

"When the Anglo-French forces attacked and captured Beijing,

Emperor Xianfeng fled to the imperial summer resort in Jehol and died there. Most eunuchs agreed that he had chosen the wrong place. Do you expect the Emperor, who was a dragon, to survive in a 'hot river'?* Before his death Xianfeng entrusted state affairs to his eight most trusted ministers, but a deadly fight ensued between Cixi and the eight ministers. As I see it, eunuchs played a key role in her success. For example, how did she pass her message to the capital from Jehol? People have made numerous guesses, but I happen to know for sure what really happened. Cixi found an excuse to beat up her favorite eunuch An Dehai and send him back to the Office of Palace Justice. He returned to Beijing and went immediately to see the Prince of Gong. He had Cixi's handwritten edict hidden in his braid! After reading the message, the prince set out at once for Jehol to rescue Cixi."

"Cixi killed a lot of people when she returned to Beijing, didn't she? "

"Yes. The leader of the eight ministers, Sushun, was beheaded. Two ministers received 'imperial white', which means they were allowed to hang themselves on white silk after eating a full meal."

"So An Dehai played a key role in the Jehol incident," Sun Yaoting said. "Cixi would surely have come to grief without him. But some people say An Dehai and Li Lianying were not really eunuchs but Cixi's secret lovers. What do you think?"

"That's sheer nonsense. Only those who have never set foot in the Imperial Palace could have come up with such wild stories! I waited on Cixi for quite a long time, and I know what I am talking about. An Dehai came from Dongguang County, and Li Lianying from Dacheng County, both in Hebei. They were genuine eunuchs. They couldn't have fooled everyone by pretending to be eunuchs all those years! They were carefully examined before entering the palace and when young must go to the Office of Palace Justice for a regular check once every two years. How could they have been fake eunuchs? What's more, Cixi was not in a position to do whatever she wanted at that time. Xianfeng and his brothers kept a watchful eye on her."

Chen Zechuan went on to describe Cixi's relationship with Xianfeng's brothers. "Among the eight imperial brothers, Cixi was most afraid of the fifth, Yimo, though he never held any important court position. Let me give you an example. On her way to the Palace of Benevolent Peace, Cixi learned

---

* Rehe, the Chinese name for Jehol, literally means "hot river".

from a eunuch that someone was already there. 'Who is it?' she asked. 'It is Prince Yimo, barefoot and stripped to the waist.' 'I am not going,' Cixi said, and headed back at once. You can imagine how she dreaded the very sight of Yimo! Well, there was constant internecine struggle in the palace, but it would be dangerous for eunuchs to meddle in it! An Dehai was a case in point. Though he achieved great merits for Cixi, he lost his head in the end."

"Why did Cixi fail to protect him?" Sun Yaoting asked. "From what I heard, she did not receive the news early enough to take action. Is that true?"

"It is not that simple. An Dehai had waited on Emperor Xianfeng for some time before he became Cixi's favorite. He wielded real clout in the palace and began to think he could afford to be arrogant toward anyone. This made him some powerful enemies. So take my advice: When enjoying good luck, watch out for ill fortune! As you know, palace rules forbid eunuchs to leave the Imperial capital. An Dehai did not think the rules applied to him because he was Cixi's favorite. When he offered to take a trip to the south to purchase dress material for Cixi, she consented. There was no train at the time, so he had to take a boat from Tongzhou. There he embarked on a journey of no return!"

"What happened to him?"

"Some people think An Dehai died in the hands of Ding Baozhen, Provincial Governor of Shandong. Actually it was Prince Gong who manipulated everything behind the scenes. An Dehai had only himself to blame. He got so big-headed that he treated Prince Gong very rudely. The ministers and eunuchs often addressed Prince Gong as 'Sixth Master', for he was the sixth imperial prince. But An Dehai called him by his pet name, 'Little Six' right in front of others. Though offended, Prince Gong did not show it. One day An Dehai asked Prince Gong, 'Little Six, what do you think of the peacock feather on my hat?' And the prince answered, 'It looks very nice, but it doesn't cover your neck.' An Dehai was so stupid that he did not catch the undertone of the Prince's words.

"As the saying goes, it takes more than one cold day for the river to freeze. Prince Gong was wearing a very precious thumb-ring when he came to see Cixi one day. 'Your thumb-ring looks nice!' she said. He took it off at once and presented it to her as a gift. The next day An Dehai saw the ring and really liked it, so Cixi gave it to him. Rather than hold his tongue, An Dehai went to show the ring to Prince Gong. 'Little Six, look what I've got here! A gift from the Empress Dowager!' Prince Gong was struck speechless with rage. There is an old maxim, 'A one-year-old master is a master, and a ten-year-old slave a slave.' An Dehai went too far and crossed the line between master and slave. He thought he had nothing to fear because of his meritorious service to Cixi at Jehol. But it did not save him from losing his head!

"As soon as An Dehai reached Shandong by boat, Ding Baozhen received a handwritten message from Prince Gong and acted accordingly. He arrested An Dehai and sent a report posthaste to Prince Gong, enumerating An's crimes such as extorting money from local officials and violating established rules of the imperial court. When Prince Gong showed Cixi the report, she pretended to be outraged. 'What a rascal! He loses all scruples the moment he slips out of my sight! He deserves to be beheaded.' She did not really mean what she said, but Prince Gong went away to have a secret meeting with Ci'an, and they sent an imperial edict to Shandong in the name of Cixi, ordering An Dehai to be beheaded at once. The next day Cixi said to Prince Gong, 'Bring Little An back to the capital. I want to question him myself.' So Prince Gong sent another edict to Shandong, but of course An Dehai was already dead by then. Ding Baozhen got a big fright when he received the second edict! Well, in the end Cixi realized what had happened, but there was nothing she could do to save the situation."

"I heard that Cixi could be kind to others," Sun Yaoting said. "The Magistrate of Tongzhou did her father a favor and she promoted him in return. Is that true?"

Prince Gong, Yixin

Prince Qing, Yikuang

"Well, it all began as a mistake. Before Cixi came to power, her father died at his official post in Hubei. As the boat carrying his coffin passed Tongzhou on its way to the capital, a messenger from the county magistrate brought them a hundred taels of silver. He had actually come to the wrong boat! When the magistrate found out about the mistake, he simply had the same amount of money sent to the right boat. Cixi learned about the gift from the magistrate of Tongzhou, but she did not know the story behind. After she took over the court, she repaid the magistrate by promoting him to prefect. So the story had a very happy ending!"

Sun Yaoting had another question. "Emperor Guangxu was the son of Cixi's younger sister. Why did she treat him like that?"

"Well, you can tell what a person she was by the way she treated her own nephew. She had a strong mistrust of him and sent four of her own eunuchs to wait on him. I was one of them. She wanted us to spy on Guangxu and tell her everything he did. Some of us made up stories just to please her, but I never did anything like that. She often sent for us and asked each of us the same question, 'What did the Emperor do today?' 'His Majesty read some books and practiced calligraphy,' I usually replied. A few days later she summoned us again to ask the same question, and I gave more or less the same answer, which did not please her. One day, when it was my turn to report, she said, 'I know what you are going to say. He read books and practiced calligraphy. Nothing else, right?' And I said, 'Yes, nothing else.' I knew Cixi had a deep suspicion of Guangxu, and the last thing I wanted to do was to stir up trouble with a loose tongue. I have my heart in the right place!" Chen pointed to his chest and heaved a deep sigh.

"In the end Cixi had Guangxu locked up in the Summer Palace. What exactly happened?"

"Well, it all began with the so-called Hundred-Day Reform. I was waiting on Guangxu at the time, so I know quite a lot about it. A few reformers like Kang Youwei and Liang Qichao advised the Emperor to strengthen the nation by implementing drastic reforms, just as Japan did in the Meiji Reform. Cixi was then staying in the Summer Palace. Guangxu summoned Yuan Shikai to the Mind Nurture Hall and revealed his plan. 'I want to strengthen the empire by reforms in emulation of the Meiji Reform of Japan, and I need your help. You must lead troops to the Summer Palace and keep a close watch on Cixi.' Yuan agreed without the least hesitation. 'I will carry out Your Majesty's edict,' he pledged. "Let thunder strike me dead if I leak the secret!' Guangxu promised to make Yuan Vice-Minister of War in the cabinet to be set up after a successful reform. After leaving the Emperor, Yuan went straight to Tianjin and told everything to Rong Lu, Governor-general of Zhili. Rong Lu hurried back to Beijing to inform Cixi."

"What a double-faced man!" Sun Yaoting said. "A despicable traitor!"

"Yes, double-dealers like Yuan could ruin anything! Guangxu was too simple-minded to see through Yuan's true nature. As Cixi planned to spend several days in the Summer Palace watching theatricals, Guangxu thought it a good chance to take action; that's why he had arranged the secret meeting with Yuan. Theatrical performance was still going on in the Summer Palace when Rong Lu arrived. Cixi exploded in fury and ordered Rong Lu to deploy his troops in the capital. The next day she returned to the palace before dawn. She went in the Gate of Divine Prowess, and Guangxu met her in the Imperial garden. He was aware that something had gone wrong, but he had not yet learned of Yuan's betrayal. Without getting off the sedan chair, Cixi hurled abuses at the Emperor. 'Look what you've done! I put you on the throne, I made you the Emperor, and you want to do me in! Dirty traitor!' We were all flabbergasted!"

"Guangxu was in big trouble!"

"Sure he was. Back in her palace, Cixi began to interrogate him. 'Who made the plan for you?' She knew Guangux better than to believe that he had taken such audacious action on his own. But the Emperor insisted that it had been his own idea. 'No one made plans for me. I want to strengthen the nation by reform; that's all. It will be good for the country and the people!' Actually, the Emperor had sensed danger when Yuan Shikai failed to send troops or pass a message and had sent away both Kang Youwei and Liang Qichao. Well, the short-lived reform failed, and many reformers died. The famous 'Six Gentlemen' were beheaded at Caishikou. Cixi moved back to the Forbidden City and had Guangxu locked up in the Summer Palace. But I continued to wait on him.

"The imprisonment of Guangxu did not bring Cixi lasting peace. Soon after, the Boxers overran the Imperial capital. I think Cixi would have dethroned Guangxu if it had not been for the Boxers. At first she decided to use the Boxers to attack foreigners. You won't believe this, but they even set up an altar for the Boxers in the palace! Then the joint troops of eight foreign powers marched on Beijing, and Cixi decided to evacuate. She summoned the ministers for a meeting to discuss where to go, and they settled on Xi'an.

The farther, the safer. As for eunuchs, we could choose to go to Xi'an or stay in the palace. After careful consideration, I asked the Emperor for a leave and did not go to Xi'an."

Chen Zechuan had personal reasons to stay behind, as Sun Yaoting knew. He had a wife in his hometown in Qing County. They had got married before he left for the capital to become a eunuch. As the joint forces of eight foreign powers stormed into China's ancient capital, Chen slipped back to his hometown to enjoy a reunion with his wife.

"I read this story about Emperor Tongzhi's death," Sun Yaoting said. "He often visited brothels in the Qianmen area and died of venereal disease he contracted there. Do you think it possible?"

"I don't think so," Chen replied. "The Emperor had lots of concubines and attending maids in his palace, so why should he want to frequent the brothels? And even if he had contracted venereal disease, the imperial physicians would have cured him. The truth is Tongzhi died of smallpox by a cruel twist of fortune."

"This is hard to believe," Sun Yaoting said. "You can find the story I just mentioned in many books. What's more, many people have had smallpox and survived. How could the Emperor have died of smallpox when he had the imperial physicians to treat him?"

"The books you read are anecdotal accounts rather than official history. If the story were true, I would surely have heard something about it from other eunuchs. Tongzhi enjoyed good relations with his Empress and three concubines. He got married at seventeen and died at nineteen, and his death had something to do with his Empress. Cixi did not like her. After a quarrel with Cixi, the Empress went to see Tongzhi to complain about Cixi's overbearing manner. To comfort her Tongzhi said, 'You know what a temper she has. She won't change a bit no matter how you storm and rage. You just have to be patient. The day will come when we get the upper hand of her.' They did not realize that Cixi had sent a trusted eunuch to eavesdrop on them. Cixi hit the roof when the eunuch reported back to her. She stormed into Tongzhi's room and swore at him angrily. As I said, Tongzhi was suffering from smallpox, which made him vulnerable to the attack of wind or anxiety. He had such a fright that his condition soon became critical. When Cixi sent several imperial physicians to treat him, they found that pathogenic toxin had already invaded his intestines. He was beyond cure. I would say Tongzhi died of fright and frustration!"

"What happened to the Empress then?"

"Well, she cried like a baby. She knew her days were numbered now that the Emperor was dead. Not knowing what to do, she sent a eunuch to seek advice from her father, Chong Qi. He was a high-ranking official at the Hanlin Academy. He said nothing but gave a food box to the eunuch to take back to her. She opened the box and found it empty. She was puzzled at first, but then she got the message. She began to fast and starved herself to death."

"This is so sad!" Sun Yaoting sighed.

"After Tongzhi's death, Cixi put the six-year-old Guangxu on the throne, though many court officials opposed it. Maybe she just wanted someone easy for her to control. Her younger sister did not dare to say no, but she wept bitterly to think of the miseries her son would surely suffer in Cixi's hands. With a child on the throne, the two Empresses dowager, Cixi and Ci'an, held court in the Emperor's place. Ci'an had little say in court affairs, and Emperor Guangxu was merely a puppet, as every eunuch could tell you.

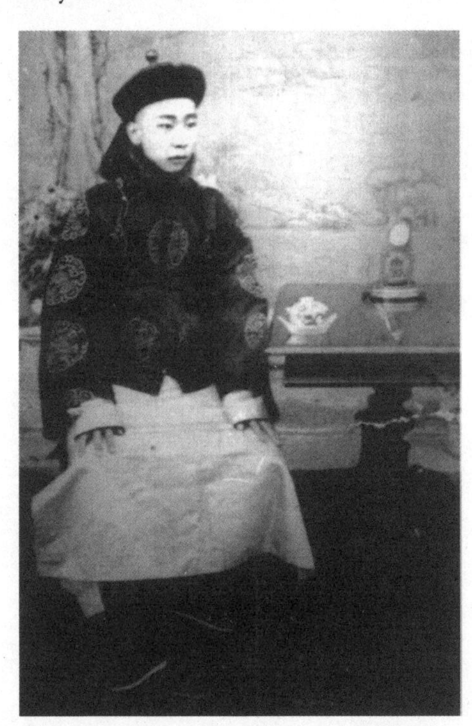

The Elder Prince, chosen as heir to the throne before Cixi replaced him with Pu Yi

"No one knows for sure how Guangxu died, though some believe Cixi murdered him. Anyway, after Guangxu's death Cixi chose Pu Yi to be the next Emperor. His father, Zai Feng, was Guangxu's brother. Well, instead of bringing joy to the Northern Mansion, the news made the whole family weep aloud. At the crowning ceremony, Pu Yi kept crying after his father put him on the throne. To comfort him Zai Feng said, 'It will soon be over.' All the officials turned pale when they heard it, and eunuchs spread these words all over the palace. It was a bad omen, and it came true. The Great Qing Empire was soon over."

"I heard that at first the Elder Prince had been chosen to be the future Emperor. Is that so?"

"Yes. The Elder Prince was Pu Juan, the son of Zai Yi. At first Cixi wanted to make him the heir apparent and had him moved into the palace. Everyone thought he was going to be Emperor someday. When we went outside the palace, some people would ask us about him. It seemed that the people had already accepted him as their future sovereign. But in the end Cixi changed her mind. She chose Pu Yi because as a three-year-old baby he was easier to manipulate. Well, Great Qing was nearing its fated end, and nothing could stop the inevitable!"

Chen paused. "It could have been worse for us," he said with a sigh. "Though we had to take shelter in a temple, at least we are not starving. Few of those powerful eunuchs ever come to a good end, you know."

Chen Zechuan and Sun Yaoting sat facing each other under the candlelight. The drips from the candles looked like teardrops lamenting the piteous fate of eunuchs.

8

HOUSE SERVANT

1. Xiaode Zhang

Early in the morning the steward of a nearby shop came to knock on the gate of the Temple of Prosperity. He headed straight for Yao Mengshan's room with an urgent message. "Mr. Zhang called from Tianjin. He wanted you and Mr. Wei to come over without delay."

"What for?" Yao asked. The steward explained that Zhang had had a bitter quarrel with his elder brother, Zhang Yunqiao. Apparently he needed Yao and Wei to act as mediators.

Yao Mengshan came to see Sun Yaoting at once. "Get packed and come to Tianjin with me. Be quick! Zhang has a big temper. We must get there before things become a total mess!"

"Yes, I'll check the train schedule right away. Then we can go and get the tickets and leave immediately." Sun Yaoting was actually quite eager to meet the renowned eunuch.

After telling Chen Zechuan about the trip, Sun Yaoting got on the train to Tianjin with the two old eunuchs, Yao Mengshan and Wei Binqing. On the train Yao and Wei began to talk about the Zhang brothers. "Yunting is used to having his own way," Yao shook his head. "He has a quick temper and hardly listens to anyone. I guess he wants us to tell Yunqiao to stop making trouble."

"But Yunqiao is also very headstrong!" Wei said. "Things must be pretty bad, or we wouldn't have been called. The fight between the brothers is for real this time!"

Sun Yaoting listened quietly, knowing too little to join in the conversation. The Zhang brothers were obviously engaged in an intense dispute over family property.

The train ride took a little over three hours. When they arrived at Tianjin East Station, two of Zhang's stewards met them on the platform. A black car took them to a large, prominent-looking housing compound in the British Concession with gates opening to the south and east. From outside one could see two three-story buildings. Xiaode Zhang lived in the building on the east, which had a basement to guard against emergencies. His son and daughter-in-law took up the building on the west. Luxurious grass and flowers grew in the open garden in between the two buildings.

Zhang met them on the terrace of the east building. "How have you been lately?" He greeted Yao and Wei with a cupped-hand salute, paying no attention to Sun Yaoting.

As the three of them exchanged pleasantries, Sun Yaoting took a close look at the notorious chief eunuch. Zhang was tall and broad-shouldered, with a straight nose, big, piercing eyes and a ruddy complexion. His hair was completely shaven. He wore a gray-serge long gown and a pair of cloth shoes.

"And who is this?" Zhang asked, looking at Sun Yaoting for the first time.

"This is Chunshou. He used to be in the palace with us." Yao Mengshan gave Sun Yaoting a tug.

"My respects!" Sun Yaoting saluted by bending the left knee.

"Get up, get up..." Zhang spread out his hands in a lifting gesture.

Zhang ushered them into the parlor fitted out with Western-style furniture. The sofas looked fashionable and the floor was covered by soft-hard wood. As Sun Yaoting learned afterward, it was here that Zhang threw sumptuous feasts to celebrate birthdays and festivals. He attached great importance to the Mid-Autumn Festival, which symbolized family reunion.

At the mention of his brother's name, Zhang began to curse and swear. The family had accumulated a fortune mostly by his efforts, but his elder brother wanted to take control merely because of his seniority. A brawl broke out between them, and neither would give in.

"Take it easy," Yao Mengshan said soothingly. "A broad-minded man like you should not be bothered by such a trifle!"

As the three old eunuchs began to discuss the matter in detail, Sun Yaoting withdrew to the adjoining room. "How did it go?" he asked when

Yao got back.

"Well, the two brothers are in a deadlock. I think Yunting will have to give in a little bit."

The three of them stayed in Tianjin for several days, with Yao Mengshan shuttling between the Zhang brothers trying to work out a compromise. "Xiaode Zhang owns many houses. Why doesn't he just give one to his brother?" Sun Yaoting asked Yao.

"That's exactly what I told him, but he wouldn't listen. He is very stubborn. And he sets great store by his houses." Yao went on to describe some of Xiaode Zhang's real estate investments.

After leaving the palace, Xiaode Zhang settled down in Tianjin. He built a three-story house in a nice location for thirty thousand dollars, then made a big profit by selling it to a battalion commander. Next he bought a piece of land in an area that was going to enjoy a property boom and built a grand Western-style house there. After a short period of time housing price in the area soared. He turned down several potential customers until Prince Zai Zhen sought him out. Zai Zhen offered to buy the house, saying Zhang could build another one for himself. "Please put up with a little inconvenience. It'll save me so much trouble."

"I am not sure if I can bear the inconvenience," Zhang said with feigned reluctance. After much bargaining, Zhang sold the house, which had cost him eighty thousand dollars to build, for a hundred and forty thousand.

Naturally he had no intention to stop doing such lucrative business. Again he bought a piece of land, and this time he built two luxury houses, one of which had a model plane perched on top. He did not have to wait long for a big customer to show up. It was none other than Pan Fu, Prime Minister of the Republic. Negotiating through his British friends, Pan finally agreed to pay half a million dollars. Unfortunately Pan Fu was ousted from office before he could make the deal. "It must be fate," said Zhang Shandai, Xiaode Zhang's steward. As the middleman he would have earned several thousand dollars if the sale had been consummated.

After listening to all the stories, Sun Yaoting began to understand Xiaode Zhang's attitude. "If he doesn't want to give his brother a house," he suggested, "maybe he could find something else to offer. It's impossible for him to settle with his brother without spending any money!"

"You are quite right," Yao Mengshan said, taking a sip of tea. "The next time I see him, I will remind him of the old saying, 'Lack of tolerance in small matters upsets great plans'!"

The next morning the three of them went to see Zhang again. Before they got to the point in their conversation, a servant announced in a loud voice, "Mr. Yuan is here!"

Sun Yaoting had no idea who the guest was, but it seemed to be an acquaintance of Yao and Wei, judging from the way they exchanged glances. The door curtain was lifted, and a young man of medium stature came in. He was dressed in an immaculate long gown and a pair of sharp-head leather shoes.

"Oh, it's Little Six," Zhang slowly got to his feet. "What auspicious wind has brought you here?" Yao and Wei also stood up to greet the visitor.

The young man sat down without much ado as Zhang ordered the servant to bring tea. He seemed to be a frequent visitor. From their conversation Sun Yaoting found out that "Little Six" was the sixth son of Yuan Shikai, the first President of the Republic.

No one mentioned the dispute between the Zhang brothers. Instead, Little Six became the center of attention. After a while they began to talk about his father, Yuan Shikai.

"Nothing could stop my father from becoming the President. Zai Feng was no match for him! He 'let the tiger return to the mountains' when he let my father return to Henan!"

"Quite so," said Zhang.

These words reminded Sun Yaoting of a conversation he had with Xin Xiuming.

"Before he died," Xin said, "Emperor Guangxu gave Zai Feng a handwritten edict, 'Kill Yuan Shikai!' Guangxu bore an intense hatred against Yuan. If Yuan had not betrayed him, he would not have come to such a miserable end."

"But Yuan wasn't killed," Sun Yaoting said.

"Well, after Cixi and Guangxu died, the new Emperor Xuantong was a still baby. It was the Regent, Zai Feng and Empress Dowager Longyu who presided over the court. They were both weaklings with neither ability nor resolution. Zai Feng wanted to kill Yuan Shikai to avenge his brother Guangxu, but Prince Zai Zhen came to speak in Yuan's favor. He said, 'It would be inauspicious to execute a minister when the Emperor has just been enthroned. Yuan has a problem in his leg. Let's send him back to Luoyang to nurse his illness.' Being a soft-hearted man, Zai Feng agreed, and let the tiger return to the mountains!"

Xin Xiuming also described a secret deal between Yuan Shikai and Zai Zhen. "When the Revolution broke out in 1911, the Imperial Court held a meeting to discuss countermeasures. It was suggested that the court send an experienced general Chen Chunxuan to lead an attack against the revolutionists. But Zai Zhen insisted on appointing Yuan Shikai to the task. In fact, the two of them had already made a secret deal: If Yuan succeeded in suppressing the revolution, he would assist Zai Zhen to ascend the throne. Well, to Zai Zhen's joy, Yuan defeated the revolutionists. But he was too naive to believe Yuan would keep his word! When the New Year was coming, Zai Zhen had his mansion decorated with lanterns and festoons, ready to celebrate his enthronement. At the year-end news came that Yuan Shikai had proclaimed himself President of the Republic. Well, Yuan was a fierce, unscrupulous man, 'producing clouds with one turn of the hand and rain with another'!"

Just then the raucous voice of Little Six awakened Sun Yaoting from his reverie. "My father was a true hero! He used those he could use, and killed those he couldn't!"

The three of them took leave after listening to the rattling of Little Six for half a day in Zhang's house. Again they had achieved nothing. Sun Yaoting felt sick turning Little Six's words in his mind. The history of the nation seemed to be littered with atrocities, betrayals, and all kinds of

Yuan Shikai

Zai Zhen, Prince Qing's son

ignoble deeds.

A couple of days later they visited Xiaode Zhang again. This time Zhang invited Yao and Wei to smoke opium with him. After enjoying a potent dose he began to prattle about his glorious past in the Imperial Palace. He referred to Empress Dowager Cixi as "Old Buddha", her own favorite epithet.

"At that time I kept the files for the Old Buddha. Before her death she made it clear that she wanted Jingyi to be the next Empress Dowager. Everyone in the palace knew she really liked Jingyi. Well, it was Zai Tao and Zai Run who escorted her coffin to the Eastern Tombs. On the way there they asked for my advice. I didn't want to get myself into trouble, so I said eunuchs were not allowed to interfere in state affairs. But they kept pressing me. They said they would act on my words and take whatever responsibility for their action. So I suggested we set up Longyu as Empress Dowager and declare it to be the oral edict of the Old Buddha."

Yao and Wei were both intrigued. "We know the story well. But was there really such an edict?"

"Of course not," Zhang replied with a satisfied smile. "But we had to pretend there was one to keep the situation under control. By palace rules members of the imperial clan, including the consorts and concubines, must pay respects to the deceased Empress Dowager for the last time after the underground tomb was completely sealed. But Emperor Tongzhi's three consorts suddenly left for the palace before the completion of the ceremony. They thought they could do whatever they wanted now that the Old Buddha was dead. By the time I got the news they must have already traveled a few dozen li in their sedan chairs. I knew perfectly well what they had in mind – the Empress dowager's gold seal. I immediately left in a carriage with a few of my men and caught up with them in the city late at night. When they entered the palace by the Gate of Divine Prowess, they must have thought the gold seal already belonged to them. But I entered the palace by the Eastern Flowery Gate and seized the gold seal in the Palace of Earthly Peace ahead of them."

"It's incredible!" Yao Mengshan exclaimed. "Someone else would have ruled the court if you had arrived a little late!"

"Exactly! I beat them to it by about ten minutes, I think. Soon Zai Tao and Zai Run returned to the palace and drafted a decree in the name of the Council of State. Early in the morning, Longyu was still in bed when I entered her room to tell her what had been accomplished. She was overjoyed. But Jingyi and the other consorts raised quite a racket over this. 'We'll stay behind to guard the Eastern Tombs and never set foot in the palace again!' 'That would be very nice,' I said. 'But we'll have to build a few houses there for them to stay!' When they were told my response, they did not know what to do next. Then I sought out General Zhang Xun. He's my sworn brother, you know. 'You must stay here to protect the three imperial consorts. You'll be held responsible if anything untoward happens to them!' 'I'll do whatever you say,' he answered. Then I told him to summon all the eunuch attendants of the consorts. 'Tell them they will all lose their heads if anything goes wrong.' In this way I held the three consorts in check, and Longyu became Empress Dowager. A couple of months afterward she made me chief of the Palace of Peaceful Longevity."

"It's common knowledge in the palace that Longyu would not have become Empress Dowager without your help!" Yao said.

"It was no big deal," Zhang smiled. "You only have to handle things with determination. Let me tell you a small incident after the Emperor's abdication. You know what happened when Pu Yi's abdication was announced? Well, all the storehouses suddenly stopped supplying provisions to the palace! Grand Secretary Shi Xu came to ask me for advice, so I told him, 'Your family has enjoyed imperial favor for three generations. I have also had my share of imperial bounty. Why don't the two of us bear the cost together?' When he sent for the storehouse keepers and announced my proposal, they realized at once that I was ready for a showdown. They all knelt and said they were willing to bear the cost themselves. Of course the money would come from the annual allowance paid by the Republic, so they wouldn't have to take a single cent from their own pocket. That was exactly what I had expected. Otherwise they would have divided the annual allowance among themselves!"

"It was their misfortune to have such a formidable adversary as you!" Yao Menshan remarked. The three old eunuchs burst out laughing.

Through the mediation of Yao and Meng, the dispute between the Zhang brothers was finally settled. Xiaode Zhang made a concession by handing over to his elder brother a pawnshop valued at some twenty thousand dollars. Thereupon Sun Yaoting returned to the Temple of Prosperity with Yao Mengshan and Wei Binqing.

Shortly afterward the Zhang brothers fell out again. Judging by the situation, the conflict seemed inevitable. Xiaode Zhang had adopted his brother's only son, Zhang Bing, by their mother's arrangement. This made Zhang Yunqiao sonless, so he married a girl younger than his own granddaughter. After bearing him three sons in succession, she raised the thorny issue of family inheritance, which triggered another round of fight between the Zhang brothers.

"You are spared a lot of trouble," Sun Yaoting said to Yao jokingly. "You don't have to go to Tianjin this time."

"You're quite right," Yao said with a bland smile. His relationship with Xiaode Zhang had turned sour because of an incident that had taken place during the interval. In Beijing's Western Hills there was a temple built by Li Lianying. After Li died, his disciple Yao Mengshan took charge of the temple. Named Baozhangsi, or the Temple of Treasure, it commanded a magnificent view in the mountains and was believed by many eunuchs to be auspiciously located. Both Liu Yincheng, the first eunuch to take Taoist order and Cui Yugui, Li Lianying's mentor, chose to be buried in the vicinity. Xiaode Zhang also took a fancy to the place. At this Yao Mengshan suggested, "If you really like it, you can come over to run the temple!"

"That would be marvelous!" Zhang was very pleased. He had the temple completely renovated, built a Western-style house, and bought a piece of land nearby. Then someone came to him to speak ill of Xin Xiuming, who happened to be residing in the temple at the time. Seething with rage, Zhang declared, "I won't let him stay there!"

Xin Xiuming refused to be intimidated. "Just let him try," he said. "I'll fight him to the end!" He went to court and filed a suit against Zhang. When the court required them to show proof of the temple's ownership, both Xin and Zhang came to Yao Mengshan for help. Xin Xiuming even prepared a written testimony for him to sign. Yao hesitated, finding himself in a dilemma. Though Zhang had built a house nearby, the temple did not really belong to him. After much deliberation Yao signed the testimony Xin had prepared. Zhang lost the case and broke up with Yao. Therefore whatever happened between the Zhang brothers, Yao could no longer act as their mediator.

2. Yao Mengshan

A great famine swept across the nation. Crowds of famine victims fled their hometowns to save themselves from starvation. Many swarmed to the capital, where they fed at the "porridge sheds" operated by charitable people of wealth. They had no home and slept in the open on Beijing's broad streets and small lanes.

Panic spread across the Temple of Prosperity when the mess stopped providing three meals a day to all. The poor eunuchs began to complain bitterly. "Heaven never seals all the exits," Chen Zechuan said to Sun Yaoting by way of consolation. "You shall not starve as long as I have something to eat."

"But I don't want to be a burden to you," Sun Yaoting replied. He knew that Chen was worried about his wife and intended to return to his hometown.

Chen decided to find Sun Yaoting a "rice bowl" before he left. At his invitation Yao Mengshan came to the temple early in the morning. After a few rounds of mahjong, they enjoyed a sumptuous meal with many dishes. Chen then sent for Sun Yaoting. "Mr. Yao," he said, "you are quite alone without a good servant by your side. This disciple of mine is not bad at all. Why don't you take him as your personal attendant?"

When Yao did not answer at once, Chen added, "when you have nothing better to do, he can entertain you by telling stories. He has a fine handwriting and can write letters for you. How about that?"

These words pushed the right buttons. Yao Mengshan looked very pleased and agreed with no more hesitation. For all his wealth Yao had no family and lived a rather lonely, monotonous life. It would be nice for him to have a servant who could read and write and tell stories.

The next day Sun Yaoting left the Temple of Prosperity for Yao Mengshan's residence at Xianyingguan, or Temple of Buddha's Presence. Yao was sitting cross-legged in a wooden armchair drinking tea from a small teapot when Sun Yaoting came in and bent one knee in obeisance. As he later found out, Yao prided himself on living in style like a Qing veteran. For one thing, he was very particular about tea drinking. He cultivated a few pots of jasmine flowers and used the petals to scent the tealeaves bought at four dollars a jin. The small teapot he used was an antique pilfered from the Imperial Palace.

Yao Mengshan sat in his armchair drinking tea from the small teapot three times a day – in the morning, after lunch and in the evening. From time to time he let Sun Yaoting take a sip after the second filling, saying, "It takes time for the flavor of this tea to come out." But he never forgot to say a word of caution: "Be very careful! Don't break it!" He obviously place great value by the teapot.

As deputy chief eunuch for Empress Dowager Longyu, Yao had made a huge fortune, which would probably last him a lifetime but for his opium addiction. In the palace the most well known opium addict had been Wei Shanqing, who smoked his pipe every day. Yet a regular opium dose lasted him two days. Yao, on the other hand, could finish five doses in any single day.

"There's nothing I can do," Yao sighed. "I am hooked on it!"

"I know you can't give it up," Sun Yaoting said, "but it would help a little if you smoke less heavily."

"There's nothing I can do," Yao repeated. He sat down on the kang, made himself comfortable in a reclining position, and picked up his pipe again.

Having waited on opium-smoking eunuchs in the palace, Sun Yaoting knew a lot about the serving procedures though he had never smoked a puff. While attending to Yao he grew very skilled at opium preparation, and Yao became increasingly dependent on him.

First he had to procure high-quality crude opium. At that time opium poppy was widely cultivated in the city of Zhangjiakou in Hebei. As many eunuchs were addicts, the Temple of Prosperity became virtually an underground opium market, where Sun Yaoting went to buy crude opium from the dealers. While preparing opium he was assisted by Zhang Yongfu, another house servant four or five years his junior. The first time he did it Sun Yaoting bought twenty liang, or a little over half a kilo, of crude opium. He placed it in a large copper ladle and melted it by gentle heating. Later, when fifty liang was prepared at a time, he had to use a copper cooker instead. When crude opium began to give off an appealing fragrance, it was time to filter it through three or four layers of paper. It took half a day to prepare twenty liang of crude opium. For fifty liang he had to work from early morning till sunset.

While cooking opium he must keep stirring it to prevent burning. He also had to dip the spoon into the opium from time to time. If the spoon sank right through, it meant the opium was still too thin. He must also prevent it from growing too thick; otherwise it would be difficult to knead into the desired shape. Thus crude opium was cooked, filtered, and cooked again. The process was three to four times depending on the quality of the crude opium, until it became a paste. In the next step opium paste was placed into a holder, roasted over a small sesame-oil lamp, and kneaded into tiny balls – the finished product. With the pipe heated up and a ball of opium put in the pipe bowl, the smoker could lie down to enjoy himself.

As the authorities periodically cracked down on opium trafficking and consumption, the balls had to be kept out of sight. When going out, Yao always told Sun Yaoting to put the opium balls into a small bag and tucked it away carefully.

"I can't live without the opium pipe," Yao often remarked after a smoke. "Sooner or later it will ruin me."

"Did you hear the story about opium smoking in the cross-talk?" Sun Yaoting asked.

"No. Tell me about it."

"All right." Sun Yaoting cleared his throat and recited a story from memory. "The solitary lamp casts shadows on the glorious past; a short pipe beats countless heroes to the ground."

"Ha-ha!" The oil lamp flickered as Yao broke into a bitter laughter. "What's the horizontal line that goes with the couplet?"

"Need I say it? I know you won't follow the advice!"

"Let me hear it anyway."

"'Never ever smoke again'!"

"You are right, I can't do it." Yao shook his head.

"So I'll have to go on preparing opium paste for you."

Yao Mengshan had a large circle of friends and acquaintances including Manchu notables, ex-courtiers as well as officials of various ranks. Among China's last eunuchs he was probably second only to Xiaode Zhang in notoriety. In his house, a horizontal scroll hanging from the lintel of the door to the main hall read: "Follow virtue without fail – for Mengshan", written by Pu Yi's brother Pu Ru in the regular script. The wording of the scroll was rather thoughtful, with the character "virtue" alluding to Emperor Guangxu, whose posthumous title, Dezong, literally means "ancestor of virtue". Yao was proud to own the scroll and often pointed it out to his guests.

One day Pu Ru, invited to write another couplet, arrived in a car just before noon. When Sun Yaoting announced the guest, Yao hastened out of the room to meet Pu Ru in the courtyard. He bent one knee in obeisance as he would have done in the palace, and Pu Ru stepped up and pulled him up with both hands. They were very courteous to each other but there was a clear distinction between master and slave.

Dressed in a faded mandarin jacket, Pu Ru had the elegant manners of a learned scholar. In Yao's house he was accorded great respect, with the servants falling on their knees to serve tea. Yao and his guest sat down to chat for a while, then a sumptuous meal was served.

After lunch Pu Ru rinsed his mouth, washed his face, and drank some more tea. Then he asked Yao for a special type of paper he used exclusively for painting and calligraphy. Yao immediately sent a servant to get the paper. When another servant brought ink and brush, Pu Ru waved him away and took out the brush, inkstand and ink slab he had brought with him. "What would you like me to write?" he asked Yao.

"Whatever you think fit."

"Where do you want to hang the scrolls?" Pu Ru dipped the brush in the inkstand and looked around.

"In my bedroom," Yao said, pointing to an adjoining room.

"Very well." Pu Ru paused for a moment to gather his concentration before committing the brush to the paper. He finished two vertical scrolls at one go, then had a servant hold them while he examined his work carefully. "Bold brushstrokes! Excellent wording!" Yao exclaimed in admiration. The couplet read, "A thin cloud takes shelter on the cliff/The lone moon dances in waves." In implicit terms it portrayed the forlorn life of a eunuch who lived all by himself. Yao liked the couplet very much and kept it hanging in his bedroom.

Yao Mengshan and Pu Ru were chatting away when a yellow cat slipped into the room meowing. Sun Yaoting went over to shoo it away, but Pu Ru stopped him. "Hey, look at the cat! It's so cute." A few days later Pu Ru sent Yao an extremely lifelike portrait of the cat. Sun Yaoting admired Pu Ru's painting and calligraphy and longed to own a piece of his work. However, he knew he was not in a position to ask Pu Ru for a gift. Then it occurred to him that Liu Ziyu had a relative named He, who had served Pu Ru for

"Young Boys in Color" by Pu Ru, courtesy of Palace Museum

many years. With He's help Sun Yaoting obtained a small mountain-and-water painting with Pu Ru's seal on it, but there was no inscription. Sun Yaoting took the painting back to He, who asked Pu Ru to add an inscription. This painting became one of Sun Yaoting's most treasured possessions.

Yao Mengshan was a shareholder of Xiangyihao, a shop located in the downtown area of Qianmen. Business seemed to be going downhill, and he enjoyed reminiscing about its past prosperity. "Xiangyihao started business just before the Xuantong Emperor came to the throne," he said to Sun Yaoting.

"Please tell me about it."

It turned out to be yet another story of Xiaode Zhang's business success. Zhang had set up Xiangyihao in the name of purchasing supplies for the Imperial Palace. Working in connivance with fraudulent merchants, he made huge profits buying at low price and overcharging the palace. He made the first deal even before the shop formally opened for business. As High Consort Duankang enjoyed watching theatricals, he procured costumes from the south at a bargain price and sold them to the Court Theatrical Office.

The shop enjoyed a booming business dealing in silk, brocade and fashionable foreign goods. Zhang invested thirty thousand dollars in the shop, with Wang Ziyuan, Wei Binqing and Li Leting contributing twenty thousand dollars each. As Yao Mengshan was his deputy, Zhang also invited him to join the venture and share the profit. When Yao said he had no ready money, Zhang put down ten thousand dollars for him. Thus the shop's total investment amounted to a hundred thousand dollars. Zhang hired Manager Jin of Shoucang, a large shop in the Qianmen area, to supervise Xiangyihao. Jin was a native of Beijing who had been doing business with the Imperial Palace for a long time. The shop yielded huge profits, but somehow Yao Mengshan failed to get his share.

"It makes me sick to talk about Xianyihao!" Yao concluded.

"What are you going to do?"

"I want to sell some land!" Yao said. While in the palace he had bought twenty-four mu of land in the village of Shuangtang that he now decided to sell to pay for his extravagant lifestyle.

"No need for you to ask around," Sun Yaoting said promptly. "I'll go home and talk it over with my family."

Sun Yaoting went home to tell his father the news, and they decided to buy the land. Yao agreed and turned down several other potential customers. The next year Yao Ziheng, Yao Mengshan's third brother, came to see Sun Huaibao, saying, "You can have that piece of land and plant whatever you like." He even agreed to get paid afterward.

Delighted, the Sun family worked hard to get the land ready for planting crops. After they had ploughed the field repeatedly for a total of eleven times, Yao Ziheng came again. "My brother is short of money. You must pay at once!" When Sun Huaibao gave him the money, Yao said it was not enough. The price they had agreed on was sixteen dollars per mu, but now Yao raised it to forty.

"What shall we do?" Sun Huaibao stamped his feet. "Where can we get all that money? And we've ploughed the field eleven times!"

In the end they bought the land, with Sun Yaoting contributing the last silver dollars he had managed to keep till then. When Yao Ziheng walked past their house a few days afterward, Sun Yaoting turned away, but his hotheaded younger brother rushed to the door with an ax, muttering, "I'll kill him!" Sun Yaoting grabbed his arm. "Stop being a fool," he said. "You are not going to change anything by acting in this way!"

3. Prodigal Sons

Yao Mengshan was in a bad mood these days. Xiaode Zhang, it seemed, took pleasure in making things difficult for him. He was informed that his debts to Xiangyihao now exceeded his stock shares. As Zhang kept pressing him to pay, he decided to sell some of his land in his hometown, Yao Village. However, he could find no buyer due to Zhang's interference. He had no recourse but to sell his housing property in Beijing.

Yao owned over a dozen houses in different districts of Beijing. Most were rented out to pay for his opium-smoking expenses. However, in times of turmoil it was no easy job to sell houses at a good price. He entrusted the job to his brother, Yao Ziheng, who cheated him out of a large part of the proceeds. With most of his houses gone, what he got in return was not even enough to pay his debts. "I must have done poorly in my previous life," he said to Sun Yaoting with a sigh. "That's why heaven has given me such a brother."

Sun Yaoting said nothing, his mind churning with emotions. For Yao Mengshan's sake, his family used to treat Yao Ziheng with great courtesy. Whenever Yao Ziheng came for a visit, the family always received him warmly and prepared the best meal they could afford. Yao Ziheng took everything for granted and ordered them around as if they were his personal servants. Sun Yaoting cursed himself when he remembered all that.

Most eunuchs adopted a son in order to "continue the family line". Yao Mengshan adopted two, one of whom was none other than Yao Ziheng's son. Instead of performing filial duties, they helped dissipate the family fortune. Yao Mengshan realized his mistake though he seldom talked about it. He remarked to Sun Yaoting once that he did not expect his two sons to look after him in his later years.

One day Sun Yaoting received two unexpected visitors from his home village, a woman with her young daughter. "You've got to help us, brother," she pleaded. "We've come all the way from Jinghai to find you." She turned to the girl. "Dezheng, come over and meet Uncle."

The girl greeted Sun Yaoting shyly. She was very thin, about fourteen to fifteen years old.

"When did you come to the capital?" Sun Yaoting asked. He knew them pretty well as they lived not far away from his family in the village.

"We've just arrived, and we've come here to ask you for a favor. Is he in?"

"No," Sun Yaoting replied. He knew she was asking about Yao Mengshan.

"You know what the situation is like in Jinghai these years. The crops do not grow so well, and we can hardly feed ourselves. So I am hoping that maybe Mr. Yao could adopt my girl."

"He's not in right now. You'd better find a place to stay and wait for a couple of days. I'll talk to him about it."

Mother and daughter thanked Sun Yaoting profusely and left. He could not help feeling the tragic irony of the situation. Some people became eunuchs in order to escape poverty, and some people wanted to be adopted by rich eunuchs as a way to make a living.

In the evening Yao Mengshan returned. When Sun Yaoting mentioned the young girl from Jinghai, he shook his head emphatically. "No, I don't need her! You know what a fix I am in right now. What's more, I already have two sons."

"Let's look at it this way. If you become bedridden someday, who will look after you? Your third brother or your sons?"

Yao Mengshan slowly shook his head.

"I know the girl very well. Dezheng has a sweet temper, something you can rarely find in young girls these days. She wants nothing from you except three meals a day. And she'll do a lot of housework."

Though Yao remained silent, Sun Yaoting could see that his interest was aroused. "You could regard it as a business deal that is mutually beneficial. She will be able to feed herself, and you will have someone to look after you in your final years. And it won't cost you a cent to conclude the deal. The only thing you need to do is to have someone write a letter of adoption."

"Who can write such a letter?" Yao asked.

"It's quite simple. I can write it for you." Sun Yaoting fetched paper and a writing brush, drafted the letter, and read it out aloud.

I am willing to have my daughter Dezheng adopted by Yao Mengshan. She shall carry out her filial duties to him, looking after him in old age and giving him a proper burial when he passes away. As word of mouth offers no proof, a written statement is hereby given.

It was the first time Sun Yaoting composed such a letter, and he did his best. At the bottom he wrote down his name as the middleman and put his fingerprint on it. Yao Mengshan nodded his agreement, finally convinced that Sun Yaoting was acting in his best interests. The following day Sun Yaoting introduced the mother and daughter to the old eunuch, and the mother signed the adoption letter. He heaved a sigh of relief, knowing that he had done a good deed.

Sun Yaoting went home and stayed there for a long period of time. Then, instead of going back to wait on Yao Mengshan, he returned to the Temple of Prosperity. When he paid Yao a visit, he was dismayed by what he saw. The old eunuch was eating steamed corn bread, the typical staple food for the poor. At the sight of him Yao came up to grab his hand and broke into tears. "I failed to do good deeds in my past life!"

As Sun Yaoting was groping for words to comfort the old eunuch, Dezheng came in and tugged at the hem of his gown. Taking the cue, he followed her out into the courtyard. "Uncle," the girl looked at him pleadingly. "Father has run out of money again. What can I do?"

"Don't worry. I don't have much on me, but take this." Sun Yaoting put a few banknotes in her hand.

They went back into the room, where Yao began a tearful account of his miserable circumstances. He made no mention of his prodigal sons, though Sun Yaoting believed they were responsible for all this. "I rely solely on Dezheng. Without her to look after me, I don't know where I would be right now."

"Hey, it's Mister Sun here! I was wondering who it could be." The sarcastic voice came from Yao Ziheng's son, who suddenly emerged from the inner room. "Take a look at my lambskin coat," he glanced tauntingly at Sun Yaoting. "It's very light and real warm."

"You'd better take a look at my coat," Sun Yaoting shot back, feeling indignant. "It may not be so light and warm, but I paid for it myself!"

"What do you mean?" The young man bristled.

"Let me ask you something," Sun Yaoting said. "How has your father been treating you all these years? But you give him coarse food to eat while you stuff yourself with meat, eggs and pancakes. Are you totally devoid of conscience?"

Listening to the quarrel, Yao Mengshan moved over as if he had something to say. "Why don't you go to bed?" His adopted son barked, glaring at him. "What are you doing here?" At this Yao Mengshan slouched away without a word.

"What the hell is going on?" Sun Yaoting cursed angrily and stormed out of the room.

A few days later Yao Mengshan's nephew Liu Jingshen called on Sun Yaoting at the temple. They both sighed deeply over what Yao was going through in his old age. Liu listened quietly as Sun Yaoting attacked Yao's adopted sons with great vehemence. "My uncle has only himself to blame for all this!" he finally said.

"Why?" Sun Yaoting asked in astonishment.

"How can you fail to see something so obvious? He's made one blunder after another! Life is hard for a eunuch to begin with, and if he keeps making the wrong choices, what else can he expect?"

"I see what you mean," Sun Yaoting nodded his head.

Liu went on. "In the Imperial Palace my uncle was Xiaode Zhang's deputy. You know how the two of them worked together? When a eunuch had to be punished, Zhang was the one to give the order, and my uncle was the one to wield the whip. He made lots of enemies in that way, taking all the blame for Xiaode Zhang without knowing it. Then he adopted Yao Ziheng's son, a good-for-nothing and an absolute scoundrel. Are you surprised that he should live in such misery in his old age?"

"Fortunately he still has a house and some money left," Sun Yaoting said. "Otherwise he would have become homeless by now."

Not long afterward he got news that Yao Mengshan had become bedridden.

9

MANCHUKUO

1. "New Capital"

On a cold winter night Sun Yaoting and Chen Zechuan sat on the kang in Chen's room. An oil lamp on the table gave off a dim light. "The Emperor has sent someone to recruit a few eunuchs here in the capital," Sun Yaoting said. "Is that true?" At that time Pu Yi was "Emperor Kangde" of Manchukuo, a Japanese puppet state in Northeast China.

"Yes. Wang Shiqing has come to the temple," Chen Ziyu replied blandly. "But he does not seem to be doing so well in Manchukuo."

Sun Yaoting sensed Chen's lack of interest and dropped the topic. He knew little about the situation in Manchukuo, but he believed he should not miss the opportunity to go and wait on Pu Yi. After all, attending to the Emperor was the best job a eunuch could ever find. Asking around, he learned that he needed an "exit certificate" from Zai Tao to go to Manchukuo. It should not be difficult for me to get it, he thought.

Zai Tao was about to leave his house when Sun Yaoting arrived at the gate. "What has brought you here, Chunshou?" Zai Tao greeted him warmly. "I haven't seen you for a long time."

"I've come to get an 'exit certificate'. I'd like to go to the New Capital to wait on the Emperor."

"No problem. Just go ahead. I have something else to do." Zai Tao left in his car.

Sun Yaoting found Jia Runqing, who took him to Lady Jiang, the princess-consort. She was having her hair combed when they came in. Sun Yaoting quickly knelt in obeisance. "Your slave pays his respects!"

"Oh, it's Chunshou. Haven't seen you for a long time."

"I've made myself busy. I am going to Manchukuo this time."

"Why do you want to go there?" The princess-consort turned away from the mirror to look at him.

"I'd like to go and serve His Majesty."

"Good!"

Just then a young woman came in. "Who is this?" She looked closely at Sun Yaoting.

"He used to work in the house," Jia replied. "His name is Chunshou." Then he told Sun Yaoting to salute the "Third Madam". After the young woman left, Jia said in a whisper, "The master married Third Madam only recently. She used to be a singer."

"You don't have to wait for the master to return to get the certificate," said Lady Jiang. "Let the Sixth Master write a note for you, and I'll stamp it with the seal."

Sun Yaoting thanked her and followed Jia Runqing to see Pu Xiu in the studio. After Pu Xiu wrote a letter of introduction, it was stamped with Zai Tao's seal. Sun Yaoting went back to thank the princess-consort again, then took his leave in satisfaction. Jia Runqing saw him off at the gate. "Be very careful when you get to the Northeast," Jia cautioned. "From what I've heard, the Emperor is extremely irritable these days. Make a small mistake, and you may lose your head!"

"Is it really as bad as all that?" Sun Yaoting asked in disbelief.

"Of course it is! The last time our master went to Manchukuo, the Emperor got very angry with him and gave him a severe dressing-down."

"Then it's really bad," Sun Yaoting said. After thinking for a long time he wrote a letter to Zhao Rongsheng, who had accompanied Pu Yi to Manchukuo. He asked specifically about Wanrong, as he wanted to wait on her again. He remembered his days in the palace with a deep longing. Attending to the Empress would give him both high status and a good living. Besides, she was kindhearted and would surely treat him well.

Zhao's reply letter, however, brought him some shocking news:

The Empress, Wanrong, had an affair and got pregnant. The Emperor was furious. ...The palace was thrown into turmoil by the incident. The Empress is now in a very precarious position. The Emperor is very bad-tempered and often has people around him beat up.

Sun Yaoting slumped on the kang, feeling dizzy in the head. The news was hard to believe, but he had to believe it. Zhao had written the letter at a risk, and there was no need for him to tell lies. Sun Yaoting did not know what to do. Just then Zhao Rongsheng suddenly returned to the capital. Sun Yaoting asked him anxiously if what he had written in the letter was true.

"Of course it's true!" Zhao seemed to be offended by the question.

"Has the Empress given birth?"

"Yes, it's an open secret in the palace. I think you'd better not go there. The Emperor was furious because he knew the baby was not his."

"How could he tell?"

"You can't be so naive! In the palace, everyone knows the Emperor is inadequate in that respect."

Zhao Rongsheng left, leaving Sun Yaoting in utter confusion. Just then old eunuch Wang Shiqing came to see him. Wang's mission was to recruit three eunuchs, preferably those who had waited on the Emperor or the Empress before, to serve Lady Tan. Pu Yi had married her in Manchukuo and conferred on her the title Worthy Lady. "Have you made up your mind?" Wang asked. "Let me take you to see His Majesty in Manchukuo!"

"I'll have to think about it," Sun Yaoting replied. For all the bad news he had heard, he still wanted to go. Maybe he should find a companion, he told himself. So he went to see Ma Deqing. "Let's go to Manchukuo together," he said. "The two of us can share weal and woe." They agreed that they would come back if things proved really bad over there.

Seeing that he had made up his mind, Chen Zechuan did not try to stop him. "You can go and try your luck if that's what you want to do. If it doesn't make out, you can always come back here."

Together with Ma Deqing and another eunuch, Guo Shaochen, Sun Yaoting took an overnight train to Changchun, the "New Capital" of the Japanese puppet regime. It felt strange to see Japanese flags flying everywhere and Japanese military men planted all over the place.

Life in the so-called "palace" was a far cry from what Sun Yaoting had known in the Forbidden City in Beijing. Early in the morning he was made to stand among a team of orderlies. When a fat man came toward them, Sun Yaoting recognized him at once. It was Yan Tongjiang, an old acquaintance from the palace in Beijing. Sun Yaoting was about to greet him when Yan suddenly announced in a loud voice, "In the inner court of the palace, you are not allowed to talk with or greet others whether you know them or not!"

Sun Yaoting could hardly believe his own ears. He lowered his head and listened as Yan reeled off one rule after another. The rules were too long and complicated for him to remember, but he got one thing clear. Heavy penalties would be meted out to anyone who broke any of the rules, and whoever failed to report on others would be considered an accomplice. Such harshness had been unheard of even in the real Imperial Palace in Beijing. "I wish I had not come," Sun Yaoting whispered to Ma Deqing when they were alone.

Among the old acquaintances he met here were several male attendants: Zhao Yinmao, Li Guoxiong, Yan Tongjiang, Wang Jianzhai and Zhao Jiantao. None of them spoke to him or even acknowledged him with a nod of the head. The whole place felt more like a prison than a palace.

2. Team of Orderlies

There was no comparison between Changchun, the "New Capital" and Beijing. Nor did Pu Yi's so-called "palace" have any of the majesty or grandeur of the Forbidden City. Instead, it had an unimpressive appearance and a rather bleak interior. Of its three gates, the first one was called Baokangmen, or Gate for Safeguarding Prosperity, with the character "kang", or prosperity, alluding to Pu Yi, now styled Emperor Kangde. The second gate was called Yinghuimen, or Gate for Welcoming Sunshine, a seemingly innocuous name. But another eunuch told Sun Yaoting what the name implied. The Chinese character "hui", meaning sunshine, consists of two parts which means "Japanese army" when written separately.

Many years later, when summoned to appear as a witness at the International Military Tribunal for the Far East in 1946, Pu Yi denied having collaborated with Japanese invaders. When asked about this, Sun Yaoting commented, "How can he deny it? He can't erase the words 'Welcoming Sunshine' from that palace gate, can he?"

Inside the second gate was Pu Yi's office, Building for Serving the People, stationed by both Japanese police and Chinese security guards. This was the place where Pu Yi attended to "state affairs". The third gate was called

Gate of Central Harmony. It led to Building of Opulence, which served as the living quarters of Pu Yi and his family. The first floor was occupied by Worthy Lady Tan Yuling. Pu Yi and Wanrong stayed on the second floor in separate chambers to the east and west respectively. Eunuchs and male attendants kept round-the-clock watch in the medicine storeroom between the two chambers. There was also a studio and a Buddhist shrine inside the building.

In the adjoining courtyard on the west stood the Hall of Mutual Goodwill, whose architectural features such as yellow glazed tiles on the roof were reminiscent of the palatial buildings in the Forbidden City. It contained a movie theatre, a dining hall, and a bathing room. The lounge was divided into two sections for receiving Manchu and Japanese guests respectively.

As nominal ruler of Manchukuo, Pu Yi attended to "state affairs" every day, but he could not even go out of his own front gates without getting permission from the Japanese army. He spent much time consulting oracles, practicing Buddhist meditation, and mingling with young students of the Aisin-Gioro clan summoned from Beijing. Apart from Wanrong and Lady Tan, Pu Yi had some other members of the imperial family to keep him company.

"Worthy Lady" Tan Yuling

Sun Yaoting had been eager to come to Manchukuo on the assumption that he would be assigned to Wanrong or Lady Tan. Shortly after his arrival he was taken to the room of the Worthy Lady, where he met both Pu Yi and Lady Tan. He knelt and kowtowed three times.

"How are things going in the Imperial Capital these days?" asked Pu Yi with great interest.

"Quite good," Sun Yaoting mumbled, not knowing exactly what to say. After asking a few more questions, Pu Yi dismissed him.

The short meeting gave Sun Yaoting much hope. The next morning he went to pay respects to Lady Tan, only to find an old eunuch Liu Chang'an standing by her side. "Chunshou, His Majesty has ordered me to wait on the Worthy Lady. You can go and join the team of orderlies!"

Sorely disappointed, Sun Yaoting went to see Yan Tongjiang, who repeated the same order. Along with Ma Deqing and Guo Shaochen, he became an orderly in the inner court of the palace. The team of orderlies, over a dozen in all, lived on the first floor of the Palace of Mutual Goodwill.

The puppet regime of Manchukuo, or at least its so-called palace, seemed to be financially strapped. The Japanese gave Pu Yi a paltry amount of sixty thousand yen each month to cover the general expenses of his inner court. For Sun Yaoting, the monthly stipend was a mere twelve dollars. From time to time the eunuchs found two or three dollars had been deducted from their salary for no apparent reason, but no one dared raise any complaint.

One day Sun Yaoting got a chance to exchange a few words with an old acquaintance, Zhao Yinmao, when they went together to fetch something from the storeroom. In the storeroom Zhao looked around to make sure no one else was in sight, then whispered, "Why on earth did you come here at such a time?"

"What?" Sun Yaoting was bewildered. "You mean..."

"Didn't you hear anything about Manchukuo in the capital?"

"Yes, but..." Sun Yaoting did not know what to say.

"You've got no idea how many people have fled Manchukuo because they can't take it anymore! Now that you are here, brace yourself for a few beatings!"

"Your words are priceless."

"But we'd better watch our tongue," Zhao said, putting a hand over his mouth.

"I understand." Sun Yaoting felt grateful to Zhao, who gave the warning at his own risk. If Pu Yi should be informed, Zhao would probably lose his head. On the other hand, Zhao was one of Pu Yi's most trusted servants. If he had lost faith in Manchukuo, things must be pretty bad indeed. Sun Yaoting knew he had to be extremely careful and keep his mouth shut.

At nine o'clock every evening Zhao Yinmao took Sun Yaoting on a daily security inspection of the palace. They checked each room thoroughly, feeling the curtains and sofas for suspicious objects and even looking at the beams. They reopened the gate of the Hall of Mutual Goodwill, checked it out, and locked it again. The audience lounge required special attention. They had to lift the carpet to see if anything was hidden underneath. They must also test an alarm under the carpet in front of Pu Yi's "dragon chair". He only had to step on it lightly to sound the alarm. It had been installed to guard against the Japanese or any guest who might have ill intentions.

Pu Yi ate supper around five or six o'clock on the porch of the Hall of Mutual Goodwill, with a few members of the imperial clan to share the table. Pu Yi was terrified of being poisoned. The cooks had been carefully selected for their loyalty, and a servant was assigned to taste the dishes before they were served. Even so, Pu Yi remained doubtful and often refused to touch a dish until someone else at the table had tasted it. The main course was followed by fresh fruits and typical Beijing deserts such as crunchy candy, preserved fruits, pea-flour cake, glutinous rice cake with sweet filling, and sugarcoated haws on sticks.

One day Pu Yi wanted to have his meal inside the Hall of Mutual Goodwill. While moving the table, Sun Yaoting and Guo Shaochen accidentally knocked it against the doorframe. Pu Yi noticed it and turned livid with rage. Male attendant Li Guoxiong shouted, "Come here, Guo Shaochen!"

"Yes." Guo put down the table and went over.

"Extend your hand!" Li ordered, taking out a long bamboo slip. "Sun Yaoting, come here!"

With the bamboo slip Li thrashed Guo's palm until it became terribly bruised. "Now remember: Never let His Majesty's table touch anything, especially the doorframe. Is that clear?"

"Yes," Guo answered, stifling a sob.

"And you?" Li turned to Sun Yaoting.

"Yes, I will always bear it in mind!"

"From now on, if you knock into each other beside the table, report to me at once! If you knock the table against anything, report to me at once! Otherwise I will punish you severely!"

"Yes, we understand!"

"You may go now."

Pu Yi watched all this without saying a word. Sun Yaoting later found out why Li Guoxiong had acted like that. In Pu Yi's superstitious mind, knocking the table against the doorframe was a bad omen because the door-gods would take offence.

A few days later Guo Shaochen, feeling nervous when adjusting the table, bumped into it. He was instantly dragged away for a ruthless beating in the confinement chamber. Commonly known as the "dark room", it was used for punishing eunuchs and other servants. In addition to a beating, the offender might be detained there for days or even months on end with barely enough to eat. Several male attendants took Guo to the dark room, threw him to the floor, stripped him naked, and used bamboo planks to beat his buttocks and thighs until they turned black and blue.

"You've been told not to touch His Majesty's dinner table," said Yan Tongjiang, who supervised the beating. "Why did you disobey the order deliberately?"

"I did not do it on purpose. I was just being too careless." Guo knelt on the floor and kowtowed repeatedly to plead for mercy.

"Now listen: If you make the same mistake again, you'll be dead!"

Already in his forties, Guo Shaochen used to enjoy high status among eunuchs as a personal attendant of High Consort Duankang. Little did he expect that he would be subjected to abuse and repeated beatings in Manchukuo. He was sunk in gloom and despondence all day.

Mealtime for Pu Yi was usually an ordeal for eunuchs. Pu Yi might explode in fury over the slightest trespass on the part of a eunuch and order him to be beaten up. Sun Yaoting soon learned to be very careful not to break any of the numerous unwritten rules. For example, when the orderlies ate together, no one was supposed to speak or make any noise. Their staple food was husked sorghum, renamed "culture rice" in the official jargon of Manchukuo. A dead silence reigned at the table; anyone who munched his bowl of "culture rice" would receive a thrashing.

A servant might do wrong in a myriad ways. Ma Deqing was quite conscientious in fulfilling his duty of cleaning up the rooms. But one day Pu Yi touched a window frame with his hand and found it a little dusty. "You are trying to fool me, you lazybones!" he said angrily. Several male attendants came up to grab Ma. They used a bamboo slip to thrash his palm, which remained bruised and swollen for several days.

Perhaps the sole benefit of being a eunuch in Manchukuo was three free meals a day. Once every few days they had wheaten food such as steamed bread or pancakes instead of husked sorghum. The dishes remained more or less the same: cucumbers, eggplants, potatoes, and bean curd. Tomatoes were often delivered to the palace but never appeared on their table.

On festivals they could eat meat, usually with "spring pancakes". After finishing his meal, Pu Yi would send for the eunuchs and look on while they attacked the food. "There's a proper way to do it," he remarked. On the table were braised pork, slices of pork tripe and chicken, scallions, and a sweet sauce made of fermented flour. "All right, let's begin!"

Sun Yaoting dipped some scallion stalks in the sauce and wrapped them up with pork into a pancake. Pu Yi looked pleased. "You seem to be an expert!"

"Thanks for Your Majesty's praise," Sun Yaoting said.

In the meantime Lady Tan began to eat at a separate table. Sun Yaoting went over to lend a hand from time to time and took the chance to grab some delicacies from her kitchen. During festivities such acts were considered acceptable. Occasionally Pu Yi summoned a group of orphans about twelve or thirteen years old to feed them with meat and pancakes. The way they gobbled up the food pleased him immensely, and he clapped his hands.

At mealtime several eunuchs laid out the table and served dishes for Pu Yi. Then they stepped back and remained standing nearby to answer his beck and call. For a period of time Sun Yaoting's sole duty was to chase flies with a flyswatter. When in a good mood, Pu Yi chatted with the attending eunuchs in an amiable tone. "Chunshou, what did you eat when you were in the capital?"

"Your slave had wheaten food once every two days and coarse grain bread sometimes."

"Are you used to eating sorghum?"

"No problem," Sun Yaoting replied with an ingratiating smile. "Every orderly eats it."

"Well, you can pick things from the table." This meant Sun Yaoting was allowed to eat the leftovers after Pu Yi finished.

"Thanks for the favor, Your Majesty!" Sun Yaoting did not mind eating Pu Yi's leftovers, which tasted better than anything on the eunuchs' menu.

The kitchen prepared Pu Yi's favorite Beijing-style food such as almond-flavor bean curd, fruit syrup and sweet-sour plum juice. In the short summer he liked to eat ice-lollies, something the Forbidden City did not have.

One day Pu Yi beckoned Ma Deqing over and pointed to some biscuits. "You can have this." To be polite, Ma turned to Sun Yaoting standing nearby. "Come and have some."

"How dare you?" Pu Yi banged the table angrily.

Ma Deqing hastily apologized without knowing what was wrong.

"The two of you must have formed a conspiracy!" Pu Yi shouted, pointing his finger.

Several male attendants rushed over and dragged Ma out of the room to give him a severe beating. Pu Yi then ordered Ma to be carried back and eat the biscuits while Sun Yaoting looked on. "Remember this," Pu Yi warned them. "No one can eat unless I tell him to!" Then he turned and walked away. Sun Yaoting and Ma Deqing were left alone in the room, staring at each other wordlessly.

In the evening a young eunuch told Sun Yaoting some unnerving news. "Did you hear about it? Guo Shaochen has run away! The Emperor is mad. "

"How do you know?"

"The whole palace is rocking with the news! Old Guo stayed here for only a short time before he slipped away without saying good-bye. No wonder the Emperor is furious!"

"But he wouldn't have been able to leave if he had said good-bye!"

"Well, who doesn't want to leave?" the young eunuch sighed. "But it's not so easy."

"It was your rotten idea to come here," Ma Deqing complained bitterly the next time he saw Sun Yaoting. "What does Manchukuo has to offer except sufferings and hardships?"

"I didn't know it would turn out like this," Sun Yaoting said. "Anyway, it's no use whining about it now."

"I didn't even tell my family when I left." Ma asked Sun Yaoting to write home for him.

"They'd beat me to death if they find out about it! But if that's what you really need me to do, I'll do it."

Having made the promise, Sun Yaoting thought carefully and hit upon an idea. Late in the evening, when everyone else had gone to bed, he hid himself in the toilet and wrote a letter for Ma Deqing with a pencil. Then Ma Deqing asked a cook to smuggle the letter out of the palace. Several months later a reply letter from his hometown in Qing County was finally delivered to him after passing through many hands. Opening the letter, Ma learned that his father was dead. He burst into tears. He had lost his mother as a child, just as he was recovering from his castration. And now he was going through hell in Manchukuo, with no one in the world to turn to.

Sun Yaoting told Ma to check his grief for fear that someone would hear his weeping and grow suspicious. Together they worked out a plan of escape. Claiming that his mother was terminally ill and needed his care, Ma obtained a leave from Pu Yi and left Manchukuo for Beijing. Of the three eunuchs recruited together by Wang Shiqing, Sun Yaoting was now the only one left.

3. Puppet Emperor

After Ma Deqing left, it was Sun Yaoting's duty to clean the rooms in the Building of Opulence. Assisted by two junior eunuchs, he tidied up the entire building regularly, wiping the windows on Monday and the doorframes on Tuesday, etc. He had to report his work plan to the chief of orderlies, a Mongolian named Duo Lianyuan. After Duo gave him the go-ahead, he set down to work, toiling from morning to evening.

One day Duo Lianyuan ran into his room to bark an order. "Go and wipe the windows at once!"

Sun Yaoting shuddered at the prospect of wiping windows. He had developed a fear of the heights after a childhood accident, when he dropped from the roof of the house into a pit of mud. Not daring to disobey, he slowly climbed to the second floor of the building and virtually dragged himself to the window. While wiping the window with a rag, he stole a glance downward despite himself. His head swam, and he clung to the handle of the window for dear life, his eyes closed and his mind a total blank. Another eunuch noticed his plight but did not call out for fear of scaring him. When Sun Yaoting finally opened his eyes, the eunuch asked, "Chunshou, are you all right?"

"Yes," Sun Yaoting answered automatically. But he felt paralyzed, unable to move his limbs.

When informed of this, Pu Yi arrived on the scene to take a look. "What's the matter here?"

"Your Majesty," replied Duo Lianyuan, "Chunshou is too frightened to get down."

"Then go up and help him!" Pu Yi snapped. "Why did you send him up there in the first place when you know he is so timid?"

Duo Lianyuan immediately told Su Huanchen and another eunuch to help Sun Yaoting get down from the window.

"Look, Chunshou has wet his pants!"

Pu Yi and his second sister walked over to take a closer look at Sun Yaoting. His face was bloodless and both trouser legs were wet. "If Chunshou is so timid, you should not make him climb the heights," said Pu Yi's sister.

Pointing a finger at Duo Lianyuan, Pu Yi ordered, "Listen carefully! Never make Chunshou climb the heights from now on! Is it clear?"

"Your slave will bear it in mind!" Duo replied, his head lowered.

Thanks to Pu Yi's order, Sun Yaoting never had to climb a ladder or wipe the windows again. However, a few days later he was taken to the "dark room" for the first time. After a period of confinement in the "dark room" for a minor offense, Duo Lianyuan was required to write a "letter of repentance" upon his release. Being illiterate, he asked Sun Yaoting for help.

It was a rather easy job for Sun Yaoting. He quickly wrote the letter, gave it to Duo, and went to bed without a second thought. He was drifting to sleep when someone gave him a rough shove. He opened his eyes to find Yan Tongjiang standing before him, a bamboo plank in hand. Yan took him to the dark room and slammed the door shut. A small opening in the wall gave out a dim light.

Without a word Yan slapped him so hard that blood dripped from the corner of his mouth.

"Did you write the letter of repentance for Duo Lianyuan?" Yan demanded harshly.

"Yes, I did. What's wrong?" Sun Yaoting was now fully awake.

"What did you write in the letter?"

Sun Yaoting got to his feet and thought for a few seconds. "Your slave, Duo Lianyuan, willingly accepts punishment for committing a mistake while on duty. Thanks to the favor bestowed by His Majesty, I am now released. From now on I will fulfill my duties most conscientiously to repay His Majesty's kindness..."

Apparently Yan had not expected Sun Yaoting to be able to recite the letter without missing a word. After a long pause, he finally said, "It's wrong for you to write a letter like that. Are you aware of your offense?"

"How am I supposed to write it?" Sun Yaoting demanded.

"You said things in Duo Lianyuan's favor. You should have written down whatever he has to say."

"I wrote the letter for him precisely because he did not know what to write," Sun Yaoting retorted. "And you think I did it wrong?"

"Since you refuse to admit your mistake, I'll show the letter to His Majesty." Yan Tongjiang left the room, locking the door behind him.

Yan came back a moment later, and his voice was less harsh. "His Majesty shows special favor to you and agrees to let you go. You won't be punished this time, but never make the same mistake again!"

Sun Yaoting walked out of the dark room after half an hour. In the courtyard he ran into Pu Yi, who smiled at the sight of him. "Chunshou, I didn't realize you are so talented! You surely know how to write a letter of repentance! Not bad! Not bad at all!"

"What your slave wrote is sheer nonsense, nonsense." Sun Yaoting muttered, not daring to look up. Pu Yi had such a volatile temper these days that one did not know what to expect from him.

"Ha-ha!" Pu Yi walked away laughing.

Thus Sun Yaoting escaped a heavy beating, and Yan Tongjiang never mentioned the incident.

Sometimes Pu Yi seemed to show a little partiality toward Sun Yaoting, who used to wait on Wanrong and therefore knew the rules and service procedures better than many other eunuchs. When fruit boxes were laid on the table in the evening, Pu Yi might call him over. "Come here, Chunshou, and have some of these. Is it sweet?"

Sun Yaoting went over to pick up a fruit and retreated as soon as he finished eating it.

One day Pu Yi, gnawing at sugarcoated haws on a stick, beckoned him over. "Come and try these," Pu Yi said, pointing to the boiled peanuts and dried fruits on the table.

After expressing his gratitude in the appropriate manner, Sun Yaoting picked up some dried fruits and stuffed them into his mouth. "It's delicious!"

Pu Yi laughed. "Eat as much as you like, but remember this: the fruits are mine, but the stomach is yours!"

There was a swimming pool to the west of the Hall of Mutual Goodwill. In winter the ice on the pool was thick enough to skate over. Whether swimming or skating, Pu Yi liked to have a large company, which sometimes included his sisters and Wanrong. Most of the time he took Sun

Yaoting with him.

"Chunshou, you should not go there without doing anything. I'll give you a pair of ice skates so you can have a try."

"Thanks, Your Majesty, but I can't skate."

"You are not too stupid to learn, are you?"

"Your slave will learn given enough time," Sun Yaoting replied. He did not think he would ever learn to skate, but he knew better than to contradict the Emperor.

At the ice rink Pu Yi skated along with his sisters and other relatives. He had given ice skates to Zhao Yinmao and a few other trusted attendants, who were skilled enough to keep him company on ice. He forgot all about Sun Yaoting until it was time to return. "Did you practice, Chunshou?" he asked.

"Your slave will," Sun Yaoting replied hastily.

If Pu Yi wanted to go for a swim in summer, many servants would have a busy time cleaning the pool before his arrival. He came fully attired, then stripped to his swimming trunks and jumped into the pool. As he could not actually swim, several attendants jumped in after him to act as lifesavers. After flopping about in the pool for some time, he climbed out, put on his sunglasses, and sat down to tan in the sun. Then he caught sight of Sun Yaoting. "Why don't you get into the water?"

"Your slave can't swim."

"You'll learn as soon as we put you in," Pu Yi said in half-jest.

"Please don't." Sun Yaoting stepped back and waved both hands frantically.

After a period of time Pu Yi seemed to think that Sun Yaoting could be trusted and gave him another assignment: escorting the attendants who carried dishes from the kitchen to the table. His responsibility was to prevent food from being poisoned along the way. At that time Pu Yi had only about ten dishes for each meal, in stark contrast to the sumptuous daily feast he had been accustomed to in Beijing.

Sun Yaoting had another routine duty in the morning. At eight o'clock Pu Yi left the Building of Opulence, walked past the Hall of Mutual Goodwill, and entered the Building of Serving the People to begin his "office hours". During the walk he was escorted by a guard of honor holding an incense box with both hands, with Sun Yaoting a few steps ahead. "Premier" Zhang Jinghui and Zhang Haipeng, commander of the guard, greeted Pu Yi at the gate and accompanied him into the building. Having thus discharged his duty, Sun Yaoting went back to the Building of Opulence.

As "Emperor" of Manchukuo Pu Yi had nevertheless few opportunities to wear the Imperial dragon robes brought from Beijing. He had been dressed in military uniform for his enthronement, though the Japanese allowed him to wear the dragon robes when offering sacrifices to the ancestors of the Qing house. On his birthday he would be sitting in his "dragon chair" and dressed in the dragon robes to receive the kowtows of the Qing veterans. Occasionally he would tell Sun Yaoting, "Hang out the dragon robes!" Then he would stand before the dress, gazing at it in silent rapture.

Pu Yi usually wore his admiral's uniform decorated with a silk ribbon and a sword when meeting with Japanese visitors such as Umezu Yoshijiro, commander of the Japanese Guandong Army and his adviser Yoshioka. There was a cloud-borne dragon beside either collar badge. The orchid-pattern "national insignia" of Manchukuo, of Pu Yi's own design, was placed below the national insignia of Japan and flanked by medals awarded by the Japanese, obviously as a gesture of humility. On such occasions Sun Yaoting must dress formally in a sort of uniform with black leather shoes and a hat, standing outside the studio ready to be summoned.

Perhaps due to his lack of proficiency in Japanese, Pu Yi was in the habit of scrawling notes on little pieces of paper when talking with Japanese visitors. Afterward he looked at the notes carefully before burning them up.

One day Yoshioka brought Pu Yi some cookies and fruits, a gift from the Empress Dowager of Japan. Pu Yi sent for Sun Yaoting as soon as the Japanese visitor left.

"Come over," he told Sun Yaoting.

"Yes, Your Majesty. What do you need me to do?"

"Look, you have something to eat here." Pu Yi pointed to a cookie box. "Open it. It is a present from the Empress Dowager of Japan."

Sun Yaoting expressed his gratitude, opened the box, and took it to Pu Yi.

"Try this." Pu Yi picked out a dainty-looking cookie from the box.

Sun Yaoting took the cookie and ate it. "It's so delicious!"

Pu Yi picked out another cookie and watched attentively as Sun Yaoting ate it. At his order Sun Yaoting went on to open the fruit box and eat an apple, a pear, and a few other Japanese fruits. Sun Yaoting finished everything with gusto and kowtowed to thank Pu Yi for his special favor. But Pu Yi had a strange look in his eyes. He scrutinized Sun Yaoting as if he were waiting for something to happen. Several of his nephews who were present also looked at Sun Yaoting in the same quizzical manner.

It took Sun Yaoting a long time to realize what had happened on that day. For fear that the Japanese might want to poison him with the cookies and fruits, Pu Yi wanted someone to taste them first, and a eunuch was of course more expendable than his own nephews. The rage and indignation Sun Yaoting felt could only be expressed in hushed whispers when he was totally alone.

4. Visitors to the Palace

From time to time Sun Yaoting saw Pu Yi sitting in the studio, his eyes closed, doing nothing. Another eunuch told him the Emperor was practicing "meditation". Pu Yi had dabbled in Buddhism and meditation for a long time and sometimes discussed it with foreign visitors. The topic came up when he received two American guests, Dr. Everett and his wife.

Dr. Everett, an eminent legal expert from Chicago, spoke first. "We are greatly honored to be granted an audience by Your Majesty. This city has left us a deep impression with its new outlook."

The young Mrs. Everett disagreed. "I am more impressed by the portrait of Guanyin in Your Majesty's parlor."

Taken by surprise, Pu Yi grunted noncommittally.

Mrs. Everett pursued the topic. "It seems that Your Majesty is interested in studying Buddhism."

"Yes, I like Buddhism and its philosophy. But I also like to learn about other beliefs in foreign countries."

"From what I know," said the young American lady, "foreigners are often drawn to Zen Buddhism, especially its meditation techniques."

Pu Yi's interest was aroused. "I like meditation too. Can you describe how you practice it?"

"Certainly. I learned this method from some Japanese monks. It is a bit different from the Chinese practice. I sit up straight, close my eyes, and clasp my upper lip on my lower lip..."

"When I feel tired, I sometimes close my eyes and sit quietly," Pu Yi said. "After a period of time I feel the nerves in my head gradually relax as I enter the state of stillness. I feel a surge of heat in my torso, and it goes on to permeate my entire body. Does the same phenomenon occur during your meditation?"

"Yes, it does. Does Your Majesty breathe deeply during meditation?"

"Yes, I breathe deeply when I enter the state of stillness."

With Mrs. Everett and Pu Yi engaged in an animated conversation, her husband could not get a word in edgewise. But she seemed unaware of it. "The Japanese monks teach people to do deep breathing very forcefully. It is important to note that different forces are applied for inhaling and exhaling. One should use his chest to inhale and his abdomen to exhale."

"Whatever method is used, the basic theory remains 'One'," Pu Yi concluded. "In other words, the cosmetic truth lies in 'One'."

Whether she knew what Pu Yi was saying, Mrs. Everett said she couldn't agree with him more. "Foreigners generally believe in the theory of oneness," she remarked.

Just then another guest was announced, and Pu Yi had to say good-bye to the Everetts. "When will be your next trip to the Orient?"

It was Mrs. Everett who answered the question. "Maybe after two years."

"Welcome to visit me again. We can have another chat on meditation."

Despite his fascination with Buddhist meditation, Pu Yi had difficulty controlling his temper. Perhaps there were so many unpleasant things on his mind that he had to vent his anger and frustration from time to time. More often than not the eunuchs took the brunt of his outbursts.

When Sun Yaoting learned that Zai Tao, together with Prince Li, had come to Manchukuo for a short stay in the palace, he decided to go and greet his former master, who had been treating him fairly well. After mealtime Sun Yaoting went over and found Zai Tao rinsing his mouth in the hairdressing room. Zai Tao caught sight of him. "Hey, isn't this Chunshou!"

"Yes! I come especially to greet you, master!" Sun Yaoting saluted him by kneeling on one knee.

"Get up, get up," Zai Tao extended a hand. "Good for you, Chunshou! You still remember me!"

"Of course! I will never forget your favor!"

Little did Sun Yaoting expect that his gesture of loyalty should displease Pu Yi, who summoned him to the studio in the Building of Opulence the same day. "Did you meet anyone today?"

Sun Yaoting was puzzled. "Whom is Your Majesty talking about?"

"You went to see Zai Tao, didn't you?"

"Yes, your slave did." Sun Yaoting could not understand why Pu Yi should feel so upset about his own uncle.

"What did you do?"

"I made my obeisances."

"Did you make your obeisances to anyone else?"

"No, no one else was present."

"What about Prince Li?"

"Oh, I did not see him. Your slave doesn't know him."

"Then why did you go to see Zai Tao?"

"Your Majesty, I used to work in his house. He is my former master."

"What did you say to him?"

"Nothing. I just went over to pay my respects."

"What did he say to you?"

"He told me to wait on Your Majesty wholeheartedly."

"That is all he said?"

"Yes, that is all he said."

Walking out of the Building of Opulence, Sun Yaoting felt troubled. Apparently an ill-intentioned servant had reported him to Pu Yi. And it was pathetic the way Pu Yi held such a strong mistrust for his own uncle. On the other hand, Pu Yi did not show the same suspicion against Zai Tao's son Pu An. When he was a young eunuch in Zai Tao's house, Sun Yaoting used to play with Pu An, who was a few years his junior. Now that Pu An had come to stay in the palace of Manchukuo, Sun Yaoting also went over to greet him.

"Oh, I didn't know you are here," Pu An said in surprise.

"How have you been all these years?"

"Not too bad."

"I've always remembered your favor." Sun Yaoting was talking of a small incident that had happened many years before. While serving tea, he dropped and broke the teacup. It was of course a terrible thing to do for a servant, but Pu An dismissed it with a sweep of his hand. "It doesn't matter. Just clean up and bring another cup." Sun Yaoting was thus exempted from punishment.

"It's nothing," Pu An said.

"If you need me to do anything for you, just tell me."

Though he learned of this meeting between Sun Yaoting and Pu An, Pu Yi did not seem to mind and never even mentioned it.

One day Pu Yi summoned Sun Yaoting to the studio. "Get ready. I may go to Japan one of these days, and I'll take you with me. Understand?"

"Yes. Your slave will always be at Your Majesty's service."

Pu Yi's words gave Sun Yaoting a little something to hope for. After all, he had never been abroad. But somehow this hope never materialized.

5. A Brutal Beating

Before coming to Manchukuo Sun Yaoting had heard about Wanrong's affair from Zhao Rongsheng. It seemed to be an open secret in the palace of the New Capital. One day he dragged Zhao into his room and asked him to tell the whole story. "Who's the man with Wanrong?"

"It's one of your acquaintances."

"Really? I can't believe I know someone so audacious! Adultery with the Empress is punishable by dismemberment!"

"It's Li Tiyu," Zhao said in a whisper.

"Are you sure? He's the one who did it?"

"Hush, please, for heaven's sake! If anyone hears us, we'll be in big trouble."

"I remember him well. We used to play together at the nine-dragon tablet in front of the Palace of Peaceful Longevity. He was only fourteen or fifteen years old then."

"He was caught in the act, you know, and the Emperor almost had him shot on the spot. But in the end the Emperor pardoned him and let him return to Beijing."

Talking about the incident many years afterward, Sun Yaoting held that Pu Yi should take the blame for what happened. Deprived of her conjugal rights because Pu Yi was either unable or unwilling to fulfill the duties of a husband, Wanrong sought solace elsewhere. In great distress she took to opium smoking and soon became addicted. Meanwhile Pu Yi was reputedly having clandestine relationships with several eunuchs and male attendants. One of his favorites was Li Tiyu, a handsome male attendant who had entered the palace as a child. He took Li to Manchukuo and had him keep night watch in the medicine room next to Wanrong's bedchamber. According to rumors, Pu Yi had set them up in order to silence Wanrong, who was probably aware of his sexual eccentricities. Anyway, Wanrong and Li Tiyu fell for each other and carried on until she got pregnant. Late one night, Yan Tongjiang and his men waited outside the door of Wanrong's bedchamber and caught Li walking out in his underwear. They took him to Pu Yi.

"Your Majesty, let's shoot him!" Yan Tongjiang suggested.

"The Japanese soldiers would rush in at the gunshot," Pu Yi said. "That would be difficult to handle."

"How shall we deal with him then?" The attendants asked eagerly, ready to spring on Li and beat him to a pulp.

"Let him go."

The attendants could hardly believe their own ears. "What?"

"Let him go!" Pu Yi repeated, then disappeared into the inner room. And that was the end of the incident.

Shortly after his arrival in Manchukuo Sun Yaoting was made to spend a night in the medicine storeroom. Feeling nervous, he tossed and turned in bed, unable to go to sleep. At around five o'clock in the morning, he heard Pu Yi walking upstairs and hurried over to salute him. "Go back and get some sleep," Pu Yi said simply and walked into his own bedroom.

This was the only time Sun Yaoting kept night watch in the medicine room. It seemed that Pu Yi had arranged it to test his loyalty. As he had waited on Wanrong before, Pu Yi wanted to find out whether he would talk with her or pass messages for her. Incredible as it may sound, Sun Yaoting saw Wanrong only once during his stay in Manchukuo. She was dressed in a cheongsam, looking as beautiful as ever. But when Sun Yaoting went up to salute her, she ignored him and walked straight into Pu Yi's room. He vaguely remembered it was her birthday that day.

Sun Yaoting did his best to establish himself in the good graces of Pu Yi. On a cold winter day Pu Yi told his male attendants to bring him a hot towel, but they could not make the towel hot even by pouring boiling water on it. One of them came to Sun Yaoting for help. "Please tell me how to do it, or I'll soon get a beating!"

"All right, I won't keep it a secret," Sun Yaoting said. "Watch carefully." He folded the towel several times, lifted it up by two corners, and poured hot water in the middle. Then he folded it backward and wrung it quickly. "You see? Do not unfold it until you take it to His Majesty."

Thus the attendants were able to bring steaming hot towels to Pu Yi. When he found out how they had learned to do it, Pu Yi scolded them, calling them "a bunch of morons".

For all his hard work and vigilance Sun Yaoting failed to keep himself away from harm. One day a eunuch named Gao Zhenpu cleaned the bathroom with a cotton flannel which, according to the rules, must be washed daily and used for no other purpose than wiping tables. Sun Yaoting noticed Gao's mistake but did not intervene for fear of getting himself into trouble. Unfortunately three male attendants, Zhao Jiantao, Qi Yuan and Wang Jizhou found out about it. "Did you know what he was doing?" they questioned him. After a long silence, he admitted reluctantly that he did.

"Put out your hand!" The three attendants took turns beating his palm with a bamboo plank until it turned black and blue. Wang Shiqing, who happened to walk by, saw what the attendants were doing and rushed to inform Pu Yi. "Your Majesty, they are beating Chunshou to death!"

"What?" Pu Yi at once walked downstairs with Wang Shiqing. "Your Majesty!" Sun Yaoting knelt and kowtowed repeatedly. "Please have mercy!" But Zhao Jiantao slapped him so hard that blood oozed out of his mouth.

"What do you think you are doing?" Pu Yi gave Zhao an angry glare. "How dare you keep beating him when he's speaking to us?"

At this Yan Tongjiang and Li Guoxiong, who had followed Pu Yi downstairs, rushed over and clubbed Zhao to the ground.

"Have mercy, Your Majesty! Have mercy!" It was Zhao's turn to moan and wail.

"All right, that's enough." With a sweep of his hand, Pu Yi turned and walked away.

Sun Yaoting happened to be on duty that night in the outer room of Pu Yi's bedchamber. Li Guoxiong came out and told him, "Go and tidy up the inner room for His Majesty."

"I'm afraid I can't do it! My hands are killing me!" Sun Yaoting spread out his bruised hands. He could hardly bend his fingers, which were all terribly swollen.

"What's the matter?" Pu Yi walked over to them.

"Your Majesty, he can't do things because his hands hurt," Li Guoxiong replied.

"Look what they've done!" Pu Yi went to the inner room and returned with a bottle of medicinal oil, which he smeared on Sun Yaoting's hands. "This is a pain reliever. You'll feel better soon. I'll get someone else to clean the room."

Back in his room, Sun Yaoting lay down to rest. After a while he felt itchy in his throat. Then he began to cough and spit blood. Another eunuch passed the news to the male attendants, and a moment later Imperial physician Dong Kuoquan arrived with his stethoscope.

"His Majesty has sent me to take a look at you." Dong gave Sun Yaoting a careful check-up. "You must look after yourself. Don't take it too lightly!"

"What's the matter with me, Dr. Dong?"

"Well," Dong hesitated. "I'll have to report to His Majesty first." He went to see Pu Yi at the Building of Opulence. He attributed Sun Yaoting's illness to "attack of liver by blood heat". "He cannot attend to Your Majesty anymore. Better let him return to the capital."

"Give him this." Pu Yi took out a bottle of medicine and handed it to Dong.

Dong came back to see Sun Yaoting in his room. "His Majesty has given you this medicine. Take it in two doses."

After that, Duo Lianyuan moved into Sun Yaoting's room and even Yan Tongjiang often came to see how he was doing. One day the telephone rang, and Duo picked it up. "Can Chunshou get up to answer the phone?" Pu Yi asked at the other end of the line.

"His Majesty wants to know if you can get up," Duo turned to Sun Yaoting.

"Yes, I can!" Sun Yaoting struggled out of bed to get the phone. "Your slave Chunshou salutes Your Majesty!"

"Are you feeling better?"

"Yes, a little bit better." Actually there had been no improvement in Sun Yaoting's conditions.

"Don't worry too much. If you like to eat anything, tell Duo to get it for you from the kitchen. If you want any fruit, let him get it from the tearoom."

"A thousand thanks from your slave! Maybe it's asking too much, but when I get well, I'd like to visit the capital again..." Sun Yaoting said tentatively.

"I'll give you the leave when you get well!" Pu Yi agreed readily, much to Sun Yaoting's surprise.

Sun Yaoting tried hard to suppress his excitement. Soon he would be able to return to Beijing! Without telling anyone, he began to pack up his luggage.

It snowed heavily in the New Capital in the third lunar month. One day Yan Tongjiang brought three pieces of watermelon. "This is for you," he said, "from His Majesty. It's good for reducing internal heat."

Sun Yaoting asked Yan to pass on his gratitude to the Emperor. But in his heart he was longing to leave.

6. Back at Home

Having more or less recovered from his injury, Sun Yaoting went back on duty. While attending to Pu Yi at mealtime, he suddenly felt itchy in his throat. He hurried out of the room and broke into a violent coughing fit. Pu Yi looked up. "Is Chunshou coughing outside?"

When Sun Yaoting was brought in, Pu Yi said, "You should see a doctor, you know."

"Yes, Your Majesty."

Sun Yaoting returned to his room, and a moment later Dr. Dong arrived. "Give me your hand." After feeling his pulse, Dong said, "You are really ill." Then he left without giving any explanation.

The next day Dr. Dong came to see Pu Yi. Pointing at Sun Yaoting, he said, "I am afraid he can no longer wait on Your Majesty!"

"Take him to the hospital," Pu Yi said promptly.

Sun Yaoting was sent back to his own room. Pu Yi, it seemed, was worried that his disease might be infectious. After a while Yan Tongjiang came. "His Majesty will send you to the Japanese hospital to have a final diagnosis. If you can get well quickly, His Majesty won't have to recruit more eunuchs from the capital. It's not easy to find someone who can do a good job!"

Accompanied by a eunuch named Wang Jianzhai, Sun Yaoting rode a horse-drawn carriage to the Japanese hospital. They had known each other well in Beijing, but Wang remained silent all along the way and when waiting for their turn at the hospital. When Sun Yaoting's name was called, Wang went in with him. A Japanese doctor told Sun Yaoting to take off his shoes and lie down. The doctor began by knocking on his chest and under his arms, then checked his lungs with the stethoscope. "What's wrong with me, doctor?" Sun Yaoting asked as the Japanese sat down to write his diagnosis.

"The first stage of lung disease," the doctor replied in awkward Chinese.

Back in the palace Sun Yaoting was given a single room to stay the night. Early the next morning Yang Tongjiang came. "His Majesty has granted you a leave. Do you want to return to the capital or Tianjin?"

After a moment's hesitation Sun Yaoting said, "My younger brother is collecting and selling scraps in Tianjin. I'd like to go and see him before I return to Beijing."

"It's up to you," Yan said curtly.

"Could you pass on a message to His Majesty for me?"

"Well, what is it?"

"I...I'd like to ask His Majesty for a favor. When I go home, I'll need a little money for my treatment."

"All right, I'll speak to His Majesty for you." Yan left and soon came back. "His Majesty gives you five hundred dollars. You can get the money from Pu Xiu in Tianjin. Is it clear?"

Sun Yaoting bowed deeply. "Thank you so much. And please pass on my gratitude to His Majesty. I cannot go and pay my respects because of my lung disease."

"That's no problem. You'll have to leave today."

"Yes!"

Xi Qia, Minister of Pu Yi's inner court, issued a so-called "cross-border certificate" for Sun Yaoting. It bore the letterhead of the Inner Court of Manchukuo and was stamped with Xi Qia's official seal. Without it Sun Yaoting would be unable to leave Manchukuo or even the New Capital.

Yan Tongjiang had a train ticket bought for Sun Yaoting and sent him to the station in a car, escorted by Wang Jianzhai. Just before the train started, Wang finally broke the silence. "When you get back to Beijing, give my regards to Mr. Chen."

"I will. When I am fully recovered, I will come back to serve His Majesty."

Wang said nothing to that.

Sun Yaoting arrived in Tianjin and collected the five hundred dollars. Though in banknotes instead of silver coins, they were good money. At that time a large sack of flour cost only five dollars.

Sun Yaoting left Tianjin for Jinghai County to enjoy a happy reunion with his parents. But life was hard in the poverty-stricken family. To add insult to injury, the attitude of some villagers made him feel ostracized. He was constantly reminded that he was different from "normal" people, an outcast or freak. Occasionally he received visitors curious about life in the Imperial Palace, but he felt reluctant to go over the past, especially his hapless days in Manchukuo.

The arrival of Japanese troops in Jinghai County shattered the peaceful life of the villagers. A few Japanese soldiers stormed into Sun Yaoting's house and dragged away his younger brother, who was made to gather grass to feed horses. Then came another team of soldiers armed with bayonets. "Chickens? Eggs?" They searched the house thoroughly but failed to find any chicken or eggs, so they decided to take away a calf.

Listening to the calf's mooing, Sun Yaoting leapt to his feet to confront the Japanese soldiers. "The calf is mine! You can't take it away!"

"Who are you?" The Japanese soldiers pointed their bayonets at him.

"I am a eunuch," Sun Yaoting said. "That calf is mine."

"Eunuch? What's that?" The Japanese soldiers did not know enough Chinese to understand the word.

Just then an interpreter came up. "Hey, what are you doing? Talking nonsense to the Japanese masters?" At this the soldiers raised their bayonets.

"I've just come back from Manchukuo!" Sun Yaoting hastily explained. "The Kangde Emperor has given me five hundred dollars to treat my illness!"

The interpreter whispered a few words to the Japanese, who looked at Sun Yaoting doubtfully and shook their heads. Sun Yaoting hurried back into the house to get the "certificate" issued by Xi Qia. "Here, take a look at this!"

The Japanese soldiers peered into the paper and dropped their bayonets at once. "You, very good!" They smiled at him and put up their thumbs. Sun Yaoting reclaimed his calf and a donkey that the Japanese had taken from another household. The next morning the Japanese sent the interpreter to see Sun Yaoting with a box of cookies. They wanted his second brother to be their road guide. Naturally Sun Yaoting dared not refuse.

The owner of the donkey soon showed up and went straight to unfasten the reins. At the sight of him Sun Yaoting was filled with rage. It was none other than a nephew of Shang Buyin, the long-time enemy of the Sun family. "What's your name?" he asked deliberately.

"My name's Shang." The man was taken aback. "This donkey is mine."

"Oh really? Why don't you pause to ask who took it back for you? You were too much of a chicken to go to the Japanese yourself, weren't you? I won't let you touch it!" Sun Yaoting's heart was burning with anger as he remembered how the Shang family had sent his father to prison on a trumped-up charge.

"If you want the donkey back, tell Shang Buyin to come and get it himself!" said Sun Yaoting's brother.

For fear that the dispute would attract the attention of Japanese soldiers, several villagers came over to mediate. Sun Yaoting finally agreed to let Shang take the donkey away after paying ten silver dollars as compensation fee.

Before long many people in Jinghai County were talking about the story of "a eunuch dispelling Japanese soldiers with a piece of paper". Sun Yaoting's family gained a certain status in the village because of the incident. However, he grew increasingly worried as the Japanese often came to visit him. "I must get out of here," he told himself, "or I would become a collaborator of the Japanese sooner or later!" He bade his family good-bye and left for Beijing.

10

SOME TURBULENT YEARS

1. An Amicable Japanese

On the train to Beijing Sun Yaoting considered what to do next. With little money and no place he could call his own, he did not really have much of a choice. He would go back to the Temple of Prosperity to get three meals a day and a bed to sleep in at night. Moreover, he had a few eunuch friends there.

The train pulled in at Beijing's Yongdingmen Railway Station, which was heavily guarded by armed Japanese soldiers. After getting off, Sun Yaoting headed for the Temple of Prosperity on foot. The temple remained more or less the same, though its gate looked battered after years of neglect.

Ma Deqing seemed to be in better spirits than when they last saw each other in Manchukuo. "You must be having a good time here!" Sun Yaoting said.

"Not really. I've been working for Zha Qi'er."

Fortunately, Chen Zechuan was still in the temple, occupying three south-facing rooms. He had a kitchen and hired an old man named He as a cook. Sun Yaoting moved into the outer section of Chen's bedroom. Once again they began to spend a lot of time together.

"Why are you back?" asked a eunuch named Zhang. "At least you had enough to eat over there!"

"I did have enough to eat, but the hardships were too much for me to bear!"

"Well, though you suffered a little bit, the Emperor awarded you five hundred dollars. You've returned home in honor!"

"What kind of honor is it?" Sun Yaoting retorted. "I wouldn't have gone there in the first place if I had known any better. Well, they are still short of eunuchs now. I can recommend you if you really want to go to Manchukuo!"

Sun Yaoting did not cherish any fond memories of the puppet regime. Sorting through his belongings one day, he found his Manchukuo uniform and insignia. He wrapped them up and sent the package all the way back to the "New Capital".

At Liu Ziyu's invitation, Sun Yaoting went to visit him at his house on Cuihua Alley, where Liu lived together with his wife, son, daughter-in-law and grandson. Liu's wife was a simple peasant woman who treated Sun Yaoting with warmth and kindness. Soon he became a frequent visitor at the house. They often played mahjong late into the night. Once, he was sitting on the kang playing mahjong when Liu's daughter-in-law came into the room. She took up his shoes, measured them, then went away. When Sun Yaoting called at the house a few days later, she took out a pair of brand-new cloth shoes. "Try them on."

Sun Yaoting put on the shoes. "They are a perfect fit!" he exclaimed in delight.

The Cuihua Alley was close to the booming market area of Dongsi. When Sun Yaoting came to visit, Liu often took his grandson to the market to buy some fish and shrimps as a special treat.

Liu was on medication for a chronic heart problem. A few days before New Year's Eve, he suddenly died of a heart attack at the age of fifty-five. Sun Yaoting went to help Liu's wife with the mourning and funeral proceedings. As head of the Accounting Office, Liu enjoyed high prestige among eunuchs. Many came to offer condolences, and the house hosted the mourners for several days on end. A grand sacrificial ceremony was held, supervised by Xin Xiuming and attended by hundreds of people.

Liu's coffin was transported by train back to his hometown, Changzhou. When the train stopped in Tianjin on its way, Xiaode Zhang set up a huge "roadside sacrificial shed" at Tianjin Railway Station and went in person to offer his condolences. This unusual display of friendship became a topic of widespread comment among eunuchs. Sun Yaoting believed he knew the reason why Zhang felt so indebted to Liu Ziyu. They both belonged to a group of forty eunuchs recruited by the Imperial Palace at the same time. Zhang used to be a reckless gambler. Once he sat playing at the mahjong table for a whole day and night. Being in bad luck, he kept losing and even had to borrow money from the banker. At the end of the game he owed three thousand dollars that he must pay immediately, so he went to ask Liu's help. "I lost a few rounds and must pay the money now. What shall I do?"

"Take it easy," Liu comforted him. "How much did you lose?"

"Over three thousand!" Zhang replied sadly. "I'll have to go to the pawnshop."

"No need to. I have the money." Liu counted out three thousand dollars and gave them to Zhang.

After that, Zhang considered Liu a true friend. One day Liu persuaded him to quit gambling. "If you listen to me, stop playing the game. It's no good for you!"

"All right, I'll give it up!" Zhang made a solemn pledge. Being a strong-willed person, he never sat down at a mahjong table again. Years later he was appointed Chief Superintendent of all palace eunuchs. He proclaimed a ban on gambling and often conducted checks against violations. By his recommendation Liu Ziyu received successive promotions until he finally became head of the Accounting Office. Zhang respected Liu for his great learning, while Liu admired Zhang's agile mind and practical abilities.

After Liu Ziyu's death his widowed wife moved to Qianzhai Alley on Nanchang Street not far from the Temple of Prosperity. Sun Yaoting often went to see her. He was also a frequent visitor at the houses of Xin Xiuming and Wang Shunshan. Like Liu Ziyu, Xin enjoyed fine food but abstained from drinking. Sun Yaoting felt quite at home in his house. If he happened to come at mealtime, Xin would surely invite him to eat together with the family. Wang Shunshan, on the other hand, never treated him to a single meal, and he learned to avoid mealtime on his visit.

By the time the Japanese troops entered Beijing, there were few well-to-do eunuchs left. Those at the Temple of Prosperity were mostly hard up. Some gathered and sold junks to earn a few extra cents. Some picked cigarette stubs in the street and wrapped the tobacco into "homemade" cigarettes, which they peddled. In winter many kept warm by burning coal cinder that they had been collecting in the street. They were all raggedly dressed on ordinary days, but for special occasions a few eunuchs might have a decent-looking long gown that had not yet found its way to the pawnshop. If a windfall happened to come their way, they usually blew it on gambling, smoking or drinking.

"Things have changed a little bit after the coming of the Japanese," Chen cautioned Sun Yaoting. "You'd better be careful when they are around."

"Yes, I understand."

"A Japanese named Hina is now in charge of all the temples and monasteries in Beijing. He seems to be quite amiable and enjoys chatting with us, for he knows we used to live in the Forbidden City. I'll introduce you the next time he comes, but remember to watch your tongue."

"If he is really concerned about the temple, why don't we ask him for a favor?"

"What kind of favor?"

"This temple looks so old and shabby inside and out. Maybe we can ask him to have it repainted."

Some days later Hina came to the temple, wearing a gray kimono and a pair of glasses. He spoke fluent Chinese and smiled courteously to everyone he met.

Hina greeted Chen Zechuan politely as he walked into the room. "Who is this?" he pointed to Sun Yaoting.

"This is my disciple," Chen said. "You can call him Chunshou."

Hina greeted Sun Yaoting in the old style, bowing slightly with clasped hands. After they had been talking for a while, Chen said, "Mr. Hina, you and I are good friends. Now look at the doors and windows of the temple. They are in such a sorry state. Can you have them painted?"

"Yes, that's no problem." Hina agreed with alacrity.

A few days later several workmen hired by Hina arrived. They erected scaffolding and started to paint the temple. At the end of two weeks the place looked almost brand-new. Because of this, Supervisor Liu paid Chen Zechuan a visit to express his thanks. "You are truly remarkable! Using the Japanese to refurbish our temple! What a feat!"

Sun Yaoting was chatting with Chen in the room when Zha Qi'er came. He was tall and had an oval face with regular features. He was wearing a bronze-colored silk gown, a satin sleeveless jacket and a pair of well-polished leather shoes.

"Mr. Zha, you've come to honor me with your presence!" Chen stood up to greet his guest. "Please take a seat."

Zha Qi'er slumped into the seat of honor without bothering to decline by way of modesty, then he noticed Sun Yaoting. "Who is he?"

"Let me introduce my disciple Sun Yaoting. He's just come back from Manchukuo." Chen turned to Sun Yaoting. "Come over and meet the eminent Mr. Zha Qi'er!"

"You're back from Manchukuo?" Zha asked.

"Yes. I came back not long ago."

"How are things going in Manchukuo? And what about the little Emperor, Xuantong?"

Sun Yaoting tried his best to answer the question, but Zha suddenly interrupted him. "Tell me, what did you do in Manchukuo?"

"He waited on Xuantong," Chen said.

"Really?" Zha turned to look at Sun Yaoting with growing interest. Sun Yaoting was neatly dressed, well mannered, and had an honest-looking face.

"I worked with a team of orderlies in the inner court for some time, then I was assigned to wait on His Majesty. My job was to tidy up his rooms."

"So you waited on the Emperor? How much did you get paid?"

Aware that Zha might want to hire him, Sun Yaoting decided to tell a lie. "I received forty dollars a month." Actually his monthly stipend was only twelve dollars.

"Forty dollars?" Zha sneered with a look of disdain. "But you could ask the Emperor for tips on festivals, couldn't you?"

"Well, yes."

"You could come and work in my house, you know," Zha finally said.

This was exactly what Sun Yaoting had been hoping for, but he showed no sign of excitement. He had already learned to conceal his feelings behind a placid face. Instead of giving a prompt reply, he turned to look at Chen inquisitively.

"Are you planning to return to Manchukuo?" Chen asked.

"No, I am definitely not going back. What's your advice?"

"Well, if you are not going back to Manchukuo, you might as well work for Mr. Zha. By the way, in his house you will meet an old acquaintance of yours, An Kuoting."

A couple of days later Sun Yaoting left the temple and began to work for Zha Qi'er.

2. Zha Qi'er

With its giant red gate and stone terrace, the house looked imposing on the narrow Wulao Alley outside the Qianmen archway. According to Zha Qi'er, his great grandfather, Zha Shibiao, was an accomplished scholar appointed to Chief Supervisor of the metropolitan civil service examination at the age of twenty-two. The family suffered a great setback when the Imperial Court sent guards to search their house and confiscate all their property. The exact cause for such heavy penalty was unknown. Maybe Zha had abused his office for personal gains or unwittingly offended a powerful courtier. Anyway, Zha Qi'er enjoyed talking about his learned ancestor as if to make up for his total lack of education.

During the reign of Empress Dowager Cixi the Zha family staged a financial comeback. Zha Qi'er's father got in touch with a distant relative who was a court minister, and through him offered an extravagant "present" to Cixi. The Empress Dowager gave the Zha family a handsome reward: monopoly of salt trades in Beijing and Xushui County in central Hebei. Such a monopoly meant enormous profits for the most inane businessman, and the Zha family soon accumulated huge wealth. Zha Qi'er grew up to be a typical profligate son, with no business acumen but accustomed to wanton extravagance. In addition to a number of ordinary servants, he already had two eunuchs to wait on him before Sun Yaoting came.

Apart from the Imperial Palace, only the Northern Mansion and a few high-ranking Manchu princes employed eunuchs as house servants in the dozen years after the 1911 Revolution. The situation changed abruptly after the mass dispersal of eunuchs in 1923. It then became fashionable for rich households in Beijing to hire eunuchs. For one thing, it did one's ego good to be waited on by eunuchs "just like an Emperor". Furthermore, it was customary for a rich man to have several concubines. Hiring eunuchs instead of male servants in the house seemed a good way to forestall undesirable liaisons.

The other two eunuchs in Zha's house, An Kuoting and Ma Deqing, had their own specific duties. An's job was to light opium pipes for Zha and his wives, and Ma was responsible for overseeing the meal service. As a personal attendant, Sun Yaoting must put himself at Zha's beck and call until bedtime, which usually meant after midnight.

The house radiated immense wealth. The spacious dining room was well lit and had an expensive marble-top table. At the corner stood a refrigerator, a rare luxury item at the time. Zha had a team of house servants: three nannies to look after the children, a few cooks and odd-job men, and a chauffeur. It took only a few days for Sun Yaoting to realize that Zha was a hopeless spendthrift. He devoted his time to mahjong and opium, paying little attention to his finances.

Zha Qi'er had two high-flying friends who lived close by, Lu Yongchun and Feng Gongdu. Lu owned a hospital named after him, and Feng was the founder of a trolley-bus company. They often got together in Zha's house to play mahjong. In some way Zha seemed to bear a striking resemblance to Pu Yi. For one thing, they both stayed up late into the night. In the evening Zha usually smoked a potent dose of opium, ate some snacks, then played mahjong or engaged in other pleasure activities until early morning. Getting up at noon, he sat down to enjoy a sumptuous meal, then left home on a pleasure trip in town.

At his new job Sun Yaoting had plenty of leisure time. He was free to do whatever he wanted after Zha settled down at the mahjong table or went to bed. But he must be careful in carrying out his special "night duty". He usually took a nap after supper and got up at eleven, when Zha would need his company. Zha was then smoking opium in bed, with his second concubine lying at his feet. Sun Yaoting sat down on a stool beside the bed to chat with the flirting couple or tell them stories. "He is having a better time than the Emperor!" Sun Yaoting said to himself. "But things like this will not last."

Zha had every reason to adore his second concubine. His principal wife only bore him a daughter. While he was too busy enjoying himself to care about it, his mother grew extremely worried that he had yet no son to carry on the family line. She began to nag him constantly until it became a standing joke in the household, with the humiliating implication that he was perhaps unable to sire a son. However, all clouds were cleared after he married his second concubine, who gave birth to five sons and a daughter.

It was mainly to show off his wealth that Zha Qi'er hired the three eunuchs, who therefore enjoyed higher status than the other house servants. They ate fairly well, with their meal delivered to their room by a cook. Each of them had two dishes and a soup, and the menu varied from time to time. Sun Yaoting, An Kuoting and Ma Deqing had never been so pampered before. "We used to wait on the Emperor, but now we feel like an Emperor!" they joked. Every month Zha gave them two or three special treats. Sun Yaoting would be delighted when Zha gestured toward the drawer where he kept his money. "You'll treat us to mutton hotpot, master?"

"Good guess! Count out seven dollars. The three of you can go and eat your fill."

Festivals meant additional dishes for the servants. Zha showed up at mealtime and told them to order their favorite dish. "What do you want to eat this time?"

"Could we have roast duck, master?"

"Of course! Now tell me, which shop do you prefer?"

"The shop at Houmenqiao is quite famous."

"All right, we'll get our duck from there."

Sun Yaoting rushed to the shop and returned with a big fat roast duck. As the eunuchs worked on it busily, Zha looked on with great satisfaction. Again Sun Yaoting was struck by the similarity between Zha Qi'er and Pu Yi. They both enjoyed watching the servants gobbling up food at their expense. "How does it taste? Is it good?" Zha kept asking.

"Meat dumplings are better," an old servant woman blurted out.

"It's real good!" Sun Yaoting said hastily. "Fresh from the oven!" He munched his food to make a big noise, knowing it would please Zha. Well into his forties, Sun Yaoting had learned to observe other people, take his cue, and ingratiate himself with the master.

As Zha spent money like water while neglecting his business, his financial situation kept going downhill. He began to sell his housing property and cut daily expenses. The three eunuchs, hired as a luxury, took the brunt of this drawback. They were no longer served three meals a day but had to pay for their own food. Zha gave them an extra fifteen dollars a month each, saying, "Now you can go out and buy whatever you like." But the food stipend was canceled soon afterward. Disappointed, both An Kuoting and Ma Deqing went away on leave to take shelter at a temple, with no intention to return. Sun Yaoting got anxious and went to see Zha. "Master, I have to go. I can't cope all by myself."

"No, you can't leave me! There'd be no one left in this house!"

"Well, if you want me to stay, I have a suggestion for you."

"What suggestion?"

"Both An and Ma have been with you for many years. If you go on paying them even after they leave, you will gain a big reputation in the capital! Besides, whenever you need them, you only have to say the word to get them back. It won't cost you a lot, either. Just skip a couple of trips to the restaurant!"

"All right." Much as Sun Yaoting had expected, Zha found it difficult to say no when faced with such flattery.

Sun Yaoting had planned his words carefully. He was afraid that An Kuoting and Ma Deqing might speak ill of him to other eunuchs; after all, they had been with Zha for much longer than he. Zha's agreement to pay An and Ma even after they stopped working for him created quite a sensation among the eunuchs in the capital.

The Japanese surrender in 1945 was followed by a few more turbulent years. Inflation gathered momentum as the national economy continually deteriorated. Even wealthy people had difficulty maintaining their extravagant lifestyle. Sun Yaoting did not know what to do with his savings kept in the Xincheng Bank. He went to a black market at Baitasi where one could buy silver dollars with banknotes. In the early morning a silver coin sold for a hundred dollars, but the price kept rising until it reached five hundred dollars at nightfall. This seemed to indicate that buying silver coins would be a good way of investment. However, Zha disagreed. "Why do you want to buy silver dollars? The *Fabi* is quite reliable!"

Sun Yaoting took Zha's advice and bought some Fabi, the paper currency issued by the Kuomingtang government. A few days later the drastic devaluation of Fabi caused him to lose a sizable amount of money. After that he grew more cautious. From several people, he learned that while everything else seemed to be depreciating, the market value of gold remained quite stable. When he was on a trip to Tianjin to buy silk and moon cake for Zha, a shop assistant gave him a useful tip. "The price of gold will rise to three thousand dollars a tael after the Mid-Autumn Festival!" At that time gold was selling for only a thousand a tael. Back in Beijing, he told the news to Zha, who got very excited. "I'll buy some gold!" he declared. Having just sold a house, he happened to have ready money.

"How much do you want to buy?" Sun Yaoting asked.

"How reliable is the news?"

Sun Yaoting repeated what he had heard in Tianjin. Zha picked up the

The White-Pagoda Temple

phone and called Liu, an assistant manager of Xincheng Bank. "Mr. Liu, I'd like to buy some gold."

"How much do you plan to buy?"

"Please come over. I'd like to talk with you about it."

Liu came and explained the situation to Zha Qi'er and Sun Yaoting. Zha decided to buy ten gold bars, then he changed his mind and bought only five. Sun Yaoting spent all his savings on four taels of gold. After the Mid-Autumn Festival the price of gold surged as had been expected. Overjoyed, Zha sold all his gold bars immediately and went out in his car to have to good time. Sun Yaoting, on the other hand, tucked away his four taels for a rainy day.

Near the year-end Sun Yaoting was forced to leave Zha's house after an unfortunate incident. Some days before, Zha had hired another eunuch, Dai Shouchen. He did not find Dai to his liking and wanted to fire him. As he could find no excuse for doing so, he sent for Sun Yaoting and told him to pick up a fight with Dai.

Dai Shouchen had never set foot in the Forbidden City but had been a house servant for several Manchu princes. After he came to work for Zha, he shared a room with Sun Yaoting. Somehow the two of them did not get along. With Zha's instigation their verbal clashes escalated until a fistfight broke out. Being taller and stronger, Dai gained the upper hand at first and threw Sun Yaoting to the ground. Sun Yaoting sprang to his feet and grabbed Dai by the waist. They fell to the ground and rolled in the dust. Both of them got hurt in the scuffle.

Much to Sun Yaoting's dismay, Zha Qi'er did not put all the blame on Dai as he had promised. For some reason he wanted to get rid of Sun Yaoting too and used the fistfight as an excuse to fire both eunuchs. Dai immediately left for the Temple of Prosperity. To stay away from him, Sun Yaoting took shelter at the Temple of Genuine Prowess on Biandan Alley. At the news Chen Zechuan came to visit him. "You are too young and impetuous. Well, just stay here for a while and try to decide what you want to do next."

"Zha Qi'er is such a bastard!" Sun Yaoting said, still fuming with anger. "I no longer hold anything against Dai because Zha is the real villain. We both fell into his trap!"

"You must have heard the saying, 'In a big forest there are all sorts of birds'. Don't take it to heart. As I get on in years, fewer things can really upset me."

Sun Yaoting found a little solace in Chen's words. As he grew older, he became increasingly attuned to this attitude of quiet resignation toward life.

3. Silver Fish and Purple Crabs

Three days before the Lunar New Year An Kuoting suddenly showed up at the Temple of the Genuine Prowess. "How have you been these days?" he greeted Sun Yaoting warmly.

"Just so-so," Sun Yaoting replied. "What business has brought you here? As they say, 'one never visits the temple without a reason'. What do you want from me?"

"Well, I've come to..." An stumbled on his words.

"Come on, I'm all ears."

"Mr. Zha wants to have you back. Now what do you say to that?"

"What?" Sun Yaoting cried in surprise. "Are you serious?"

"Mr. Zha has thought things over and realized you are the best servant he's ever had. Well, if you really don't want to come back, that's fine. He just wants you to buy something for him."

"Is it silver fish and purple crabs again?" Sun Yaoting gave An a quick glance.

"Exactly!"

"I'm afraid I'm not up to the job," Sun Yaoting said quickly, though he was not sure if he really meant it. Among wealthy households in Beijing it would make the host immensely proud to treat his guests to silver fish and purple crabs in wintertime. Just before the Spring Festival in the previous year Zha suddenly decided he wanted silver fish and purple crabs for his house feast on New Year's Eve. As the two delicacies were available only from Weishui River in Tianjin, Ma Deqing was sent there to get them. He bought the fish and crabs and tried his best to keep them alive, but they were all frozen to death on his return. This enraged Zha, who had been waiting anxiously to win admiration from his guests with the rare dish. He cursed at Ma fiercely and dumped the dead fish and crabs in the courtyard. This had been one of the reasons why Ma finally decided to quit.

Sun Yaoting felt ambivalent about the offer, not knowing whether to accept or decline. He hated the idea of going back to work for Zha, who had proved to be a capricious, trustless master. On the other hand, he did not have a choice, for he must find a way to make a living. "I'll have to think about it," he told An Kuoting. When An came again the next day, Sun Yaoting said he would do it.

"Here's four hundred dollars."

"I'll be back tomorrow, right on New Year's Eve," Sun Yaoting said. "Wait for my good news."

"Don't get them frozen again," An warned.

"You can trust me," Sun Yaoting said, showing more confidence than he actually felt.

Sun Yaoting left for Tianjin without delay. Instead of going to see his younger brother, he headed straight for the market, where he visited several shops dealing in aquatic products. He found out that Qian's Fishmongers offered fish fresh from the river, whereas many other shops dealt in frozen goods only. Unfortunately the day was too windy for fishing boats to set out. He stayed in Tianjin overnight and went to Qian's early the next morning, when fishermen had just brought in their first catch. He picked several silver fish and some purple crabs the size of one's nail, then put the fish in a pail

Stalls selling silver dollars

filled with water and the crabs in a well-sealed basket. Without a moment's delay he rushed to the railway station and caught the first train to Beijing.

It was almost nightfall on New Year's Eve. Staring out of the window, Zha Qi'er began to despair of getting the silver fish and purple crabs in time for the evening feast. Just then Sun Yaoting arrived, and Zha rushed out to receive him. He cried out in joy to see the silver fish swimming in the pail and the purple crabs crawling over one another in the basket. "Wow! How the guests will admire me! Thanks so much! Well, now that you are back, you don't have to leave."

"I have to leave them a message at the temple," Sun Yaoting said, pleased at what he had done. Having to endure prejudices in daily life, many eunuchs felt a strong urge to prove their worth by outshining "normal" people. Thus Sun Yaoting was filled with satisfaction when he had completed the difficult task. In a lighthearted mood he trotted back to the Temple of Genuine Prowess to get his belongings, then returned to Zha's house for dinner.

After the meal Sun Yaoting added up the expenses of the trip, which amounted to just over two hundred dollars. Zha was surprised. "How come?

You spent no money on food in Tianjin?"

"I ate with my younger brother," Sun Yaoting lied. In fact, he did not have the time for any regular meal there.

"You did a good job for me," said Zha, looking impressed. "And you did it on such a cold day! Well, I'll let you keep the money left."

"Thanks." Sun Yaoting took the money and stayed.

Zha had moved to Yangrou Alley only recently. The house had a spacious front yard with five rooms, a kitchen and an awning that served as a garage. There was also a big backyard and a separate compound for servants. One day Sun Yaoting overheard a servant complain, "This house is unlucky. It's shaped like a coffin." Though he did not quite believe in fengshui, he was well aware that Zha's continued extravagance did not bode well for them.

The financial situation of the family had gone from bad to worse since the Japanese surrender in 1945, when the Kuomintang government revoked its long-time salt monopoly. "I'm going downhill every day," Zha complained to Sun Yaoting. "In a few years I'll probably be more wretched than you. At least you can take shelter in a temple."

"If you would listen to me," Sun Yaoting said, "it's time for you to make a 'big to small' change."

"What do you mean by that?"

Sun Yaoting explained that Zha should stop living beyond his means and settle for a simple lifestyle. After a long pause, Zha conceded that he was right. Some days later Zha sold his house. With Sun Yaoting's help he leased the western yard of the Temple of Buddha's Presence for eighty dollars a month. It was a nice little compound. Sun Yaoting had the rooms cleaned up, all the walls whitewashed and the partition boards pasted with silk. Zha was quite pleased with his new home.

"This house is fairly comfortable," Sun Yaoting said. "But if you want to live here comfortably, there are two things you must do."

"Which is?"

"You must quit opium. Sooner or later it would ruin you. Then you must reduce the number of servants in the house. If you can do these two things, you will be able to live a comfortable life with what is left of your wealth. Maybe you should also sell some jewelry and decorations that you don't really need."

Zha agreed to curtail the servants, but he was too addicted to give up opium. Sun Yaoting tried to reason with him. "You must do it for the sake of your children. Your eldest son is already eleven and will grow up in a few years. You don't want your five sons to live in poverty, do you?"

For all that Sun Yaoting said, Zha continued to smoke opium every day with his second concubine. However, he made a point of not smoking right front of Sun Yaoting.

When Zha was lying asleep in bed one day several policemen stormed into the house and took him away. As it turned out, the government had recently launched a campaign against gambling and opium smoking. Because of his bad temper Zha made a lot of enemies, one of whom had reported him to the police, accusing him of hosting gambling and opium-smoking parties. Knowing Zha's reputation for great wealth, the police considered it a good chance to extort some money from him. His arrest terrified all his family members, who tried every means to get his release. Finally an in-law who was a Kuomingtang official agreed to lend a hand. He went to see the chief of police and succeeded in getting Zha out of prison.

On his return Zha looked unkempt and dejected. "Quit opium," Sun Yaoting said. "Otherwise you'd get into trouble again!" Zha nodded his head without uttering a word.

As Zha went on in his old ways, Sun Yaoting began to worry about his own future. Just then he got a message from Chen Zechuan, who had fallen seriously ill. Chen was then staying in the Temple of Great Bounty behind the Drum Tower. He had left the Temple of Prosperity, which no longer provided meals for resident eunuchs.

Sun Yaoting went to ask Zha for a leave. "Mr. Chen is ill. I must go and see him."

"Let's go together," Zha said. They got in the car and arrived at the temple.

"Thanks for coming," Chen Zechuan greeted them in bed. A few days before, he had fallen and dislocated his hip joint.

Sun Yaoting had come in a hurry without bringing any money. Once outside the room, he borrowed two hundred dollars from Zha and handed the money to Wei Ziqing, who was looking after Chen. "I'll come again tomorrow," he said.

The next day Sun Yaoting came alone to the temple. "Well, I'll probably remain bedridden," Chen said with a sigh of resignation. He shifted his position in bed, and the cigarette in his hand dropped to the floor. Sun Yaoting realized that Chen had difficulty holding things. An idea suddenly occurred to him. He should come over to wait on Chen, who had treated him well for all these years.

He went back to see Zha Qi'er. "I keep worrying about Mr. Chen. He looked so ill when I saw him today."

Zha seemed to read his mind. "All right, you can go and look after him. Come back when he gets well."

Thus Sun Yaoting left again for the Temple of Great Bounty. A few days later, he came back to ask Zha for a long leave. Zha looked reluctant this time, aware that Sun Yaoting did not intend to return. After a long pause, he nodded his consent. "But I'll continue to pay you," he said, "even if you stay away for three or five months. How about that?"

Sun Yaoting packed up his belongings and quietly moved out of Zha's house.

4. Death of Chen Zechuan

For over two months Sun Yaoting tended Chen Zechuan in the Temple of Great Bounty. It was during this time that he heard of Yao Mengshan's death. According to a story, Yao had been so bitter over the unfilial behavior of his adopted son that he swore in his deathbed, "When I die, I'll take him with me!" Sure enough, the son died of a sudden illness soon afterward.

At the news Sun Yaoting pondered over the old saying, "A man will be repaid for his good or evil deeds". Yao's adopted son had certainly come to a bad end that he fully deserved. But Sun Yaoting could not help wondering when the saying would come true for him. He had never done any evil deeds but was yet to enjoy a life of peace and comfort.

Unable to sit up straight in bed, Chen relied on Sun Yaoting to do everything for him. He kept the habit of drinking a cup of tea in the morning. "For morning tea," he said, "seven or eight tea leaves would be enough." Chen had always been very thrifty. A small pack of cheap jasmine tea could last him over a week. While he slowly sipped his tea, Sun Yaoting sat by the bed and chatted with him. Chen grew weaker by the day until he had difficulty speaking, though he remained sober. Sun Yaoting often had to guess what he needed from his inarticulate words and gestures.

One day a sudden surge of energy enabled Chen to sit up in bed and speak in a clear voice. Beckoning Sun Yaoting over, he said, "I know I won't be long for this world. I need you to do something for me."

"I'll do my best, master."

"I need you to oversee my funeral. Don't forget about my 'treasure'!" Chen closed his eyes as if a great weight had been lifted from his mind. After a while he repeated, "Don't forget about my 'treasure'!"

Sun Yaoting bent down to whisper in Chen's ear. "Trust me, master. I'll take care of everything. I won't forget what you tell me!"

After a violent coughing fit Chen took his last breath. Restraining his grief, Sun Yaoting began to discuss the funeral arrangement with Zhang Shandai, the temple's abbot. Like most eunuchs, Chen attached great importance to his own funeral and had purchased a very costly fir wood coffin many years before. As Chen had left no money, Zhang Shandai suggested that they sell the coffin and use the proceeds to buy an inexpensive one and fund a grand funeral. "But where's his treasure?" They started searching all over the room. According to popular belief a eunuch should be buried with his well-preserved genitals tucked in place; only then would he be accepted in the underworld as a "complete person". Failure to do so might cause calamities in his afterlife and even cause him to be reborn as an animal. But Chen had died before disclosing where his genitals were kept.

The funereal proceedings lasted over a dozen days, complete with the erection of a sacrificial awning and the chanting of Buddhist sutras. Many eunuchs in the capital came to offer their condolences, and the lavishness of the funeral became the talk of the town. Before the burial of the coffin Sun Yaoting and Zhang Shandai made a last attempt to find the "treasure". They opened an old suitcase to see a small box in the bottom. Inside the box, wrapped up with dry chaff in

Ruined tombstone of Chen Zechuan at Landianchang

many layers of oilpaper, were the long-sought-after organs, withered but otherwise intact. "We've found the treasure!" they cried out in joy. The other eunuchs all rushed over to take a look. "Mr. Chen was a man of virtue after all!" remarked Liu, a eunuch in his late eighties.

"Come on, let's 'complete the body'!" Zhang urged.

"Yes, let's do it right away." With Zhang's help, Sun Yaoting put the "treasure" squarely between the thighs of Chen's body in the coffin.

"Is it in the right place?" asked Liu.

"Yes, trust me," Sun Yaoting replied.

"It should keep contact with the body," Liu added. At his instruction Sun Yaoting adjusted the "treasure" so that it closely adhered to the body.

On the day of the burial Sun Yaoting, dressed in mourning, led the funereal procession together with Zhang Shandai. The coffin was buried at the eunuch cemetery in the area of Landianchang in western Beijing, and a tombstone set up. Chen Zechuan was believed to be the last eunuch to enjoy such a grand funeral, as the founding of the People's Republic of China was just a couple of years away. Many people who witnessed the funeral scene agreed that a real son could not have showed more filial piety than Sun Yaoting, and that Chen must have done lots of good deeds in a previous life to deserve all that.

11

COMMUNIST TAKEOVER

1. Temple of Great Bounty

After Chen Zechuan passed away, Sun Yaoting moved into the Temple of Great Bounty. Zhang Shandai, the abbot, was good at farm work and therefore spent most of his time in the Temple of Mounted Lord Guan located at Landianchang, which had a lot of farmland. Wei Ziqing, the abbot of Lord Guan's Temple, often stayed at the Temple of Great Bounty because he had to look after a couple of shops he owned in the city center. Thus Sun Yaoting got to know Wei quite well. When Wei rented out a house in the city or sold burial lots at Landianchang, it was usually Sun Yaoting who drafted the contracts for him.

Young palace maid

Over a dozen eunuchs lived in the Temple of Great Bounty. Sun Yaoting got along well with them and had a few good friends such as Ma Deqing, Zhou Ziqing and Cai Yachen.

Though he lived in the temple most of the time, Wei Ziqing had a house on Nian'er Alley that he shared with a pretty woman who used to be a palace maid. She had waited on

Duankang, doing most of the needlework for the high consort. Wei had been a high-ranking eunuch serving Cixi, Longyu and Duankang successively. A secret liaison developed between the senior eunuch and the palace maid. He took her home after Pu Yi's expulsion from the Forbidden City, and they lived together like husband and wife.

"Mr. Wei, can I visit you at home today?" Sun Yaoting asked.

"Of course," Wei smiled. "It's my wife that you really want to see, isn't it? Come on and admit it. I don't mind."

For Sun Yaoting, a visit to Wei's house was always a pleasant experience. A variety of flowers and other plants grew in the small, quiet courtyard. The moment he stepped into the gate, he was greeted by the fragrant smell of incense.

After Wei ushered Sun Yaoting into the room, the woman came out bringing a cup of jasmine tea on a saucer.

"You are being too kind, sister-in-law!" Sun Yaoting stood up to greet her. Dressed in a close-fitting cheongsam, she was tall and slim, with regular features and creamy white skin. She should be in her thirties but looked younger than her age, perhaps because she had never borne any child.

"Make yourself at home," she said in her soft and melodious voice. "Have a nice cup of hot tea." She put the teacup with lid and saucer on the table and soon withdrew to the inner room. Sun Yaoting knew that she ran the house all by herself without hiring a single servant. She stayed home most of the time and never gave Wei any reason to worry. Many eunuchs envied Wei his beautiful and virtuous wife and often compared him to Xiaode Zhang, who kept several beautiful concubines at home.

While Sun Yaoting sat chatting with Wei, the woman came out from time to time to pour tea. Sun Yaoting noticed that the teacup, with its fine texture and colorful design, was made in the reign of Emperor Qianlong. Apparently it was a precious item pilfered from the Imperial Palace. But in his eyes Wei's young wife was far more attractive.

When Sun Yaoting took leave, the woman bade him goodbye at the door. With her hands placed on the left side of her chest, she made a slight bow. "Do come again when you have time."

"See you next time," Sun Yaoting said. The faint fragrance of the small courtyard haunted him for a long time afterward.

Sun Yaoting began to pay frequent visits to Wei's house mainly to see the pretty woman. He made clumsy attempts to strike up a conversation with her, for which Wei often made fun of him. However, after moving back to the Temple of Prosperity, he stopped going there, for it was too much trouble after all. He had to dress neatly for the visit and would feel embarrassed if he failed to bring a present for the host.

One day Sun Yaoting took a stroll to the Temple of Great Bounty. "You had visitors this morning," said a eunuch named Wei Ziming.

"Who is it?" Sun Yaoting asked in surprise. It was rare for a poor person like him to have visitors these days.

"You'll never guess. It's Dezheng! She thought you still live here."

"Did you tell her I've moved to the Temple of Prosperity?"

"Yes. And she brought some news. She is now married to Li Lianying's grandson! The couple came together this morning."

"That's wonderful!" Sun Yaoting felt very happy for the girl, who had finally gained what she fully deserved, a life of security. "Good and bad deeds will be repaid in kind", he thought, "at least for some people."

What happened to another of his acquaintances seemed to bear out the same truth. Mu Haichen, head eunuch of High Consort Duankang, had amassed a great fortune in the palace and bought seven housing compounds in the capital. After leaving the palace he settled down in a great mansion near Huanghuamen. A lot of eunuchs stayed in the temples nearby, but few went to visit him. He often called on the temples, and Sun Yaoting had met him once, but they did not have much to say to each other.

Mu's two adopted sons, Dashun and Ershun, were both compulsive gamblers. With him lying ill in bed, they played mahjong day and night, paying little attention to him. At his death they arranged the funeral in a perfunctory way. As a high-ranking eunuch for many years Mu had been an eminent figure in the palace, but few eunuchs showed up at his funeral. Dashun and Ershun couldn't have cared less. The moment the ceremony was over, they hurried home and sat down for another round of mahjong without bothering to change out of their mourning dress. As typical prodigal sons they managed to spend the family fortune left by Mu in a couple of years. Some eunuchs considered it divine retribution. Sun Yaoting agreed. "I used to doubt the old saying, 'A fortune gained through unrighteous means will not bring long-lasting bliss'. Now I realize how true it is!"

One day Zha Qi'er suddenly came to the temple and tried to persuade Sun Yaoting to come back with him. Sun Yaoting declined. "I don't want to go back. More people means higher cost for you. What's more, your wife cooks well. You don't really need lots of servants."

Zha left in disappointment. A few days later he came again. "I should have listened to you. Now it's too late!" As it turned out, Zha had finally succeeded in squandering all his money.

When Zha called again, he was looking more haggard than ever.

"What's the matter now?" asked Sun Yaoting.

"I need you to speak up for me. You must give me a hand!"

"Tell me what it is about," Sun Yaoting said cautiously. He was not sure that he really wanted to help.

"My good days are now gone! I don't even have a place to plant my feet!"

Zha had got himself into a terrible mess. The Temple of Buddha's Presence had sued him for failing to pay his rent and selling the partition boards that belonged to the temple. Zha refused to move out because he had no other place to go. And he had no money to hire a lawyer. Therefore he wanted Sun Yaoting to represent him in court and testify for him. After a moment's hesitation, Sun Yaoting decided to say no. "I used to work for you and should help you out when you are in such difficulty. On the other hand, you must remember that it is I who negotiated with the people at the temple to lease you the house. I owed them a favor. How can I turn against them now?"

"But you can't let them drive me out to the street! My family must have a place to live!"

"Yes, I know. But you don't own the house; it belongs to the temple. So you have to pay your rent on time. And you shouldn't have sold the partition boards; you know perfectly well they are the temple's property. If I were to testify in court, I would only say what is within reason."

Zha left in a huff. However, he often came back to pester Sun Yaoting. Partly to avoid him, Sun Yaoting moved to the Temple of Great Bounty and stayed there for over a year. He heard no news about Zha until many years later, when he met a lawyer named Ma who had been Chen Zechuan's good friend.

"Do you know Zha Qi'er?" Ma asked.

"Yes, of course."

"What do you think of him?"

"He's a good-for-nothing."

"You are quite right! He's been arrested, you know."

"Really? What for?" Sun Yaoting was astonished.

"He committed house robbery with a fake pistol!"

That was the last time Sun Yaoting heard of Zha.

2. Lord Guan's Temple

The Temple of Mounted Lord Guan had been small and inconspicuous until chief eunuch Liu Chengyin funded a major expansion and refurbishment. Liu seemed to be a true devotee. After taking Taoist order, he spent tons of money building temples in the capital. He got himself into big trouble when he diverted water from Jade Spring Hill to one of his temples without official permission. The enraged Empress Dowager Cixi ordered him to be banished to Heilongjiang in the Northeast. Fortunately he was a close friend of Li Lianying, Cixi's favorite eunuch. The day after the edict for Liu's banishment was issued, Li Lianying made a tearful appeal to Cixi, who eventually relented and agreed to let Liu return to the capital.

Liu Chengyin did not go back to the palace but settled down at the

Lord Guan's Temple, now a cultural site under state protection

Temple of Mounted Lord Guan in western Beijing. He had the small temple completely rebuilt and the statue of Mounted Lord Guan reconstructed. The number of worshippers surged. For a long time afterward it was one of the most prosperous temples in the area.

Troubles always abounded where eunuchs got together. After a big quarrel with a few other eunuchs at Lord Guan's Temple, Zhang Shandai left in a rage and returned to the Temple of Great Bounty. A few days later several local notables from the Landianchang area visited him. "Please come back," they pleaded. "No one else is more suitable to run Lord Guan's Temple. Without you it will fall into ruin someday!" Their concern was genuine as the temple played an important role in the local economy.

As Zhang Shandai remained adamant, Wei Ziqing came to ask Sun Yaoting for help. "Chunshou, can you come to Lord Guan's Temple with Mr. Zhang?"

"Didn't they just have a terrible fight? What am I supposed to do there?"

"You must give me a hand. Mr. Zhang would not go back with no one to accompany him."

"Why do you think he'd agree to go back if I'm going with him?"

"Well, the two of you get along quite well. If you agree to go, he won't refuse."

"But there's something else on my mind. I don't want to deal with Bian Fachang. He's such a bully, you know."

"All right, I'll tell him to behave. And I promise to side with you if you ever get into a fight with him."

Eventually Sun Yaoting returned to Lord Guan's Temple with Zhang Shandai. Zhang no longer wanted to oversee the daily affairs of the temple himself but relegated most of his duties to Sun Yaoting. "I'll do my best," Sun Yaoting pledged. The temple did not seem to be well managed, as no one knew the exact amount of land the temple let out and the annual yield. Together with his old friend Zhao Rongsheng, Sun Yaoting embarked on an investigation tour. As it turned out, Lord Guan's Temple owned an impressive amount of cultivated land and real estate property in addition to a large vegetable garden and a cemetery, where successive abbots of the renowned White-Cloud Temple were buried. A sizable portion of the most fertile land owned by the temple had come from Cui Yugui, a favorite eunuch of Empress Dowager Cixi. After Cixi's death Cui left the palace, first staying at the Temple of Great Bounty and later moving into Lord Guan's Temple. He appeared very benign and generous in his later years, probably because he felt guilty for murdering the Precious Consort by pushing her into the well and wanted to do good deeds in atonement. While talking with his disciple Li Shouchen, he learned that people at Lord Guan's could barely feed themselves with the yields from its land. Thereupon he donated a large tract of fertile land at the village of Dashun to the temple. Thanks to him, eunuchs at Lord Guan's Temple never went hungry even during the chaotic years of Japanese occupation and the subsequent civil war.

"This place must be run in a different way," Sun Yaoting suggested to Zhang Shandai in the evening.

"How?"

"We can begin by selecting a few supervisors, each with his respective duties."

Sun Yaoting's proposal was adopted. The temple appointed four supervisors, with Sun Yaoting in charge of daily affairs, Zhao Rongsheng keeping the storeroom, Bian Fachang tending the vegetable garden, and Zhao Yaru handling mess arrangements. In winter Sun Yaoting introduced another reform. The temple had a large open stove that burned up a lot of coal and must be extinguished at night to avoid gas poisoning. Thus everyone woke up shivering with cold in the morning. At Sun's suggestion over a dozen safety stoves were installed in the temple, bringing warmth to every room.

One day Zhao Rongsheng came to see Sun Yaoting, looking very upset. Deyuancheng, the shop that supplied their daily provisions, suddenly refused to allow the temple any credit. Now they had to pay ready money even to buy vinegar or soy sauce. "They can't do this!" Zhao said indignantly. "The shop itself belongs to the temple!"

"We have to sit down and talk it over," Sun Yaoting said. "Would you please go downtown and get Mr. Wei to come here?"

In the evening Sun Yaoting discussed the matter with Wei Ziqing and Zhang Shandai. Wei and Zhang agreed that the shop's demand was unreasonable. "The temple and the shop always give each other credit and settle accounts at the year-end. This has been going on for generations! After all, the temple owns that place!"

"Can you go and negotiate for us?" Zhang Shandai finally asked Sun Yaoting.

"All right, I'll have a try."

The next day Sun Yaoting went alone to Deyuancheng to meet its manager, Zhang Dehui, a native of Shandong. "If you want ready money from us, we'll also demand ready money from you," Sun Yaoting told him. "This house belongs to the temple, and the monthly rent should be at least five hundred kilograms of millet!"

"You are asking for too much! This is unacceptable!"

After much bargaining they settled on two hundred and fifty kilograms of millet. Sun Yaoting made Zhang sign an agreement stipulating that the money rent was to be calculated by the market price of millet as listed in the newspapers. "The current price of millet is six cents a kilograms," Sun Yaoting said. "That means sixty-five dollars a month, enough to pay for all the soy sauce we need!"

On his return Sun Yaoting was greeted warmly by Zhang Shandai. "You've done an excellent job!"

At Lord Guan's Temple Sun Yaoting made a point of avoiding any contact with Bian Fachang, a difficult fellow who was always ready to pick up a fight. He often took things from the vegetable garden he was assigned to look after. One day Sun Yaoting heard a noisy disturbance outside the temple and went out to take a look. Bian was scuffling with a peasant. They seized each other by the collar, swearing loudly.

"What's the matter?" Sun Yaoting went over to separate them.

"He stole a tree from our temple!" Bian said. The day before, someone had cut and stolen a tree from the temple. Unable to locate the thief, Bian went out in the street to curse at the top of his voice. "I'll keep on cursing his ancestors until the thief shows up!" he declared. Sure enough, the peasant who had stolen the tree could not bear the obscenities hurled against his ancestors and came out to fight Bian. Many of the peasant's relatives gathered in front of the temple, forming a circle around Bian.

"Fuck you! Fuck your grandmother!" Bian was getting desperate.

"Everyone knows you are a eunuch!" the peasant sneered. "You have nothing to fuck anyone with, do you?" His words sent the crowd into a boisterous laughter.

Sun Yaoting turned red in the face, feeling humiliated. All eunuchs hated to be reminded of their mutilation. However, the peasant's family members and relatives were gathering into a big crowd, which might turn into a mob at any moment. "Come back at once!" Sun Yaoting shouted, dragging Bian inside and closing the gate behind them.

Zhang Shandai shook his head when informed of the incident in the evening. "You brought insult and humiliation to all of us!" he told Bian. "If Chunshou had not acted as wisely as he did, they could have beaten you to death!" Bian lowered his head and said nothing. It was the closest he came to admitting he had been in the wrong.

The area of Landianchang was undergoing drastic change and rapid development. A few years after Chen Zechuan's burial, his grave had to be removed to make way for a new asphalt road. Sun Yaoting wrote to Chen's adopted son, Chen Xiuhe, asking him to come over at once. However, it was Chen's wife who showed up. Sun Yaoting explained that the coffin had to be dug up and moved away and that they could take the opportunity to transport Chen's remains back to his home village. She nodded her consent. They opened the coffin to find the body fully decomposed with only the bones left. It would be unpractical to have the coffin transported back to Chen's hometown. Sun Yaoting brought some pieces of paper and used them to mark the bones. Then he packed the bones into a bundle and accompanied Chen's wife to the railway station.

Some days later Sun Yaoting had a visitor from Cangzhou, Liu Ziyu's hometown.

"Mr. Liu's wife just passed away," the man said. "They sent me to ask for your help."

Sun Yaoting started at the news. "I'll do whatever I can," he promised.

"Before she died, she said she wished to be buried in a coffin rather than get cremated. But the authorities won't allow it because there's no more room for burial in the village."

"Does she have a coffin?"

"Yes, the coffin's ready."

"Wait for me." Sun Yaoting went at once to see the township head of Landianchang. "Please do me a favor. Chen was my mentor, and I really feel I owed him a lot."

"All right," the township head agreed with alacrity. "You can have him buried here."

By Sun Yaoting's arrangement the coffin of Liu Ziyu's wife was transported to Beijing and carried to Landianchang. After a few days of mourning and sutra chanting, the coffin was buried on a hill.

3. People's Liberation Army

The civil war was coming to an end. After successive defeats in the battlefield the Kuomintang was preparing to make its exodus to the island of Taiwan. People at Landianchang often heard cannon fire in the distance and the roaring of planes overhead.

One day Sun Yaoting heard a clamor outside. "Somebody is dying!" He went out to see a crowd gathering on a bridge nearby. A wounded Kuomintang soldier lay unconscious on the ground. Taking pity on him, an old man brought a bowl of hot water. After a while several people carried the soldier away and put him outside the wall of the Summer Palace.

"There's going be trouble!" Sun Yaoting muttered to himself as he slipped back into the temple. That night a sudden banging noise woke him up. Flinging a coat on his back, he went out to open the gate, and some armed Kuomintang soldiers swarmed in. "Who moved away the wounded soldier?"

"I don't know," Sun Yaoting replied.

"Nonsense! How could a dying man have moved all that distance himself?"

Sun Yaoting suggested that people from another temple might have been responsible for it.

"Even if you are telling the truth," said a soldier, "you cannot get away without paying for it. Let's get to the point. We know you have coffins at this temple. You must donate one!"

"This is not our responsibility!" Sun Yaoting said firmly. "Why should we give a coffin to someone who is neither friend nor relative? The neighborhood head is the person you want!"

"All right." The soldiers gave in. "But you must get a mat to cover up the body first. We can talk about the coffin later."

"That'll be easy," Sun Yaoting said.

Just as he had expected, the soldiers returned shortly afterward, accompanied by a police officer. "The temple can provide the soldier with a coffin, but on one condition," he told them. "The neighborhood head and the local elders must share part of the cost. You can't expect the temple to give away coffins for free." They soon reached an agreement, and the matter was settled before dawn.

The siege of Beijing went on for a long time. One day a uniformed young boy wearing a white lambskin hat came to Deyuancheng. When asked, he revealed himself to be a soldier of the People's Liberation Army. The news spread like lightning at Landianchang, causing widespread panic among the landlords and rich merchants. They decided to set up an office to deal with the PLA takeover, but before they could do anything the troops began to arrive in large numbers. Exhausted by many days of forced march, the PLA soldiers went to sleep in the open, leaning their back against the wall.

No one dared to go out to meet the troops. People at the temple turned to Sun Yaoting. "How about you?"

He tried to decline. "I've been here for only a short time. I'm not the most suitable person for the job."

"Yes, you are," Zhang Shandai declared. "You can go and speak for all of us!" The others all agreed.

At the head of a six-people delegation, Sun Yaoting arrived at the PLA headquarters, where a benign-looking officer wearing a pistol received them. "Your office belongs to the Old Society," he began in a kindly voice. They started, staring at each other in dismay.

"Let's rename it," the officer suggested. "We can call it 'joint office of military and civil affairs'. How about that?"

"Yes, it sounds great!" They replied in unison, heaving a collective sigh of relief.

The six members of the office received specific duties, with Sun Yaoting in charge of grain and fodder supplies for the army. A newly carved official seal in hand, he had the authority to allocate and deploy provisions in the entire township of Landianchang, which was serving as a bridgehead for the People's Liberation Army marching on Beijing. He took sixty hectoliters of grain from the huge stores of Deyuancheng to feed both men and horses, and organized local residents to prepare corn cakes and steamed bread for the army. He must also carry out various other assignments at very short notice. When the army wanted some road guides, he immediately took several strong-bodied young men to the headquarters. An officer invited them to sit down and explained that he needed them for the sole purpose of leading the way.

"That's no problem!" one of the young men responded. "I know the area like the back of my palm!"

"You don't have to do anything else," the officer said. "When you hear gunshots, lie down and make no move. Don't budge even when some of our soldiers get wounded. There's no need to be afraid as your safety is our first priority!"

Soon afterward Sun Yaoting helped organize a team of stretcher-bearers, which set out at nightfall with the troops heading for the city of Beijing.

As the number of troops gathered at Landianchang kept growing, Sun Yaoting's responsibilities became heavier. At his suggestion ninety-six people were selected from the over two hundred households in the township to take duty shifts around the clock. He provided them with millet porridge from the temple and pickled vegetables from Deyuancheng. The six members of the "joint office" also took night shifts. After the initial shock in the richer sector of the population, the arrival of PLA did not cause great chaos or confusion in the area.

One day Sun Yaoting returned to the temple at midnight. He had barely got into bed when there came a loud pounding on the gate. He went out to see a fellow member of the "joint office", the deputy neighborhood head. "It's too bad!" the man said in a trembling voice, his face white as sheet. "I just had a clash with the PLA!"

"You quarreled with them?"

"Worse!" Some minutes before, over a dozen mounted soldiers suddenly arrived. They told him that more troops would soon follow, and that he must get ready to feed and accommodate five hundred men and horses. "But that's impossible!" he exclaimed. The officer in charge lost his impatience. "The troops will be here any moment! What am I supposed to do?"

The deputy neighborhood head was a very stubborn man. "I can't get things done at such short notice," he insisted. "Shoot me if you want!"

"Shoot you?" the officer said with a sneer. "I'd rather save my bullet for better use!"

After the deputy neighborhood head returned home, the more he thought about it the more fearful he grew, so he finally came to Sun Yaoting for help.

Sun Yaoting immediately went to see the army officer to make an apology. He prepared hot water and a little fodder so that the dozen men and horses could settle down and take some rest. Then he drove several carts around the neighborhood collecting hay, which he mixed with corn grains from the temple. Early in the morning they got ready to feed a host of cavalry, only to learn that the troops had gone in another direction. Wiping off perspiration on his forehead, Sun Yaoting turned to the deputy neighborhood head. "You are lucky. If the troops belonged to one of the warlords, they would have shot you on the spot!"

Just then Zhao Rongsheng came running. "What shall we do?" he asked. "The troops went around the neighborhood asking for cabbage, but no one would give them any. Now they have come to the temple."

"How much do they need?"

"At least two hundred and fifity kilograms!"

"Let's take them to the cellar of our vegetable garden."

By Sun Yaoting's arrangement the PLA soldiers eventually carried away over five thousand kilograms, or five tons of cabbage. Many eunuchs at the temple pulled a long face. "The cabbage belongs to the temple," they said, "and you let them take away so much just like that. Who will pay us the money?"

"It's my decision and I will take responsibility for it!" Sun Yaoting said firmly. A few days later the troops paid for the cabbage at a good price, much to the relief of the eunuchs. "We should have sold them more!" one of them remarked.

Two pigs raised in the vegetable garden, weighing nearly two hundred kilograms, caught the attention of a unit of troops stationed nearby. Several men came to negotiate with Sun Yaoting. "It is our duty to help the army as much as we can," he said. "On the other hand, the New Year is just around the corner. We have more than twenty elderly people here in the temple, and there is no other source of meat."

"How about giving us the chitterlings?" one of the soldiers asked.

"That would not be treating you right; I can't bring myself to do that. Now here is my suggestion: We keep one of the pigs and let you have the other one, and you will take the trouble to slaughter them." The men from the army agreed.

A couple of old eunuchs began to worry again. "Will they pay us after they've eaten the meat?" When the money was sent over just before the Lunar New Year, even the most skeptical eunuchs had to admit that the PLA was indeed drastically different from all the other troops they had dealt with before.

During this hectic period, when he had to take frequent night shifts, Sun Yaoting picked up smoking to keep himself awake in the long winter nights. He settled on the cheapest brand, Greenleaf. One day he was holding a cigarette in his mouth when a soldier said jokingly, "Throw away that cigarette! Try a better one." He brought out a pack and offered it to Sun Yaoting.

"Save it for yourself," Sun Yaoting said. "I am too inexperienced a smoker to tell the difference!"

"Lord Guan's Temple is immensely rich," the soldier said. "So why are you so closefisted?"

"The temple does have a little money, but it's not mine!" Sun Yaoting was a bit incensed by the question. "I don't have the right to waste a single cent!"

Because of his heavy smoking habit, he coughed frequently and was soon diagnosed with bronchitis. Ten years later he made a vow to give up smoking. To the surprise of his fellow eunuchs, he kept his word and never had a single smoke again for the rest of his life.

Late one night several policemen suddenly came to the temple to take Sun Yaoting away. They locked him up in a dark room and kept him there for a whole day. The next evening Wang, head of the local police station, interrogated him. "Sun Yaoting, you must tell us everything you know about the bullets. Confess to all that you have done!"

"I have no idea what you are talking about!" Sun Yaoting cried out. Only then did he learn that the day before some bullets had been unearthed in the pigsty at the western yard of Lord Guan's Temple.

"You are the one who runs the temple. Are you trying to tell us you know nothing about the matter?"

"I really know nothing about it," Sun Yaoting said. "You can go and ask the people around."

Fortunately an old servant who had spent all his life at Lord Guan's Temple came to testify for Sun Yaoting to the police. "What a joke! Of course Sun Yaoting knows nothing about it! The bullets were buried right after the Japanese surrender; Mr. Shi and Mr. Li were in charge of the temple at that time. How could Sun Yaoting have known anything about it?"

"How long have you stayed in the temple?" Wang asked Sun Yaoting.

"I've been here for only a year or so, from August of forty-eight. You can ask the township head about this!"

Thereupon Sun Yaoting was set free after his one-day imprisonment.

4. "Big Landlord"

After a PLA land reform taskforce arrived at Landianchang, the ten remaining eunuchs at Lord Guan's Temple were summoned to a meeting in the courtyard of the township government, where a list of landlords and rich peasants were publicly announced. All the eunuchs were designated "landlords", with Sun Yaoting's name topping the list.

After the meeting "Sun Yaoting the big landlord" enjoyed sudden notoriety in the Landianchang area. When he went home for a visit, his father asked in great perplexity, "How did a poor man like you suddenly become a big landlord? It's really beyond me!"

Back in Landianchang, Sun Yaoting learned from Zhao Rongsheng that some people at the temple were secretly planning to divide up its property before the government came to confiscate everything. At that time Zhang Shandai remained the nominal head of Lord Guan's Temple, though Sun Yaoting had been attending to its daily affairs. Zhang Shandai's attitude was noncommittal when Sun Yaoting went to seek his advice. "But you have to take a decision in such an important matter!" Sun Yaoting urged.

"I leave everything to you," Zhang said. "I will go along with whatever you decide to do."

"All right." Sun Yaoting made up his mind. "Let's hold a meeting tonight where everyone can speak his mind openly. No more under-the-table maneuvers!"

The atmosphere was tense at the meeting. Sun Yaoting spoke first. "I have thought about your proposal to divide up the temple property. It won't work! We have the township government to our west and the police station just across the street. Tell me, what on earth can we possibly do?"

"We have considered it very carefully," a eunuch said. "And we have agreed on a single word: divide!"

Sun Yaoting's eyes bulged and his voice trembled with anger. "Don't you realize what this really means? The moment we start dividing the property, they'll take me out and shoot me!" He paused to regain his composure. "Let's not rush to a decision. Hold whatever you plan to do and allow me a little time to check things out first."

After the meeting Sun Yaoting went straight to the township government. After hearing him out, Zhao Biao, the township head, patted him on the shoulder. "You've done the right thing! If they should divide up the temple's property, you'd be the one to account for it! You'd be labeled a landlord guilty of stirring up trouble and shot for trying to sabotage the land reform!"

The tumultuous days of the land reform movement kept Sun Yaoting on edge. Sometimes he stayed awake for several days and nights. Getting up one early morning, he found to his dismay that his hair had turned gray overnight. Eventually he emerged relatively unscathed from the movement.

The People's Republic of China was founded in October 1949. Shortly afterward the Korean War broke out. The township head of Landianchang summoned the "landlords and rich peasants" to a meeting, calling on them to donate money for the Chinese troops fighting in Korea. While the other eunuchs gave ten or twenty dollars each, Sun Yaoting alone donated sixty. Some days later the head of the local police station came to collect another round of donations, which would be used to buy fighter planes. Though people were supposed to contribute money on a voluntary basis, the temple had a quota to fulfill: three hundred dollars. Sun Yaoting gave a hundred dollars at first. The total donation of other eunuchs amounted to a hundred and eighty dollars, so they were still twenty dollars short. At this Sun Yaoting produced a hundred and twenty dollars. Thus Lord Guan's Temple surpassed its donation quota. Sun Yaoting and the other "landlords" at the temple were awarded a collective citation by the township government.

12

AFTER LIBERATION

1. An Investigation and a Lawsuit

One day Sun Yaoting left for the downtown area in early morning. On his return late that night he learned that the police had come to look for him several times. He immediately went to the police station. The police officer in charge, also named Sun, did not show his usual affability. "What do you know about the death of Wang Guangquan?

"I didn't know he was dead," Sun Yaoting said in astonishment. "I left for the city early this morning."

"You know nothing about his death? Wang hanged himself last night!"

Sun Yaoting realized why he became a suspect. He had "vanished" from sight soon after Wang's death.

"Do you have any idea why he committed suicide?"

"I would say he failed to understand the policy of the government," Sun Yaoting answered promptly.

"Why do you say so?"

"In my opinion, his suicide can only be explained by his unreasonable fear. It all started when Wang slaughtered four pigs raised at Deyuancheng without official permission. Someone at the township government told him that he had done something illegal by trying to evade tax, and that he had to pay a fine. This made him very upset. He thought it was a gross injustice. Why should he alone be held responsible when the meat from the pigs was shared among all the people at Lord Guan's Temple?"

"Did he talk to you about it?"

"Yes, he did, and I tried to comfort him. 'We all know you feed pigs for the temple rather than for yourself,' I told him. 'Explain it to the government people, and you'll be all right. The temple can pay the fine; it's no big deal!' But my words fell on deaf ears."

"When did you leave this morning?"

"I left at dawn. I went in town to buy a few things and handle some temple affairs." Sun Yaoting went on to describe in great detail his day in downtown Beijing.

"Do you have witnesses?"

"Yes!" Sun Yaoting began to relax as he rolled out the names of the people he had met during the day.

"You can leave now."

Sun Yaoting stumbled back to the temple and explained what had happened to his adopted son and daughter-in-law, who were staying with him. His adopted son, Sun Changnian, felt puzzled. "Why do they think you should have anything to do with Wang's death?"

"Isn't it obvious, Changnian? Every morning you and your wife went to Deyuancheng to collect the manure there, didn't you? Wang gave the manure to you rather than to someone else because he and I got along well. When he suddenly died, and I happened to be away for the entire day, the police are bound to get suspicious. But I am not really worried. What is true will not prove to be false, and what is false will not prove to be true!"

For all his professed belief in justice Sun Yaoting did not sleep a wink that night. A few days later the police notified him that a thorough investigation into the case did not link him to Wang Guangquan's death.

What happened next took Sun Yaoting completely by surprise. Bian Fachang, together with his adopted son Hou Shilin, sued Sun Yaoting and Sun Changnian on a charge of appropriation of public funds. They claimed that Sun Yaoting and his adopted son had been living off the temple's property without doing any work. The local court sent someone to Lord Guan's Temple to investigate the case. "Bian's accusation is totally groundless!" Sun Yaoting said indignantly. "If you don't believe me, go and ask around in the township!"

Zhang Shandai spoke in Sun Yaoting's favor, citing many examples to prove that it was Hou Shilin who lived off the temple doing no work in return. "Bian is accusing Changnian of what his own son has been doing all along! How ridiculous!"

Several old eunuchs, as long-time residents of the temple, also testified for Sun Yaoting. They agreed that Changnian had never used Sun Yaoting's position to gain extra advantage. He was paid for his labor on a daily basis; if it happened to rain in the afternoon, he would only get half day's pay.

The court finally rejected Bian Fachang's accusation. At Lord Guan's Temple many eunuchs blamed Bian for making trouble. "Why should a eunuch fall on another eunuch?" one of them remarked.

"Changnian gets the nicknamed 'Silly Changnian' because he is so simple-minded," another eunuch said. "He's the last person to take advantage of the temple!"

"Without Yaoting to look after everything, the temple would have come to ruins," declared a third eunuch. "He has run this place for years without making any profit for himself. He's not the kind of person to favor his son at the expense of the temple!"

Thus Bian Fachang's abortive suit ended up elevating Sun Yaoting's status at Lord Guan's Temple.

One day Sun Yaoting was doing the accounts when a eunuch told him that a military officer had just arrived in a car to visit Liu Chengyin's grave. "Who can it be?" he wondered.

Zhang Shandai came over at the surprising news. "Liu did not seem to have a son!"

"You never know for sure," Sun Yaoting said. "It might be his adopted son who has made it!"

"Let's go and take a look," Zhang suggested. They walked over to the cemetery, where they found an officer of large stature standing quietly in front of Liu's tombstone. "He must be a high-ranking officer judging by his manners," Zhang whispered. "Go and ask him."

Sun Yaoting would not. "What can I possibly say? You go ahead if you want to ask him anything."

Not daring to approach the officer, Zhang went over to strike up a conversation with the chauffeur. "Who is that officer, brother? He seems to be a man of great standing!"

"You guess correctly. He's a field officer in charge of the Military Museum."

Back in the temple Zhang Shandai commented, "How lucky for Liu to have adopted a son like that! He must have done good deeds in his previous life. Well, I have no one to carry on the family line. I doubt if anybody will ever visit my grave."

"Why worry?" Sun Yaoting said. "Your job is to eat well and sleep well so that you can enjoy a long life. Taoism teaches us to cultivate ourselves in the present lifetime, doesn't it? Never mind what will happen in the next!"

2. The Fate of Xiaode Zhang

After 1949 Xiaode Zhang continued to live in peace and comfort in Tianjin. One day his long-time steward, Wang Fu, called on Sun Yaoting at Lord Guan's Temple, bringing a present of two boxes of fried dough twist, a famous local product of Tianjin. Wang Fu introduced Zhang's youngest grandson, San'er, a boy about seventeen, and explained that Zhang wished to consign San'er to the temple.

"You mean Mr. Zhang wants his grandson to earn his living by doing manual labor, just like everyone else here?" Sun Yaoting asked incredulously, knowing that Xiaode Zhang was perfectly capable of supporting his family.

"Mr. Zhang wants San'er to stay away from Tianjin and stop relying on the family fortune," Wang Fu said. "Manual labor will do him good. Mr. Zhang wants to make sure that whatever happens to the family in the future, San'er will be able to get by on his own."

"If that's what he wants, no problem," Sun Yaoting said. "San'er can eat at the same table with me, and I'll find some work for him to do. As long as my rice bowl is full, San'er won't starve."

San'er was a simple, good-natured boy, showing no sign of a spoiled son from a rich family. He did whatever he was assigned to do, laboring from morning to nightfall. He often worked side by side with Changnian, cleaning up the pigsty, propelling the waterwheel, and transporting manure to the field on three-wheel carts. He ate the same meal as other laborers, with steamed bread and pickled vegetables as the staple food every day. Gradually Sun Yaoting came to realize that Xiaode Zhang had made a wise choice for his favorite grandson.

Somewhat later another visitor from Zhang's family came to the capital. At that time Sun Yaoting had become an official of a sort, as a member of the temple administration office on Luomasi Street. "You have a visitor," the doorkeeper told him. "A pretty woman."

"Who is she?" Sun Yaoting asked in surprise.

"I don't know. She just asks to see you."

Walking out to the door, Sun Yaoting recognized the caller at once. It was Xiaode Zhang's wife, Zhang Xiaoxian. Wearing a trendy hairstyle, light make-up, and a tender green cheongsam, she looked quite attractive for a middle-aged woman.

"Sun Yaoting, Mr. Zhang has sent me to ask you for a favor. That's why I have come all the way from Tianjin."

Sun Yaoting noticed that instead of his palace name, Chunshou, she had addressed him by his regular name out of respect, in accordance with the common practice in the post-1949 era. Having met her before, he knew a little about her past. She had been an extremely popular courtesan in Tianjin before she caught Xiaode Zhang's fancy and became his concubine. She enjoyed great favor with him and was finally elevated to the status of principal wife.

"Come in please." Sun Yaoting invited Zhang Xiaoxian and her accompanying servant to come into the office.

"You are an old friend of our family," Zhang Xiaoxian said, "so I'll get straight to the point. Mr. Zhang is now terminally ill. He wishes to be buried at the Temple of Gold-Hill Treasure."

As Sun Yaoting had known all along, Xiaode Zhang was unlikely to enjoy a long life on account of his overindulgence in wine and women. But the news still came as a shock.

"This is his last wish." Zhang Xiaoxian looked expectantly at Sun Yaoting. "Do you think it would be easy to arrange?"

"Let's give it a try. Mr. Zhang has treated me well all these years. Actually you don't have to come down here in person. Just send me a message, and I'll try my best, though I can't make any promise."

As it was getting late, Sun Yaoting arranged for Zhang Xiaoxian and her servant to stay the night. Early the next morning they set out in two pedicabs, heading for the Temple of Gold-Hill Treasure in the Western Hills. They found the temple practically deserted, which was not very surprising. At that time the entire nation was mobilized to smelt steel, with the unlikely goal of turning China into an industrialized country in a few years' time. Even monks and nuns had to contribute their share of labor. Walking around the graveyard, Sun Yaoting spotted a small cabin and went over to find an old grave-keeper.

The grave-keeper had been hired to watch the graves of some senior eunuchs, but now he supported himself by planting crops and vegetables in the field. "Xiaode Zhang wants to be buried here?" he stared at the unexpected visitors in surprise. While Sun Yaoting and Zhang Xiaoxian stood waiting, he went away for a while, apparently to get instruction from the person in charge. "It won't do," he told them on his return.

Zhang Xiaoxian left Beijing in disappointment. Shortly afterward Xiaode Zhang died. He was eventually buried in a cemetery at Beichang about fifteen kilometers outside the city of Tianjin.

3. Back in the Temple of Prosperity

After being labeled a "landlord" Sun Yaoting began to pay extra attention to his speech and conduct. Though the label was later removed, he still thought it a good idea to keep his mouth shut and mind his own business. However, entrusted with the day-to-day management of Lord Guan's Temple, he inevitably got caught up in the successive political campaigns and often felt that he had to steer a course through a minefield.

As part of its blueprint for a brave new world, the government took measures to gradually eliminate private ownership. In the first step to take over private businesses, it advocated a form of "joint state-private ownership". The announcement of the plan in the newspapers caused a great furor among the people at Lord Guan's Temple, who had shares and various other interests in Deyuancheng. The shop, along with its branches, was enjoying a booming business. Its estimated market value amounted to forty thousand yuan, at a time when one could live comfortably on thirty yuan a month. Opinions varied as to what to do with the shop.

"I think it would be wise for us to support the government and hand over the shop," said one of the eunuchs.

Another disagreed. "Why should we do that? People in this temple depend on the shop for a living. Why give it away without a fight? At least let's wait and see what others will do."

"The newspapers call on people to 'follow the socialist road'," Sun Yaoting said. "If we don't listen to what the government has to tell us, we'll soon regret it. I think we should hand over the shop." In the evening he met with a few elders at the temple to discuss the matter. They all agreed that they should not hesitate to answer the government's call; otherwise they might end up with a label nastier than "big landlord".

Early the next morning Sun Yaoting and Zhao Rongsheng went to the government office of Haidian District. On behalf of Lord Guan's Temple they offered the shop Deyuancheng for "joint state-private ownership". An official received them warmly. After hearing them out, he said the government would discuss the matter and that they could come over the next day.

The same official received Sun Yaoting and Zhao Rongsheng the following day. "The district government has decided to accept your offer. Each of the temple's supervisors will get a monthly salary of thirty yuan. Would that be acceptable to you?"

"No, we won't take any money," Sun Yaoting said firmly. "Every person should support himself by his own labor. The temple still has some land and a vegetable garden left, and we can do other things to earn a little extra income. That'll be enough for us to make a living." He did not mention that the temple had houses to let, which constituted an important source of their "extra income".

"What about your shares in the shop?"

"Shares? We don't need them anymore!"

Deyuancheng turned out to be the first private business to be handed over to the government for "joint ownership" in Haidian District. However, Sun Yaoting had to face a lot of criticism and complaints at the temple. When the district government offered to reward the temple a sum of money, Sun Yaoting declined, saying, "We have simply returned to the people what has always belonged to them!" This brought him another round of criticism. Some accused him of currying favor with the government at other people's expense. Zhang Shandai alone spoke up in his defense. "What's the use of a little extra money? The ability to support ourselves is the only thing we can count on!"

"People like us must face reality," Sun Yaoting said. "I consider myself lucky to have lived to this day. Enough to eat and wear is all that I will ever need."

What happened next proved him right. The "joint ownership" was soon enforced not only in Beijing but all over the country. The eunuchs who had vociferously opposed Sun Yaoting finally realized how naive they had all been.

With all their valuable properties, including the temples where they had been staying, handed over to the government, the remaining eunuchs in Beijing moved en mass into the Temple of Prosperity. By the time Sun Yaoting came to the temple, there were already over thirty people there, most of them eunuchs. Each received a monthly stipend of sixteen yuan – ten yuan for buying food and six yuan as pocket money. In winter they enjoyed a special subsidy of eight yuan for buying coal. Initially, when the government persuaded eunuchs at various places to move to the Temple of Prosperity, many had been reluctant. Some eunuchs thought the stipend too small and demanded twenty-five yuan instead. Wei Ziqing, who had by then lost his beloved wife, the fair "palace lady", showed an attitude of resignation. "I don't care how much I get paid, as long as it's enough to keep me alive," he remarked. "What's the use of any extra money? You can't take it with you when you die!" Wei enjoyed a measure of prestige among the eunuchs. After he moved into the Temple of Prosperity, others followed suit.

Thanks to his literacy and the ability to keep accounts, Sun Yaoting became a member of the temple's management group, earning thirty yuan a month. His hard work soon earned him a raise of five yuan. Subsequently he joined the temple administration office of Beijing and was put in overall charge of the Temple of Prosperity.

At the temple Sun Yaoting met many of his old friends and acquaintances. Wang Yuezheng, who had been rich enough to own a sedan-chair shop in Tianjin, told Sun Yaoting that his shop had closed down many years before. He had returned to his hometown in Qing County once and found the attitude of his fellow villagers not at all friendly. On the whole Sun Yaoting found Wang to be much more amiable than before.

If there were such a thing as happy eunuchs, Sun Shangxian must be one. He had got married before undergoing castration to become a eunuch. Thus he had a wife and a married daughter. From time to time he went to stay at his daughter's house for a few days. Thanks to his happy "family life", he always seemed to be in good humor.

Chi Huanqing, who used to be immensely rich, had become impoverished after he took to drinking and smoking opium. His clothes were in tatters, and his cloth shoes had holes in them. Being ambidextrous, he had learned the practical skill of welding tin pots. Whenever he was about to starve, he would go around the city to earn a little money by mending teapots. Taking pity on him, Sun Yaoting decided to offer a little help. "You are now too old to travel around. When there is any repair work to do, I'll give you the assignment and pay you well. How about that?"

Chi accepted the offer gladly. Sun Yaoting often gave him various odd jobs at the temple, such as sealing windows and repairing stoves. But Chi persisted in his old ways. The moment he got paid he would slip into a wine shop nearby to get drunk.

Like Sun Shangxian, Liu Zijie had a daughter, but he did not seem to get along with her and never visited her at home. Well educated and with an aptitude for numbers, he also became a member of the temple's management. Sometimes he was assigned to sell meat and vegetables for the temple, and he took the chance to make personal gains. On one occasion he managed to save some fish for himself by giving short weight to customers. When he took the fish back to his room and cooked them, the smell gave him away. But he was completely unabashed and paid no attention to the complaints and ridicule of other eunuchs.

Liu Zijie turned out to be a troublemaker when Chen Yan, a woman cadre from the Religion Office of the municipal government, came to the temple for an inspection. No sooner had she stepped in the temple than Liu led her to his room, where he embarked on a vicious attack of other eunuchs who did not get along with him. But many other eunuchs went to see Chen afterward, and she became bewildered by all the mudslinging, not knowing what to believe. "Liu Zijie suffered a lot in the Old Society, didn't he?" she asked. At that time it was a widely acknowledged truth that one who had endured great sufferings in the Old Society must be politically conscious and therefore trustworthy.

"We all suffered a lot in the Old Society!" responded the eunuchs.

But Liu Zijie had something to say about Sun Yaoting's past. "He's no ordinary eunuch. He waited on the 'Empress' for quite a long time in Beijing, and then he went to Manchukuo to serve its 'Emperor', Pu Yi. He's a cursed big landlord!"

When Chen Yan came to Sun Yaoting to verify what she had heard, he did not hesitate to rake up Liu's faults. "Yes, I waited on the Emperor. So what? Do you suppose a eunuch had the right to say no when the Emperor needed his service? What really matters is one's character. When Liu Zijie left the palace, he borrowed Shao Xiangqing's fur coat but never returned it. He even had his own name embroidered on the coat afterward! What a nasty thing for him to do! Shao was none other than Liu's mentor, you know."

Liu Zijie proved himself a very resourceful infighter. "We don't have enough food these days," he complained to Chen. "Many people are too weak from hunger to get up!" He took her to several rooms in the temple, where all the eunuchs were lying in bed.

"Too hungry to get up?" Sun Yaoting exclaimed when Chen came to talk about the "food problem". "What nonsense! They are sleeping in the daytime because they have nothing else to do! If you don't believe me, go and ask them."

Chen went back to knock on doors, but she asked the wrong question. "Are you short of food?" Unsurprisingly, all the eunuchs answered yes. Therefore she took Sun Yaoting for a liar and praised Liu Zijie for showing deep concern for his fellow eunuchs. The implicit assumption was that Sun Yaoting had embezzled the other eunuchs' food rations at the temple. A few days later Chen's boss, Chief Li, sent for him. "What have you been up to, Sun Yaoting? You must give the other eunuchs enough to eat! You can't let them starve!"

"Who says they are starving?" Sun Yaoting was indignant. "Did anyone starve to death at the temple?"

"How did Zhang Shandai die?"

Sun Yaoting was almost amused by the question. "He died of overeating!"

"We've got a report that he was starved to death."

"His death is no mystery at the temple," Sun Yaoting said. "You only have to make a little investigation to find out the truth. Just before he died, he gobbled up eight pieces of steamed bread and a large bowl of fish at a single meal. I would say he ate himself to

Shao Xiangqing, Liu Ziyu's mentor

death!"

Liu Zijie went on to sow discord and stir up trouble among the eunuchs, making life difficult for Sun Yaoting. Eventually officials of the Religion Office realized what was going on and removed Liu from the temple's management group. A measure of peace was finally restored in the Temple of Prosperity.

4. Quarrels and Fights

The relocation of a group of nuns to the Temple of Prosperity created a tumult. Some were quite young and, in the eyes of eunuchs, great beauties. The temple had only one toilet, and it seemed unnecessary to build another when the nuns first came. The traditional housing compound in Beijing had a single toilet for all its residents. Anyone going to the toilet simply signaled by clearing the throat; no response meant the toilet was unoccupied. But the arrival of the nuns at the temple was soon followed by a series of "toilet incidents". Several eunuchs would barge into the toilet without warning when they knew perfectly well that a woman was inside. When this happened too often to be accidental, the nuns raised a clamor of protest. Finally an earthen wall was built to separate the toilet into two sections.

"Toilet incidents" stopped, but quarrels and conflicts between eunuchs and nuns went on unabated. During a fight the nuns sometimes resorted to shoes and rolling pins and the crudest swearwords available in the local dialect. The eunuchs, though advanced in years, were hardly less combative. In the meantime a few young nuns, unable to resist the allure of money, succumbed to the amorous advances of the eunuchs. Thus eunuch-nun "couples" were occasionally seen strolling the street. The temple management was powerless to intervene in such clandestine affairs.

Hostilities among the eunuchs were common and sometimes escalated into serious fights. Ren, in his eighties, was the oldest eunuch at the temple. He occupied three rooms in the front courtyard together with his adopted son, daughter-in-law and two grandchildren. With the temple's kitchen near his room, he was among the first to arrive when the bells rang at mealtime. During a housing reallocation the temple management asked him to move to the rear courtyard. The old eunuch hit the roof. "What's it all about? Stop harassing a poor old man like me!"

Though the temple management did not force him to move, Ren brooded over the matter all day. Then he got into a brawl with another eunuch named Tian Bichen over a trifle. Accustomed to respectful treatment from other eunuchs due to his seniority, Ren found Tian's insolence and contempt hard to swallow. "Where do you get all that swagger?" he flaunted. "You couldn't even afford to wear boots when you were in Prince Zai Xun's house!"

"What about you?" Tian shot back. "You entered the palace as a child but did not even have a button on your hat when you left as an old man! What makes you believe you are so superior?"

These words touched a raw spot, and Ren went away burning with rage. After a sleepless night, he got out of bed early in the morning and slipped into Tian's room holding a pot of boiling water. Tian just had enough time to raise a hand to shield his head when Ren emptied the pot over him. Hearing Tian's horrible shriek, the other eunuchs ran over to his room. He was groaning in misery, with terrible scalds on his face and hands. "You bastard!" cursed Ren, walking out of the room. "You deserve to be scalded to death!"

Tian had to be taken to the hospital for emergency treatment. He returned to the temple determined to get even with Ren, and Sun Yaoting spent a long time trying to dissuade him. The following day happened to be October 1, the National Day, when Sun Yaoting had to join a parade on Tiananmen Square in the morning. Coming back in the afternoon, he learned that Tian and Ren had had another terrible row, with Ren's daughter-in-law joining in the fight. The situation got so serious that two officials from the temple administration office came to give Ren and his daughter-in-law a severe dressing-down. Ren regarded this as an additional insult. After the two officials left, he stormed into Tian's room to embark on a new round of verbal attack.

Sun Yaoting dragged Ren back to his room and, on behalf of the temple management, offered some concessions to pacify the old eunuch. Ren did not have to move to the rear courtyard against his will. People at the kitchen would always leave some food aside for him, so that he never had to worry about coming late for his meal. As Ren seemed to be mollified, Sun Yaoting went away with relief.

The next morning Sun Yaoting was awakened by a hired hand of the temple. "What's the matter?" he asked sleepily.

"It's terrible! Mr. Ren hanged himself!"

"What?" Sun Yaoting could hardly believe his own ears. "What did you say?"

"Mr. Ren hanged himself! He's dead!"

Flinging a coat on his back, Sun Yaoting followed the man to Tian Bichen's room. The night before, Ren and Tian had got into another fight when they ran into each other at the toilet. With no one else present, Tian shouted a lot of obscenities to the old eunuch. Ren felt he could not swallow such humiliation. He slipped into Tian's room in the dead of night and hanged himself on a beam.

Ren's body was taken down and he was pronounced dead. Sun Yaoting went to the local police station immediately to report the case. The police soon arrived on the scene to examine Ren's body and collect relevant information. At the end of the day they reached the conclusion that Ren had committed suicide.

However, Ren's family members called Tian a "murderer" and kept clamoring for "justice". Among them the daughter-in-law was most vociferous. "My father hanged himself because you had insulted him!" she barked at Tian. "You must pay for it with your life! Otherwise we will crush ourselves to death in front of your door!" His face still covered in bandages, Tian Bichen kept to his room not daring to make a sound.

When consulted about Ren's funeral affairs, his daughter-in-law staggered the temple management with her demands. She wanted a mourning canopy to be built at the temple's expense. Tian Bichen, she said, must keep vigil by the coffin for three days. She also wanted a grand funeral complete with mourning dresses, the chanting of Buddhist sutras, and a long funereal procession. "No way," the management group told her. "We are not living in the Old Society anymore!" Finally the family agreed to have Ren buried in the eunuch cemetery at Enjizhuang west of Beijing.

One of the many things Sun Yaoting did and later regretted was a proposal he made to Beijing's Religion Office. For the sake of efficiency, he suggested, the sixty-one Buddhist and Taoist temples in Beijing could be brought under unified management. His proposal, adopted by the municipal government, made him a "traitor" in the eyes of many Taoist followers. During the next May Day Parade, Taoist and Buddhist followers met at the Temple of Prosperity and set out together for Tiananmen Square. Several Taoist priests pointed their fingers at Sun Yaoting, cursing and swearing. When lining up, both Taoists and Buddhists strove for positions on the north side in order to

The Temple of Great Charity, once the site of Beijing's temple administration office

get a better glimpse of Chairman Mao, who would be viewing the parade from the Tiananmen gate-tower. As the authorities habitually regarded eunuchs and religious devotees with some suspicion, they were eager to demonstrate their political correctness. When it was their turn to shout "Long live Chairman Mao", they did it whole-heartedly and at the top of their lungs. Before setting out, each of them was given a white-paper lotus flower to wear. "This has symbolic meaning," an official explained. "You are like lotus flowers which have 'emerged unstained from the filth'!" Sun Yaoting did not take it as a compliment. "Why do they think we came from the filth?" he muttered to himself.

News of his mother's death overwhelmed Sun Yaoting with grief. He went back to his home village, where he bought a high-quality coffin and arranged a proper funeral. Favorably impressed, the villagers agreed that the deceased was "fortunate" to get buried in such a decent manner. Some even called Sun Yaoting as a filial son. Words could not express how much solace Sun Yaoting found in such comments. As an old saying goes, "Of the three unfilial things to do, the worst is to have no son." For a eunuch to be called filial was perhaps the highest praise he could ever aspire to.

In the Temple of Prosperity Sun Yaoting often met with Xin Xiuming. One day he learned that Xin had already finished his four-volume work,

Anecdotal Accounts from the Qing Palace. "May I have a look at your completed manuscript?" he asked.

Xin agreed with some reluctance. He unlocked a drawer and took out four volumes of manuscript. "Return it as soon as you finish reading. Do not show it to anyone or tell anyone about it."

"I promise," Sun Yaoting said. "You watched me grow up in the palace; you know I can be trusted."

After reading only a few pages, Sun Yaoting became convinced that the book had great historical value. Xin had recorded in great detail his experiences in the Imperial Palace for several dozen years. Written in small characters in the regular Chinese script, the manuscript was also a fine work of calligraphy. A few days later Xin came to take it back. "I've just received a publishing offer!"

"That's great!" Sun Yaoting said. "I'll wait to read the printed book!"

However, the book did not find its way to print. The next time Sun Yaoting asked about it, Xin heaved a long sigh. "At first the publisher told me they would print my book and pay me five hundred yuan. But I did not hear from them for a long time after they took away my manuscript. And you know what the problem is? Someone has accused my work of eulogizing Guangxu and Cixi! What nonsense!"

"What will happen next?" Sun Yaoting asked. "Many people are still waiting to read your published work!"

"Well, they told me they wouldn't publish the book as it is. They wanted to have someone revise and edit it, but I said no. It is my book, and I won't let anyone change a single word of it!"

Finally Xin Xiuming took back his manuscript. "I'll hide it in the mountains and wait for the highest bid!" he declared, quoting an old saying.

13

LIFE IN THE NEW SOCIETY

1. Narrow Escape

Because of his proposal to unify the management of Taoist and Buddhist temples in Beijing, Sun Yaoting made quite a few enemies who regarded him as a "traitor to Taoism". But on the whole he was cautious and prudent in his conduct. This enabled him to emerge from the many political campaigns more or less unscathed. He had a narrow escape though during an "anti-embezzlement and theft" campaign. For four months the eunuchs attended numerous meetings, at which they must expose and denounce one another. Sun Yaoting's name was called.

"Sun Yaoting, you must confess to all your wrongdoings!"

"We know all that you have done! Do you really need us to remind you?"

Sun Yaoting quickly admitted that he had made a couple of secret deals. He had bought four monk's garments at two yuan apiece and sold two of them to a commission shop for twenty yuan. He had also bought a pair of cotton-padded shoes for two yuan and sold it for ten. After he handed in his "illicit income", the case was closed, as the officials in charge seemed convinced that he had made a clean break of it. In contrast, two other members of the temple administration office who adamantly denied all charges of embezzlement came to a miserable end. They were both arrested, and one of them died in prison.

Life usually regained a measure of normality during the intervals between political campaigns. In his daily work as member of the temple administration office, Sun Yaoting got acquainted with quite a few high-level officials in Beijing's religious circles.

One day an editor from a publishing house came to interview him about Pu Yi's past. "Did you meet His Majesty recently?" Sun Yaoting asked.

"Yes," the editor said. "He's now living in Beijing. He has become an ordinary citizen." Pu Yi was then working on an autobiography with the aid of a ghostwriter, and the editor hoped to learn more about his life both in the Imperial Palace of Beijing and in Manchukuo.

"I have very little to say." Sun Yaoting thought it wise to hold his tongue.

Undaunted, the editor came to visit him repeatedly. At last Sun Yaoting told the incident when Pu Yi threatened to shoot him with a revolver. "I remember clearly the way he grabbed me by the ear in the Mind Nurture Hall. The memory still makes me tremble with fear!"

When Pu Yi finished his autobiography, *From Emperor to Citizen*, the publishing house sent Sun Yaoting a large-type typescript to solicit his opinion. Many eunuchs at the temple came to borrow it, curious to know what the "Emperor" had to say about them. At Sun Yaoting's suggestion a new section on eunuchs was added. After the book's publication, Sun Yaoting received a complimentary copy. He read it carefully and sighed with deep emotion. "It's no easy thing for His Majesty to have revealed so much!"

2. A Forum of Eunuchs

One day Sun Yaoting had an unexpected chance to meet some of his old friends and acquaintances at a forum of eunuchs sponsored by the culture and history committee under the National Political Consultative Conference. A total of fifteen aged eunuchs received invitations to give "witness accounts" of the final years of Qing, China's last imperial Dynasty.

Dressed in blue or gray Mao suits, the eunuchs arrived at the office of the National Political Consultative Conference located in the former residence of a Manchu prince. They exchanged greetings warmly, bantering with one another. One of the eunuchs, Wang, had waited on the prince once. "So you are back after all these years," a friend of his joked.

When the opening of the forum was announced, the eunuchs quieted down and took their seats. Tea was served as the official in charge explained the agenda of the meeting. "Today we are gathered here to do one thing only: talk. All participants are eunuchs, so let's make this our topic. We can talk about whatever is on our mind and hopefully will offer some useful data for researchers of the history of late Qing Dynasty."

All the eunuchs had a lot to say about why they had become eunuchs in the first place. No matter which part of the country they came from, poverty seemed to be the prime reason. "In late Qing, people came to Beijing in large groups in order to be eunuchs," said Chen, who had stayed in the Northern Mansion for many years. "Many came from Leling of Shandong Province. I know there was a 'Shandong clique' in the palace; these people bound closely together and helped one another. Parents who sent their boy into the palace cherished the hope that he would enjoy a bright future by becoming a personal attendant of the Emperor. There were also many people from various areas in Hebei, such as Heijian, Dacheng, Wen'an, and Cangzhou."

"I know a story about the eunuchs from Leling," a eunuch named Zhang interjected. "Because of its good fengshui, Leling was destined to produce a hundred great scholars who would succeed in the imperial examinations. Unfortunately the local people built a pagoda in the wrong location. With its fengshui damaged, the place ended up producing a hundred eunuchs!" At his words everyone in the room burst out laughing.

Chen waited for the laughter to subside, then went on. "Eunuchs could come from any place under heaven. Chunshou, for example, is from Jinghai County, isn't he? Even areas near the capital such as Pinggu and Changping are known to have produced quite a few eunuchs. Poverty left people with no choice. Otherwise parents would not have the heart to do such a thing to their son!"

"That's true," agreed Ma Deqing. "Families that sent their children to be eunuchs did so out of desperation. I was born in a village in Tianjin. My family was too poor to own a house or piece of land. My father could barely make a living by selling medicinal plasters. My mother also came from a very poor family; she did not even have any dowry when she married my father. There was never enough food on the table. A distant relative named Li Yuting became a eunuch and got rich. He bought a big house and lots of land. When my father heard this, he thought he had found a way out for me.

He didn't realize that few eunuchs could become that rich!"

"It's almost the same story with me," Sun Yaoting said, "except that my family was a bit better off than his. We owned an adobe house and a small piece of land. My father had high expectations for my future; that's why I learned to read and write. It was my father who castrated me." His voice cracked with emotion as he remembered the most painful moment in his life.

"It was also my father who castrated me," Ma Deqing said, his eyes brimming with tears. "After so many years it's still hard for me to talk about it. It happened in the thirty-first year of Emperor Guangxu's reign. I lay on the kang, and my father cut off my 'root of life' with a knife. There was nothing to relieve pain or stop bleeding. I simply passed out, woke up, and passed out again. As you all know, a tube had to be planted into the urethra, otherwise you would be left with no pee hole after the scab formed, and you would have to go through the 'operation' all over again. It took about a hundred days for the wound to heal; in the end I was more dead than alive because of the terrible pain. What grieved me most was my mother passed away just when I was able to walk on my feet again. She did not live to see the day when I entered the Imperial Palace!"

When it was Zhao Rongsheng's turn, he described the "training" he received before entering the palace. "I got into the palace the year after Ma Deqing got his 'operation'. But first I had to spend a few days at the Office of Palace Justice to learn all the rules. You had to know the proper way to greet all kinds of people, the way to bow, kneel and kowtow. If you saluted the Emperor in the wrong way, you might even lose your head! But when it comes to palace rules, Mr. Wei certainly knows a lot more than I do."

At this Wei Ziqing took over and made a long discourse on palace etiquette. "To sum up, you must do whatever the master or mistress told you to do," said Wang Yuezheng, one of the few well-educated eunuchs. "Nothing was beneath your dignity because you had none. To put it bluntly, a eunuch must not consider himself a human being!"

"I couldn't agree with you more," said Liu Zijie, who had been Pu Yi's personal attendant. "The Emperor regarded himself as the 'Son of Heaven' and all his subjects as inferior beings. To wait on the Emperor did not always bring good fortune to eunuchs. When in a good mood, he might call a eunuch by his pet name and make him crawl on the floor barking or meowing. When in a bad mood, he might order a eunuch to be beaten on the spot."

"No one surpassed Cixi in caprice and malice," remarked Liu Xingqiao, who had once waited on the notorious Empress Dowager. "She liked others to address her as Old Buddha, but she took offence over the most trifling matter, and not a day passed without a eunuch getting chastised or beaten. When one of her eunuchs made a mistake, the others would get implicated. That's why she always had a crowd kneeling in the hall waiting to receive a beating! I'm sure you all know about this incident: In a rage she forced an old eunuch to eat his own feces. He was eventually tortured to death in this way."

The eunuchs responded with deep sighs and murmurs of agreement. At this Sun Yaoting spoke up. "As a rule, eunuchs seldom came to a good end. A few senior eunuchs managed to save enough money to live in comfort after leaving the palace, though that did not necessarily mean they were happy. Life was much harder for low-ranking eunuchs like us. Those who had no money on leaving the palace became homeless vagabonds; some of them were starved or frozen to death on the street. Those who got enough money to secure a place to stay at a temple should consider themselves lucky."

"You are right on that!" many eunuchs nodded their agreement. "We should consider ourselves extremely fortunate to have lived to this day!"

3. The Great Turbulence

The Cultural Revolution that began in 1966 turned many things upside down in China. The remaining eunuchs in Beijing, along with Buddhists, Taoists, Catholics and Christians, were gathered at a farm in Xibeiwang of suburban Beijing to undergo "reform through labor". The temple administration office was turned into a "production management team". Sun Yaoting became a member of the team's leadership along with Luo Fulin from the Southern Cathedral at the Xuanwumen and Shao Fengyuan from the Protestant Church at Xisi. Some eunuchs considered this something to be proud of. "We have a eunuch in our leadership!"

A few days after his appointment, Sun Yaoting saw a big-character poster at the front gate. The title screamed: "How can eunuchs – the

Emperor's slaves in the Old Society – lead the Great Proletarian Cultural Revolution?" It was signed by "revolutionary Catholic and Christian masses".

Under the volatile atmosphere what Sun Yaoting did next proved very unwise. When he went to the canteen for lunch as usual, the pancake he bought was only half-cooked. After eating some of it, he gave up and went to enjoy a good meal at a small restaurant nearby. Soon another poster appeared to denounce his "decadent bourgeois lifestyle". Sensing imminent danger, he found an excuse to leave for the Guanghuasi, the Temple of Great Deliverance.

The moment he stepped into the temple the old gatekeeper took him aside and told him in a whisper, "You are lucky to be here! The Red Guards are beating Ma Deqing!"

"How come? Everything was all right at Xibeiwang when I left in the morning!"

"I'm telling you the truth!" the gatekeeper said. "I just received a phone call. They said the Red Guards are looking for you. You would be the first to suffer if you stayed there!"

After thinking for a while, Sun Yaoting went to see Li Guang, director of the Municipal Religion Committee. "They can't do this!" Li said. He picked up the phone and asked for the person in charge at Xibeiwang. "No beating is allowed! Is that clear? It is against the Party's policy to beat up a man just because he's a eunuch! For many years Ma Deqing has been working for the repair and maintenance of temples in this city. He has done a good job. You must guarantee his safety!"

The phone call probably saved Ma Deqing's life, but it had little effect on the general political climate. The national mania of the Cultural Revolution reached a crescendo when Chairman Mao Zedong ascended the gate-tower of Tiananmen Square to review Red Guards coming from all across the country. At the Temple of Great Deliverance people were summoned to listen to live radio broadcast of the event. They sweated a lot in the summer heat, feeling apprehensive about their future. Sun Yaoting got unusually thirsty and went out to buy several ice-lollies, which he finished at one go. Soon he began to feel funny in the stomach. He suffered loose bowels and made numerous trips to the toilet while the other eunuchs listened to the crowds at Tiananmen shouting themselves hoarse.

Sun Yaoting had every reason to worry about his future. He had saved three taels of gold as protection against old age. But anything could happen at such a hectic time. Some people, tucking away a little gold just as he did, had been accused of "hoarding gold to sabotage the Cultural Revolution" and clubbed to death by Red Guards.

In the initial period of the Cultural Revolution the Red Guards overran the country. Among other things, they set out to eliminate the "four olds" – old ideas, old culture, old customs and old habits. Temples and churches, regarded as "bastions of superstition", became the targets of vicious acts of vandalism fueled by political fervor.

A team of Red Guards stormed into the main hall of the Temple of Great Deliverance, tied ropes on the gilded statue of Buddha, and pulled it to the ground. The statue broke into pieces of clay amid a thick fog of dust. Several eunuchs saw it happen right in front of their eyes, but they dared not utter a word, let alone intervene. An old saying occurred to Sun Yaoting: "Even gods fear evil people."

Suddenly there rose a big racket outside. He walked out to find several Red Guards perching on the roof of the main hall. They were removing the decorative animals and throwing them to the ground, where they crashed into pieces. The other Red Guards watched and cheered.

"Hold it!" A lanky old man came out from the rear courtyard to confront the Red Guards. "What do you think you are doing?"

"We are eliminating the four olds as Chairman Mao has taught us!" The leading Red Guard answered. "Who are you?"

"I'm a religious worker!"

"Whatever worker you are, if you dare stand in our way, we'll crush you to pieces along with the four olds!" A female Red Guard barked, waving a leather belt.

An old monk went up to the leading Red Guard. "This is Comrade Li Guang, director of Beijing's Religion Committee!"

"Since he is an official, he has the duty to support us in eliminating the four olds!"

"Such acts as yours cannot be supported!" Li Guang said firmly. "You think you are eliminating the four olds? You are destroying our cultural heritage! The Temple of Great Deliverance is a cultural site under state protection!"

The leading Red Guard hesitated, then beckoned those on the roof to come down. After a short discussion with some of his companions, he came to address Li Guang in a polite tone. "We didn't realize this is a cultural site under state protection. We won't break the animal figures on the roof, but you must guarantee that no activity of feudal superstition will ever be held here in the future!" With this the Red Guards beat a retreat.

It was hard to tell what would come to be classified as the four olds. From another eunuch at the temple, Sun Yaoting learned that the Red Guards had dug up Li Lianying's tomb at Enjizhuang. "You won't guess what they found in the coffin! A head without the torso!"

Sun Yaoting did not say anything. Having been to the eunuchs' cemetery at Enjizhuang many times, he knew the grave quite well. It stood apart from the other tombs and had two stone tablets. Li's family continued to visit his tomb every year even after 1949. The discovery of the severed head reminded Sun Yaoting of a conversation between Xiaode Zhang and Yao Mengshan many years before.

They were in the parlor of Zhang's house in Tianjin. While Zhang and Yao sat chatting, Sun Yaoting stood by their side in attendance.

"Li was an astute man, but he did not plan well for his future on leaving the palace," Zhang remarked. "So I made sure that I wouldn't commit the same mistake again. As you know, the three consorts of Emperor Tongzhi hated me because I helped make Longyu the Empress Dowager after Cixi's demise. At Longyu's death I knew I had to get out of there."

"The situation looked pretty bad for you," Yao agreed. "I was

Li Lianying's tomb in western Beijing

wondering why you hadn't run away earlier."

"I couldn't even if I wanted to, because I was closely watched. I would have come to the same end as Li Lianying if I had left the palace immediately. Apart from the high consorts, I also had many enemies among the eunuchs. From what I heard, they planned to beat me up the moment I stepped outside the palace. So I went to the Palace of Peaceful Longevity to offer condolences to Longyu, knowing that no one dared touch me when I was dressed in mourning. But instead of a formal mourning dress, I put on a sheepskin coat inside out. After I kowtowed to Longyu's coffin, I left the palace by the Western Flowery Gate without stopping to change clothes."

"We gathered at the Eastern Flowery Gate waiting to see you off," Yao said. "There must be hundreds of people there. Some had it in their mind to beat you up. But you never showed up!"

Zhang laughed. "I knew they were waiting for me! That's why I told everyone I would leave at the Eastern Flowery Gate but arranged for General Zhang Xun's men to meet me at the Western Flowery Gate. I did not even stop at my house in the capital but went straight to Tianjin by train."

Both the conversation between Zhang and Yao and the latest discovery of the head in Li Lianying's tomb seemed to bear out speculations that Li did not die a natural death but was murdered by his enemies.

Sun Yaoting's youngest brother suddenly paid him a visit. "Things are going rough in the village. What shall we do about your 'treasure'?"

Sun Yaoting hesitated, feeling a bit dazed. His brother was talking about his severed genitals, which the family had kept all these years. On New Year's Eve they used to bring out the "treasure" and hold a sacrificial ceremony to pray for peace and good fortune on his behalf.

"They are wiping out the 'four olds' in the village, and we've been told we must get rid of the 'treasure'. What can we do?"

Sun Yaoting scratched his head. "Throw it away then. That'll save us a lot of trouble!"

"What?" His brother was flabbergasted. "I thought you'd want me to bring it here!"

"No need to do it," Sun Yaoting said curtly, with a sweep of his hand. Thus the "treasure" that had been well kept for over half a century was thrown away.

Shortly afterward Sun Yaoting was made to face the music. In the evening some Red Guards took him to a separate room in the temple for interrogation. "You must make a true confession! You were a slave to the 'Emperor' and 'Empress' in the palace. How much gold and silver do you hoard?"

"I don't have any gold or silver."

"That's impossible!" A Red Guard rolled up his sleeves threateningly. "You must tell us the truth!"

"I only have three taels of gold left," Sun Yaoting finally said. He did not want to die for the gold.

"Where is it?"

"I sewed it inside my cotton-padded trousers."

"Where are you hiding your trousers?"

"It's in the luggage I sent to the train station."

"What a deceitful eunuch!" The Red Guards decided to escort him back to his home village.

4. Homecoming in Disgrace

The Beijing Railway Station was thronged with young people wearing red armbands. Instead of announcing arrivals and departures, the loudspeakers kept blaring the most popular song at the time, "Rebellion Is Reasonable".

Led by four Red Guards, two boys and two girls, Sun Yaoting threaded through the crowds and finally came before the train he was to board. Large characters written in black ink marked out the compartment for "Reactionary Elements". As soon as he got on board, Sun Yaoting was given a wooden placard designating him as "Big Landlord" to hang on his neck. Looking around, he realized that he was very much in his own company. The passengers all belonged to the "Five Reactionary Categories", namely, landlords, wealthy peasants, counterrevolutionaries, "bad elements", and Rightists. Each was escorted by several Red Guards. Before the train started they were warned against "talking and acting irresponsibly".

The trip lasted two hours. The moment the train stopped at the station in Tianjin, a band of Red Guards jumped on board. They walked up and down the compartments surveying the "reactionaries", each holding a broad leather belt. A young girl with her hair worn into a plait sticking upward was going around shouting in a harsh voice. "You, five reactionary categories! Behave yourselves! Our leather belts are not for decoration only!" Much to Sun Yaoting's horror, she noticed his hairstyle and came up. "You, five black categories! Why do you have your hair parted like that?"

Sun Yaoting was too nervous to say a word. The strong Tianjin accent of the young girl, sounding so familiar yet so strange, sent a shiver down his spine.

"Come here," the girl called to a male Red Guard nearby. "Cut his hair!"

The boy brought out a pair of scissors from the military satchel he was carrying. It took him less than a minute to finish his job, leaving Sun Yaoting half-bald. He examined what he had done with a satisfied look. "You know what this is? It's called the yin-yang head! It marks you out as a black-five, so anyone can tell what you are!" Sun Yaoting kept silent, showing no sign of his indignation.

The Red Guards retrieved Sun Yaoting's luggage at the station and searched the cotton-padded trousers for the gold. They exchanged suspicious looks when they found it. "This is so small! Does it weigh three taels?"

"I don't know how I can make you believe it, but it does weigh three taels." Sun Yaoting gestured with both hands. "A sixteen-tael gold ingot in the palace is only this size!"

"All right. If we should find out you've lied to us, we'll make you pay for it!" A female Red Guard warned him, shaking her fist.

Sun Yaoting's homecoming had never been so dramatic. Two of the Red Guards entered the village first, spreading the news. When the other two Red Guards escorted him into the village, hundreds of people came to watch.

"Hey, Sun Yaoting is coming home again!"

"He was a eunuch attendant for many years, you know. He has seen the world!"

"So what? Isn't he taken back home now? He must have done something bad!"

It so happened that the Tianjin police had just put a white-haired old man on their wanted list. Many people, including some of Sun Yaoting's fellow villagers, thought the police was after him. The Red Guards in the nearby villagers all hurried over at the news. After checking him against the photo of the wanted man, they realized it was a mistake. They tried to decide how to deal with him, and some suggested they simply let him go.

"Shall we call a meeting to denounce him?"

"Well, he's a temple administration worker in Beijing."

"But he's also a big landlord! We should make him do penal labor under surveillance!"

Two Red Guards took Sun Yaoting to his home. On the way Sun Yaoting met his younger brother, who greeted him warmly, "So you are back!"

"You know him?" asked a Red Guard.

"He's my big brother!"

"Don't you realize he's a landlord?"

"He's a landlord?" Sun Yaoting's brother shot back. "I don't know if he's a landlord or not!"

In Sun Yaoting's house they met another Red Guard whose armband designated him a "platoon leader". He turned out to be Sun Yaoting's nephew.

"How can a landlord's nephew be a Red Guard?" The Red Guards from Beijing murmured in puzzlement as they left.

Sun Yaoting's nephew burst into tears. "How did you become a landlord when our family was so poor all along?"

"This is a political campaign," Sun Yaoting explained, "when things like this just happen."

"But they can't make an accusation that's totally groundless!"

"Well, they classify me as a landlord because of the land that actually belongs to the temple," Sun Yaoting said. "It doesn't matter all that much."

"Yes it does! I can't be a Red Guard platoon leader when my uncle is a landlord!"

The next morning the nephew went to the township government to hand in his Red Guard armband. In the meantime rumors about Sun Yaoting's wealth circulated in the village. According to a story, he had a hoard of four gold bars and two gold ingots. Sun Yaoting responded to such rumors with a sad smile. His lifelong savings amounted to three taels of gold, now taken away by the Red Guards. He did not bother to explain, knowing no one would believe him.

Sun Yaoting was assigned to work in a vegetable garden. He did not mind manual labor, but he stooped under the weight of the large wooden placard the Red Guards ordered him to hang on his neck. For a whole morning he carried the placard around in the garden. After lunch Mei Dakui, group leader in charge of the garden, told him to remove it. Sun Yaoting hesitated. "The Red Guards wanted me to keep wearing it!"

"Do as I tell you. Here at this garden, whatever I say goes!"

"I don't want to get you into trouble."

"What are you so afraid of? Everyone in this village knows what a kind of person you really are!"

A few days later the four Beijing Red Guards left. Then the Party secretary of the village sent for Sun Yaoting. "Our village just suffered a crop failure and is short of food. Is it possible for you to go back to Beijing?"

"I was taken home by Red Guards, wasn't I?" Sun Yaoting replied. "I must return to Beijing in the same way."

"If you want the Red Guards here to take you back, you'll have to pay for their expenses."

"That'll be no problem. I need them to prove my return is authorized."

Thus Sun Yaoting returned to Beijing accompanied by two Red Guards from his home village. He entered the Temple of Great Deliverance and greeted Li Guang in the hall.

A bit surprised, Li Guang nevertheless did not hesitate to welcome him back. "His return saves us from sending clothes to the village," he said to the Red Guards. "It's getting cold these days."

"What about the luggage he left in the village?" asked the Red Guards.

"You have to return him everything," Li Guang said firmly.

Sun Yaoting made a return trip home to take his luggage, this time with no wooden placard hanging on his neck.

Quite a few old eunuchs died during the most turbulent period in the Cultural Revolution. Some of them, such as Sun Yaoting's old friend Sun Shangxian, died of illness and old age. It was his daughter who informed Sun Yaoting of his illness. Sun Yaoting immediately paid him a visit, then went to see Li Guang to explain the situation. Li promptly agreed to give the dying eunuch a special subsidy of fifty yuan. Sun Shangxian passed away a few days later.

The death of Liu Zijie, a well-known hoarder, had something to do with the Red Guards. Through the years he had accumulated a few pieces of expensive clothing, which he seldom wore but guarded jealously. With Red Guards smashing and looting all over the city, he entrusted the clothes to his mentor. Unfortunately they all disappeared after some Red Guards ransacked his mentor's house. Overwhelmed with rage and regret, he became seriously ill and soon died of a broken heart.

For several eunuchs including Feng Leting, Zhao Rongsheng, Zhang Xiude, Bian Fachang and Wang Yuecheng, one of the biggest calamities inflicted by the Red Guards was the destruction of their coffins kept in the Temple of Prosperity. With one foot in the grave, they counted a coffin of quality wood and fine workmanship as their most treasured possession. Some shed tears of grief over what they regarded as an irretrievable loss.

After a couple of years of anarchy the People's Liberation Army was called in to restore order in the country. Even the Temple of Great Deliverance was placed under military control. Army officers called discussion meetings at which each eunuch had to make a statement of his position. They invariably admitted to being "dregs of feudalism" and professed firm support for the "Great Cultural Revolution". Sun Yaoting and Ma Deqing, among others, received official rehabilitation thanks to their sincerity of attitude. Liu Zijie, Tian Bichen and a few others failed to impress the authorities favorably and were "shelved" indefinitely. Full of fear and anxiety, Tian left the temple for his home village and died shortly afterward.

For a long time during the Cultural Revolution, Xibeiwang served as a quasi labor camp for people from Beijing's temples and churches. Against the backdrop of the scenic Western Hills eunuchs toiled side by side with Buddhists, Taoists, and Christians.

On the farm Sun Yaoting made quite a few new friends. Fu Tieshan, Liu Futing, Sun Shang'en, Song Guo'an, and Shi Yukun from the Southern Cathedral worked so hard that they gained the epithet "five tiger-generals". Sun Yaoting also made a name there by his good winnowing skills.

When winter was coming, people all over Beijing began to buy and store Chinese cabbage, the main if not the only vegetable for the entire season. On the farm they had to move tons of cabbage into cellars. Despite his old age, Sun Yaoting worked in the cold and damp cellar for hours stacking cabbage. When he finally got out, soaked in sweat and aching all over, he had already contracted rheumatism in the legs.

One day he complained about his rheumatism when chatting with Ma Deqing. "I met someone a few days ago," Ma said abruptly. "You'll never guess who it was!"

"So who was it?" Sun Yaoting asked. "And why are you looking so cheerful?"

"I was suffering from diarrhea for a quite some time, and the medicine they gave me didn't work. Then I found out that Dr. Dong is practicing in a hospital in Dongcheng District. He recognized me when I went to see him! I took the two herbs he prescribed and got well in no time."

"I'm not surprised," Sun Yaoting said. "An imperial physician is no ordinary doctor! I wish I could be a doctor and do good deeds every day."

Toward the end of the Cultural Revolution the eunuchs moved back to the Temple of Great Deliverance to spend their remaining years in peace and quiet. Several of Sun Yaoting's old acquaintances such as Wei Ziqing and Dai Shouchen passed away here.

14

THE FINAL YEARS

1. The Last Eunuch of China

In the early 1980s Sun Yaoting, Ma Deqing and Liu Xingqiao in the Temple of Great Deliverance were the last remaining eunuchs in China. Sun Yaoting lived in a room on the east while Ma Deqing stayed in the west courtyard. They had visitors from all over China and other countries. Sun Yaoting certainly had much knowledge and information to impart. After leaving the palace, he had stayed at several temples and worked for years at the temple administration office; thus he became an expert on Beijing's temples. Quite a few researchers in the field came to consult him. When the annals of Haidian District were being compiled, the editor called on him and learned, among other things, valuable information about the history of Lord Guan's Temple. Though not strong enough to speak for long periods of time, Sun Yaoting received the guests warmly and enjoyed answering their questions.

Sun Yaoting with his great grandson in the Temple of Great Deliverance

In contrast, Ma Deqing did not like to chat with visitors. His idea of a good time was a drink or two followed by a sound sleep. When urged, he would say a few words on his favorite topic: how poverty had driven him to be a eunuch. He evaded all other questions, saying, "Go and ask Mr. Sun. He has a better memory."

Unlike Sun Yaoting, Liu Xingqiao and Ma Deqing did not enjoy good health. In a few years they both passed away. Sun Yaoting asked them the same question: "Where is your 'treasure'? Are you still keeping it?"

They both gave the same reply. "No, it's long gone! It got thrown away when we were 'reactionary elements'!"

The deaths of Liu Xingqiao and Ma Deqing made Sun Yaoting the only living eunuch in the country. Born in 1902, he witnessed the course of Chinese history for nearly a century from the unique perspective of a eunuch – the early days of the Republic, the puppet regime of Manchukuo, the Japanese occupation, the rule of Kuomingtang as well as the Cultural Revolution. Scholars and journalists from China and overseas took great interest in his life experience.

Though Sun Yaoting generally enjoyed chatting with people, occasionally there were moments of sadness and flashes of anger when he received the assortment of visitors. One day a visitor from a Western country lingered for a long time on a topic that was especially painful to Sun Yaoting: his physical mutilation as a eunuch and its effects on his life. At one point he choked on his words and burst into tears. But the visitor continued with his relentless questions. Among other things, he wanted to know if a eunuch had sexual desires and outlets. Startled by the bluntness of the question, Sun Yaoting responded with silence, and the visitor left with his curiosity unsatisfied. Back home, he sent Sun Yaoting a letter care of the Municipal Bureau of Religion, whose officials opened it to find a poker card showing an oversize male organ. They decided not to give the letter to Sun Yaoting.

Another Western journalist had a similar interest but was less subtle in his approach. He asked lots of mundane questions during the allotted interview time. When the interpreter went away for a short moment, he suddenly picked up his camera and in halting Chinese asked Sun Yaoting to take off his trousers for a close-up shot. Sun Yaoting's face turned crimson with rage. "Get out of here!" he shouted, pointing his finger at the visitor.

"You'll get paid!" The visitor hastily brought out a stack of dollar bills from his pocket. "Here, take it!"

This enraged Sun Yaoting even more. "The Chinese have no use for it!" He roared, hitting the floor with his walking stick. "Get out of here! Get out!"

Xiu Ming (right), the abbot of the Temple of Great Deliverance

After the visitor went away, Sun Yaoting flopped into the chair, breathing heavily. "What the hell!" he cursed.

Most visitors were friendly and courteous. Sun Yaoting got very well acquainted with a West German journalist stationed in Beijing who spoke fluent Chinese. One day he came with a Chinese woman. "This is my wife," he told Sun Yaoting.

The woman walked up to greet Sun Yaoting and shook hands with him. "My name is Yuan Hong."

"Are you a Beijinger?" Sun Yaoting asked.

"Yes, I am. Do I sound like one?"

"Yes, you certainly do. You have a Beijing accent."

"Do I look like a Red Guard?"

"What?" Sun Yaoting started.

"Are you afraid of the Red Guards?"

"Why shouldn't I be afraid of them?" Sun Yaoting asked in reply. What had happened in those chaotic years remained vivid in his memory.

"I was a Red Guard!" she declared, laughing. "But you don't have to be afraid of me!"

Sun Yaoting scrutinized her closely, trying in vain to find a trace of the Red Guard in this vivacious and stylish woman. "Yuan Hong... Well, isn't it a good name!" he finally said.

Sun Yaoting also received a lot of Chinese journalists. A few days after the Lunar New Year a journalist came to the Temple of Great Deliverance to interview him. Leaning on his walking stick, Sun Yaoting greeted the visitor at the gate and ushered him into the room.

"Are you having a good time during the New Year holidays?"

"Yes. Look!" Sun Yaoting pointed at the food on the table. "I've got nothing to complain about! The Religion Bureau has sent me beef, chicken, and meatballs. And the cook at the temple made this bowl of meat dumplings especially for me! They've been really nice to me!"

"Are the apples for you, too?"

"Of course! I have very good teeth!" Sun Yaoting opened his mouth to show his white teeth. "Do you think this is the only thing I can eat?" he asked, picking up a box of cake. "I can eat this also!" He picked up a pear and burst into happy laughter.

"How did you spend the New Year when you were in the palace?" the visitor moved closer and asked in a loud voice.

"You don't have to yell at me," Sun Yaoting looked a bit displeased. "I can hear you all right! The New Year celebration was not much fun for junior eunuchs like me because we had to kowtow to all kinds of people all the time. You couldn't afford to break the rules of etiquette in the palace, which might mean the difference between life and death."

"When did New Year greetings begin in the palace?"

"On New Year's Eve and New Year's Day, we went around kowtowing nonstop. If we ran into the Emperor or the Empress followed by a team of head eunuchs, it would take us a long time to get on our feet again! It gave me bruised knees and a swollen forehead!"

"Nowadays you no longer need to do it," a young man at the temple remarked. "People come to greet you instead!"

"I am lucky to have survived," Sun Yaoting said with a smile. "In the old days homeless people used to starve to death on the street on New Year's Eve."

"How much do you get paid each month?" the reporter asked.

"I have a monthly salary of more than forty yuan," Sun Yaoting replied. "For me it's more than enough. I get my meals from the canteen, I have someone to wash my clothes for me, and when I get ill they send for a doctor. I have newspapers delivered to my room every day. If I want to eat something special, I can just ask anyone in the temple to buy it for me."

One day a journalist asked Sun Yaoting to demonstrate his calligraphic skills. Picking up the writing brush, Sun Yaoting wrote from memory a stanza from Du Fu's poem, "Song of Eight Immortals":

> Inspired by a pot of liquor, Li Bai composes a hundred poems,
> Then nods off in the wine shop on the street of Chang'an.
> The boat from the Son of Heaven calls for him, but in vain.
> "When drunk, I become an immortal," he declares.

Impressed, the journalist subsequently wrote an article in which he speculated why Sun Yaoting, a teetotaler, should like such a poem about eight "drunkards". The former eunuch attendant, he thought, must be showing his admiration for Li Bai, a great Tang poet. Though he once served as a court official, Li Bai refused to curry favor with his imperial master at the expense of personal dignity.

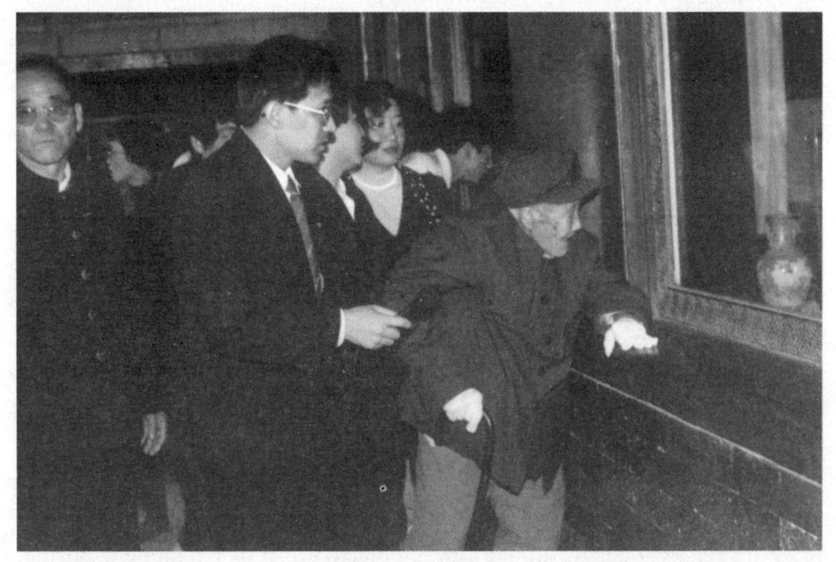

Sun Yaoting got out of his wheelchair before the Palace of Gathering Elegance

Apart from receiving a lot of journalists, Sun Yaoting kept in touch with his friends and acquaintances. Fu Tieshan, Archbishop of Beijing's Catholic Church, visited him several times. They had remained good friends since meeting on the farm at Xibeiwang in the Cultural Revolution.

One day a man came to the temple, saying he was from the Public Security Bureau of Beijing. Sun Yaoting looked at him with apprehension.

"You used to know Zhao Rongsheng, didn't you?" the man asked.

"Yes, he's an old friend of mine."

"I am his adopted son."

"Oh!" Sun Yaoting had actually met him before but could not recognize him after many years. In their conversation Sun Yaoting learned for the first time how Zhao Rongsheng had come to an unhappy end. Zhao returned to his home village in Cangzhou in the late period of the Cultural Revolution. Accustomed to living in the capital, he felt ill at ease at his own home and died soon afterward.

"He shouldn't have gone back," Sun Yaoting sighed. "He was such a nice person, and we got along so well. He wouldn't have died so early if he had chosen to stay in Beijing!"

Some days later Sun Yaoting again failed to recognize an old acquaintance. "You look very familiar to me," he told a visitor about sixty years old. "But I can't remember who you are!"

"My name is Zhang Jihe."

Sun Yaoting looked blank.

"Uncle, I'm Xiaode Zhang's second grandson!"

"Oh!" Sun Yaoting bowed with clasped hands. "Excuse me for my bad memory. I'm really old now!"

Of Xiaode Zhang's three grandsons, Zhang Jihe was the smartest. After 1949 he sold his luxury mansion to the government and moved into a much smaller house. His elder brother, on the other hand, was living in an old people's home. His younger brother, who had worked as a hired hand at Lord Guan's Temple, never got married. "Why don't you help him build a family?" Sun Yaoting asked with a look of disapproval.

"Not much of a chance," Zhang Jihe replied. "He's going on fifty already."

Zhang then revealed why he had come: to ask for a written statement about his past signed by Sun Yaoting. Subjected to unfair treatment during the Cultural Revolution, he was collecting the documents needed for his rehabilitation. Afterwards Zhang Jihe came to Beijing to visit Sun Yaoting once every year, and they kept writing to each other. After completing a book on his notorious grandfather, Zhang sent the manuscripts to Beijing to solicit Sun Yaoting's suggestions and criticism.

2. Revisiting the Forbidden City

At the age of eighty-three, Sun Yaoting revisited the Forbidden City, now called the Palace Museum, for the first time in sixty years. Nan, a cadre from Beijing's Bureau of Religion and Xiaoling, a girl working at the Temple of Great Deliverance, took him there on a pushcart.

They arrived in the early morning, entering the palace by the Gate of Divine Prowess. Sun Yaoting looked at all the familiar sights, his mind awash with memories. "There," he pointed out the absence of threshold at a gate. "The Emperor had it chopped off when he was learning to ride a bicycle."

They turned west. "It was Xiaode Zhang who supervised the construction of this road," Sun Yaoting pointed to a path paved with

Sun Yaoting with the author's wife (left) and daughter (right)

broken stones. "Take a close look at its design and you'll get an idea what an audacious man he was!"

"Wow." His two companions marveled at the picture of a man kneeling on a washboard to ask for his wife's forgiveness. "A manifesto of sexual equality in the Imperial Palace!"

Sun Yaoting smiled. "Xiaode Zhang was quite an extraordinary person, I assure you!"

When the pushcart entered the Palace of Gathering Elegance, Sun Yaoting's eyes lit up as he surveyed the surroundings. "This is Wanrong's bedchamber. Look at the side room to the north. Eunuchs on night duty slept on the floor in that room. And this is where Wanrong played on the swing." He pointed out the iron rings to Nan and Xiaoling. "Though the swing has been removed, the rings are still there!"

"You have excellent eyesight!" Nan said. "Yes, I see the iron rings now!"

"I can describe a lot of things with my eyes closed," Sun Yaoting said with a satisfied smile.

"Where was Pu Yi then?" Xiaoling asked.

"The Emperor usually stayed at the Mind Nurture Hall and seldom came here. When he did, we felt so happy for Wanrong that we clapped our hands in secret! I don't know why we felt so happy for her!" Somehow Sun Yaoting found the topic very funny and kept chuckling to himself.

At the Gate of Heavenly Purity he pointed out the "Three Great Halls" to the south – the Hall of Supreme Harmony, the Hall of Complete Harmony and the Hall of Preserving Harmony. "We eunuchs could not go there," he said. "They were taken up by the warlords."

They followed a stream of crowd into the Mind Nurture Hall, which happened to be holding an "Exhibition of the Life of the Last Emperor and Empress". "Let's take a look," Sun Yaoting said. With Nan and Xiaoling supporting him on either side, he walked up the steps into the dimly lit hall. A rope stretching across the hall stopped visitors from going further. "Nothing has changed," he said.

"Look again," Nan said. "This place is newly painted!"

At this the young female guide on duty walked up to them. Sun Yaoting might appear somewhat familiar to her, for he was featured in a recently released film, *Legends of Old Beijing*. Nan introduced Sun Yaoting. "This is Mr. Sun, who used to wait on the Empress in the palace!"

"Welcome! You are an honored guest!" The guide invited Sun Yaoting to enter the roped area for a closer look. The news spread quickly among the visitors. Ignoring the "No Photography" sign, some raised their cameras for a snapshot of the last eunuch back in the Forbidden City. On leaving the hall Sun Yaoting apologized to the guide for causing trouble.

At noon they exited the Forbidden City by the Gate of Divine Prowess. "It's been sixty years!" Sun Yaoting sighed. "I will come back again sometime!"

3. Peaceful Old Age

One day a young man at the temple came to Sun Yaoting's room. "Mr. Sun, I find your name in today's evening paper!"

"But I've met no reporter recently," Sun Yaoting said. "What's the article about?"

"Here, take a look."

It was a short notice at the bottom corner saying a "Taiwan compatriot" had sent a letter to Beijing looking for Sun Yaoting. He was puzzled. "Who could it be?"

Sun Yaoting at Tian'anmen Square

When he opened the letter, which the young man fetched for him, tears welled up in his eyes. It was sent by Liu Ziyu's adopted son, who had left for Taiwan as the civil war was raging on in the late 1940s. For the next forty years he was out of contact with Sun Yaoting. Then, accidentally, he learned from a newspaper article that Sun Yaoting was still alive, so he sent a letter to Beijing. Sun Yaoting was eager to write a letter in reply, but a severe attack of diarrhea confined him to bed for several days. After he recovered, he was able to write a long letter in a shaky handwriting.

A little short-tempered as a young man, Sun Yaoting grew calm and good-natured in old age. People around considered him an affable old man and pleasant company. Young novices at the temple often came to ask about his life in the Imperial Palace. The gatekeeper also enjoyed chatting with him. A bricklayer who did some temporary job for the temple made a walking stick for Sun Yaoting, saying the stick had the function of preventing numbness of the limbs and paralysis. "In the second half of my life," Sun Yaoting said, "I've met lots of people who are very kind to me!"

Though still in good health, Sun Yaoting began to have difficulty moving about. The Buddhist Association arranged for Gao, a sixty-year-old woman from Anhui Province to take care of him. Sun Yaoting already knew her quite well, for she had come to help him from time to time while looking after two aged monks at the Temple of Great Deliverance. Now that both monks had passed away, she was reassigned to look after Sun Yaoting. She soon found out that Sun Yaoting could be very finicky. One day he gave her some money to buy two jin of sugar for him. When she handed him the sugar and the change, he asked, "How much a jin is it?" She said she didn't know. "How much does this weigh?" he asked again. "Is this exactly two jin?" She didn't know that either. "I'll go back to the shop and ask them," she finally said.

When Gao returned to tell him the price of sugar, Sun Yaoting smiled. "I know how much sugar costs. I just want to make sure you are clearheaded."

After this incident Gao complained to several people at the temple about Sun Yaoting's parsimony. "He's not really a miser," one of them told her. "He just likes to keep clear accounts. That's his specialty. He used to be the bookkeeper for all the temples in Beijing."

Despite his old age Sun Yaoting enjoyed doing things with his own hands. It was Gao's duty to sweep the yard every day. When she went on a

Sun Yaoting and Mrs. Gao

sick leave for three days, Sun Yaoting took up her job voluntarily and kept the yard very clean. Though hardworking, Gao did not pay much attention to details. For one thing, she wiped the table in a perfunctory way so that a thick layer of oily filth accumulated on its surface. While she was away on sick leave, Sun Yaoting scrubbed the table with hot alkaline water. On her return she found the table shining with cleanness. "How did you do it?" she asked in amazement.

Sun Yaoting grinned. "That's one of the basic skills I learned as a eunuch in the palace!"

One day he handed Gao five yuan.

"What's it for?" Gao asked in surprise.

"You work hard all day long, and I know you don't earn a high salary. So I'd like to pay you a little extra out of my own pocket."

"How can I take your money?"

"Please do. If you go on doing a good job, I'll give you an additional five yuan every month."

"Thanks so much," Gao said gratefully.

"You are welcome," Sun Yaoting smiled. He felt genuine sympathy for this old woman from Anhui, an underdeveloped province in east China famous for its export of household servants. On the other hand, he really savored the moment of tipping her. Having spent the better part of his life as a servant, he derived immense satisfaction from giving such tips "just like a master".

For dozens of years after 1949 the Temple of Great Deliverance was closed to the public. During the day it occasionally received prearranged groups of worshippers. Otherwise it was a quiet and secluded place, and Sun Yaoting lived there almost like a hermit. For him, Gao was more than a servant; she was also an almost indispensable companion. After supper he usually sat down for a chat with her. When winter came, life got a bit difficult for him. With no central heating in the temple, he had to keep a coal stove burning in his room. If the fire went out at night, he would be freezing the next morning and sometimes catch a severe cold as a result. Gao suggested that she stay the night in the outer room to better look after him. Sun Yaoting thought it a good idea at first, but dropped it eventually. At that time the unreasonably rigid public attitude toward male-female relationships made it unthinkable for a sixty-year-old woman to sleep in virtually the same room with an old eunuch.

When the Temple of Great Deliverance was getting ready to open to the public, the management somehow thought it would tarnish the image of the temple to keep a woman servant. Gao lost her job and had to leave for her home village in Anhui. Sun Yaoting gave her some money as a parting gift. "Come to visit me when you are back in Beijing next time!"

"Sure!" Gao said. "I will come to see you!"

However, they both knew that they would probably never see each other again.

After Gao left, Sun Yaoting suddenly felt terribly lonely. He had felt the same way when his long-time companion Ma Deqing died some years before. In the evening he slipped into bed and turned on his portable radio, drifting into sleep with Beijing opera still playing by his ears.

To replace Gao, the temple management first sent a couple of young monks. Then an old monk named Juexiu moved into the outer room. He had entered a monastery at Miyun in suburban Beijing at eight, over half a century before.

Going on ninety, Sun Yaoting began to feel rigid in his legs and could not walk for long distances even on his stick. He was told not to leave the temple on his own. However, he wanted to have the freedom to move around and felt reluctant to be always accompanied, so he had a carpenter make him a specially designed four-wheel handcart that he could both lean on and sit in.

On a fine day he would leave the temple leaning on his handcart, which held a bottle of drinking water, a towel, and a cotton-padded cushion. Having found a spot to his liking, he sat down in the handcart to bask in the sun.

4. Secrets to Longevity

As the last surviving eunuch of China, Sun Yaoting met a lot of people curious about his "secrets to longevity". He claimed to have no secret, attributing his long life to his attitude and lifestyle. To live long, he said, one must be broadminded. "In the course of life everyone will have to endure adversities, either big or small. If you take them to heart, brooding and sulking all day, surely you won't live to a ripe old age. I've had a lifetime of frustrations and hardships. Being a eunuch, I am deprived of the family happiness many people take for granted. So there is less reason for me to take other worldly desires too seriously, and this attitude saves me a lot of worry and anxiety. The older I grow, the more relaxed and carefree I become. I would not have lived to this day if I let myself be troubled by all the unpleasant things in life!"

According to Sun Yaoting, one must eat well to live a long and healthy

Sun Yaoting with visitors from his home village

life. Joining the All-True Sect of Taoism and spending dozens of years in Buddhist temples did not turn him into a vegetarian. "How can one stay healthy without getting enough nutrition?" he argued. Even in the Imperial Palace, where eunuchs must dress well, he gave his first priority to food. This partly explained why he had failed to save much money, a fact many people found hard to believe. Some tried to coax him into a confession. "Come on, you served the Emperor and the Empress for quite a few years and must be hiding a small fortune somewhere. A starved camel is still much bigger than a horse!"

Sun Yaoting smiled. "You want to know where I put all my money? Well, it's right here, in my stomach!"

He was not too particular about food, though he adjusted his diet to seasonal changes. He believed in "following the course of nature". When he felt like eating something, he reasoned, it was probably because his body needed it.

Sun Yaoting had never used a fan in his life. "Why don't you use a fan?" A visitor asked him the question on a summer day, when it was hot and stuffy in his room.

"When I was young," Sun Yaoting explained, "I was an attendant in the palace and had no right to use a fan. Imagine me standing by the Empress and fanning myself! So I got used to it. Even after leaving the palace, I've never felt the need to use a fan no matter how hot it is. One day I happened to sit opposite someone who kept fanning himself, and I caught a cold! After that I always stay away from fans!"

In the palace another eunuch had told him that castration resulted in a lack of yang energy. The remedy was to wash one's feet in hot water before going to bed and rub the soles of feet vigorously to stimulate blood circulation and generate yang energy. Sun Yaoting kept doing it all through the years. At his age he remained mentally alert and curious about what was happening around him. One day he read a newspaper article that claimed the process of aging started at both ends of the human body, the head and the feet. He smiled proudly, saying, "I've long been trying to keep my head and feet young!"

Though affable and easygoing, Sun Yaoting had a strong point of view on many things. "Mr. Sun is certainly no muddle-headed old man!" an acquaintance once commented. When his grandson was getting married, Sun Yaoting sent for him to ask about the wedding plan. "What kind of guests are you going to invite?"

"Many of our colleagues, classmates, and relatives will come," the grandson replied. "We want to make it a big occasion, so people will be really impressed and have a high opinion of our family! We'll also invite the West German reporter and his wife."

"Do you think that would be a proper thing to do?"

"Why not? He's an old acquaintance of yours, isn't he?"

"Think carefully. They are foreigners. Do you expect them to bring you a wedding gift?"

"Well, I haven't thought about it."

"We don't really know them well enough to accept their present. On the other hand, all the guests to the wedding are expected to bring presents. Either way, it would cause some embarrassment."

The grandson pulled a long face. "All right, I'll forget it."

"This is my advice," Sun Yaoting said. "After the wedding, you can send them a message along with some 'happiness candies'. How about that?"

"I'll do as you tell me."

One day his grandson showed him a newly bought watch. "Can you guess how much it cost?"

"Well, I bought my British watch for a hundred and sixty-five dollars. I know watches are much cheaper now, so it should not have cost you more than a hundred yuan."

"It cost me five yuan!"

"What? How can it be so cheap?"

"Because it's an electronic watch!" The grandson had to explain the difference to him.

Sun Yaoting considered himself lucky to have adopted Changnian. When he was recovering from an illness, he went to stay with Changnian, and they lived together like a happy family. He went to bed at eight and got up early to take a stroll, joining several elderly people in the neighborhood chatting and basking in the sun. Changnian's wife usually arrived in a short moment with a folding stool to help him sit down in a sunny place without draught. "Is that your daughter?" one of the elderly men asked.

"She's my daughter-in-law!" Sun Yaoting replied proudly.

"You are lucky to have such filial children!"

It must be very gratifying for Sun Yaoting to hear such comments. On the whole he was more generous to Changnian's family than to himself.

On an early winter day his daughter-in-law took him in his handcart to a department store. It was his intention to buy her a down overcoat, but in the end she persuaded him to let her buy one for him. After wearing it only once, he gave it to Changnian, saying it felt a bit tight on him.

The Temple of Great Deliverance was finally opened to the public. For the sake of his health, Sun Yaoting was dissuaded from attending the grand opening ceremony that lasted a whole day. However, many people took the opportunity to visit him. By that time he had become a "national treasure", and no one was allowed to call on him without obtaining official approval in advance. But he could not bring himself to turn away the visitors. He still enjoyed an outdoor walk in the vicinity, either to Shichahai Lake or the Drum Tower. Occasionally he ran into an old acquaintance in the street and stopped for a chat. Most of the time he just moved on at a leisurely pace, the serene expression on his wrinkled face showing no sign of the trials and tribulations of a life that spanned almost a century of turbulence, metamorphosis and rejuvenation in this ancient country.

15

GRAVESTONE IN SILENCE

It was deadly quiet in the backyard of the Buddhist Guanghua Temple, where I do not remember how many times I looked at the weather-worn face of Sun Yaoting and listened to him tell of his hard and eventful life. I was shocked by what he had gone through.

What I heard from this ailing old man was not only the personal sufferings inflicted upon him by the feudal system, but bad luck, too. His story was a history of the late Qing Dynasty told from his unique perspective. After thinking it over I came up with a long scroll of paintings depicting events that took place during the past 100 years and the folklore of the cities of Beijing and Tianjin.

I wanted to record down the arduous life of Sun Yaoting. So I confined myself within the room and began to write his story. I would sit at my desk for 15 to 16 hours a day in high summer when temperature rose to 37 to 38 degrees Centigrade. I continued to write even when I ran a fever of 39 degrees and suffered from persistent diarrhea. I was racing with time because I had made a promise to publish the biography before the old man died.

It turned cooler as autumn arrived. I finished the manuscript which I called "Long-Hidden Secrets Revealed by China's Last Eunuch". I went to the temple to get the old man's consent if I could ask Pu Jie, brother of the last Emperor of the Qing Dynasty, to write a preface to the book. The old man was excited but a bit skeptical. He asked, "Why would the Second Master write the preface for me?"

It was unnecessary for the old man to worry. Pu Jie, a friend of mine despite our age difference, agreed immediately after I told him the gist of the book. He refused to use the preface I had drafted for him but wrote a poem himself instead. Pu Jie had always denied there were secrets in the Imperial Palace. But he wrote in the preface to this book, "It is not easy to hear the secrets in the Qing Imperial Palace. Now they are revealed through heavy clouds..."

I ran to the temple in excitement and spread Pu Jie's preface before Sun Yaoting. I said to him, "Look at this."

"What is it?" The old man asked, raising his head from his lunch. When he saw it was the preface written by Pu Jie, he put down his rice bowl and stood up immediately and took the paper. Recognizing the familiar handwriting of Pu Jie, the old man's hands began to shake and tears flowed down his wrinkled face.

He said, "I never thought the Second Master would write the preface for this book. I was only his bondservant! It is really true what they say 'One will become known far and wide as soon as he has made a name.'"

After the book was published, Sun Yaoting became very famous. Among his visitors were many foreigners from abroad, too. The old man shed a lot of tears. From time to time, he would tell me what he saw and heard during the time he served the imperial court as a eunuch. I taped our conversations, amassing more than 100 hours of recordings. I also made a dozen hour-long videos about the old man's daily life and recollections.

Sun Yaoting became a rare "national treasure". He was about the only authority left in China who had lived through the last years of the Qing Imperial Court. When the film "Eunuch Li Lianying" was being made, Director Tian Zhuangzhuang and leading actor Jiang Wen and leading actress Liu Xiaoqing paid him a special visit, consulting him on the protocols and customs in the Imperial Palace. They wanted to meet a second time, but he was ill. Afraid he might not be able to go through a lengthy interview, he made a phone call asking me to help. Over several hours of the interview I helped him explain the customs at the Imperial Court. The film stars were very pleased with our insights.

In those days I went to see him almost every week. He enjoyed meeting me, too. If I did not show up for a while he would call or send me a letter. We became bosom friends despite our considerable age difference. I fell ill in the second half of 1992 and was confined to bed. I could not go to Guanghua Temple to visit him for many days. He made many phone calls asking about my health.

One day, his servant Cui came to my house and told my mother that his master had sent him over to find where I lived. He wanted to deliver some salted eggs. My mother declined with many thanks. But his servant Cui brought the salted eggs to me anyway. He had two small bamboo baskets with him. In one basket were salted hen's eggs and in the other basket were fried meat balls. Servant Cui brought a message from Sun Yaoting: "Let Yinghua try the meat balls. I cooked them according to the standards of the Imperial Kitchen. They are different from those sold on the street."

All in my family ate the imperial-style meat balls cooked by Sun Yaoting and savored the profound friendship he showed to me.

Sun Yaoting called me on the phone again, asking me to come over immediately. My mother thought it must be something urgent. I was seriously ill. She asked someone to accompany me to the temple. The old man came up to grab my hands with his and did not say a word for a long time. Then he told me he had a dream last night. He dreamt of me but he could not tell me what happened in the dream. I saw tears shimmering in his eyes.

As I was about to leave, the old man tell me that I died in his dream and was laid on a bare wooden bed. No matter how hard he tried he could not wake me up. He became so worried he called me at home immediately after he got up in the morning. He could feel at ease only when he saw me in person. The old man burst into smile and said, "From ancient times people have been saying, 'what one dreams goes contrary to reality: death is living.' I know it is an omen of your sure recovery..."

I do not know if it was because of the old man's auspicious remarks or not, I recovered from an illness which doctors had deemed hopeless.

As I recovered from my illness, the old man's health kept deteriorating with each passing day. One year later he looked much more fragile. He kept saying he wanted to go back to his native village in Jinghai. His mind would be clear for a while and then become muddled. I went to see him one day in early September. He took hold my hand and said, "Yinghua, you must ask them to send me back to my birthplace after I die."

I knew very well the old man was talking about the arrangements of his death. Two years earlier when he fell seriously ill he had also told me he wanted to be buried in his native village after he died. He also wanted to erect a tombstone with an inscription by Pu Jie. For this I made a special visit to Pu Jie who promised to write the inscription without any hesitation.

Unfortunately Pu Jie died before Sun Yaoting. During a casual talk, Sun Yaoting said to me, "You wrote an epitaph for His Majesty. Could you write one for me?"

He said, "I cannot care about what it will say after I die." His clouded eyes seemed to open wider. He said, "I won't mind what you write. It's up to you. I had hoped the Second Master would write it. But he died before me. You write it. I won't mind what you write."

I knew this was a solemn request the old man made for the arrangement of his death. It was also a deathbed wish of his to return to his roots.

"You rest assured," I said, grabbing his two bony hands in mine. I held his hands tightly and watched him falling slowly asleep.

During the holiday of the National Day on October 1st, I came to Guanghua Temple again. Sun Yaoting was half awake in bed. His face brightened when he saw me and he said, "Yinghua, I feel stuffy here and want to take a walk outside."

His servant Cui and I helped him to his wheelchair and pushed him along West Gulou Street. Watching the endless flow of motor vehicles the old man said with emotion, "Look, there are more cars in Beijing today than were rickshaws in the old times."

He seemed to talk to me and to himself at the same time. He talked about a tour of Beijing the government arranged for him two years ago. He said, "Good. Beijing is really good."

When we reached Yinding Bridge he asked me to take a photo there. He had often told me this was the spot where Wang Jingwei tried to kill Zaifeng, Emperor Pu Yi's father, with a bomb. It began to rain as we were strolling along the shore at Shichahai Lake. We hurried back to the temple. After he lay down on bed he asked me to sit by him and said in a weak voice, "I feel I am dying." After a while he began to tell some anecdotes in the Imperial Palace, such as the Empress loving jasmine tea, and other stories. His mind seemed to have returned to those old days. Then he said to me, "Don't leave. Stay here and have a meal." But, with these words, the old man suddenly fell asleep.

It was December 18th in the same year. I was attending a conference of Chinese writers. Someone came over and told me my family wanted me to return home immediately. I called and learned that Sun Yaoting had died.

I rushed to Guanghua Temple. There I learned that the previous night Sun Yaoting had asked his servant Cui for an apple. Cui said to him, "An apple is tough to bite. Can you eat it? Let me boil some water with a pear in it. The juice will be good for you." The old man nodded his approval.

After the old man had drunk the pear water, his servant Cui went about tidying up things in an outer room and while talking to the old man who was in the inner room. When Cui no longer heard the old man's voice for a long while, he went in and saw Sun Yaoting's head tilted to one side. He had died.

At 6:50 on the afternoon of December 17th, 1996, Sun Yaoting, the last eunuch from Imperial China, died quietly in Guanghua Temple by Shichahai Lake in Beijing at the age of 94.

No one expected his death would arouse extensive interest within and outside China. Overseas news media paid special attention to this event. China Xinhua News Agency, AP, Reuters, AFP and Jiji all released stories of Sun Yaoting's death. A French TV station produced a special program showing aspects about life in China before and after his death. Within a day, more than 100 major news agencies worldwide carried the news. Many said that the death of China's last eunuch marked the final passing of Imperial China.

The funeral of Sun Yaoting began at 12 o'clock on December 20th at Babaoshan Mortuary House and his remains were cremated there afterwards. At 13:30 his oldest adopted son and I collected his ashes and wrapped them in a bundle of red silk. In the afternoon, his friends, relatives and I escorted his ashes to his native village of Xishuangtang in Jinghai County, Tianjin Municipality. The next day, more than 100 of his friends and relatives witnessed the burial of his ashes, placed in a cypress coffin in a graveyard not far to the northwest of Xishuangtang Village.

But the old man's wish for erecting a tombstone was not an easy task. I made five trips to Jinghai and three trips to a quarry in Fangshan which was a designated stone supplier to the Imperial Palace. I got an ideal piece of stone for the tombstone. But the local government did not allow me to erect it there. I was determined to fulfill the old man's last wish no matter how difficult it was. Only after many setbacks did I succeed in erecting the tombstone at the old man's grave during the Qingming Festival in 1999.

It was early spring when all things came back to life. The earth had

The mourning hall in West Shuangtang

turned tender green. Inscribed on top of the 2-meter-high tombstone are four Chinese characters: "The Last Palace Eunuch". The five large Chinese characters carved in the middle of the tombstone read: "The Tomb of Sun Yaoting".

The epitaph carved on the back of the tombstone tells the history of the eunuch service in Imperial China and the life of Sun Yaoting, the last eunuch. To a certain extent, Sun Yaoting's personal experiences were a reflection of a particular period in Chinese history. The epitaph reads as follows:

"Alas! The wine cup is brimming over with sorrow. The eunuch system had existed for several thousand years. It continued throughout the feudal society, with one Imperial Dynasty replaced by another.

"I wrote these words in memory of Sun Yaoting, an old bosom buddy of mine despite of the great difference in our ages. He was the last eunuch from China's Imperial times. Sun Yaoting was born at Dongliumu in Jinghai on the outskirts of Tianjin on November 30th in the 28th year of Emperor Guangxu's reign and died on December 17th of 1996 in Guanghua Temple in Beijing. He was born into a very poor family. In order to avenge his father, he underwent castration when he was eight years old and entered the Imperial Palace when he was 15 years old. He first served Empress Dowager

The author pays last tribute to Sun Yaoting's body.

Duankang and then Empress Wanrong. He continued to serve Pu Yi who was made Emperor Kangde of Manchukuo, a Japanese puppet regime in Northeast China. After he returned to Beijing he lived in a Buddhist temple for many years in the company of monks chanting scriptures and striking on bells and chime stones. After he was appointed an official in charge of religious affairs he continued to enjoy his life in the Buddhist temple. He told me his life and the events from the late Qing Dynasty, giving me unreserved help for writing the book entitled "Long-Hidden Secrets Revealed by China's Last Eunuch". He wrote the preface to the book himself. The book has been translated into fifteen foreign languages in part and read all over the world.

"Sun Yaoting revisited the Forbidden City in his later years. The many anecdotes he told and the video recording he made during his visits have become precious reference material. He wrote a couplet to summarize his life-long experience. It reads: "When the country is on the correct course Heaven will bless it; when the officials are honest, the people will live in peace." This couplet is much read in Beijing. I had written the epitaph for Pu Yi, the last Emperor in China. And I had the honor to write an epitaph for Sun Yaoting, the last eunuch from the imperial times.

"Was it the will of Heaven? Recalling my meeting with Sun Yaoting in

A poster for the documentary "The Last Eunuch Revisits the Forbidden City", shown daily at the Palace Museum

his later years I shed tears before his tomb. Deeply grieved by his loss I cherish his friendship even more. Here I pay him my respect.

"Sun Yaoting lived a long life and witnessed several historic changes in the national rule of China. He was like a drop of clear water that can reflect the waves on the sea. He died in his bed of a ripe old age without suffering any illness. His death, however, marked the end of the final vestiges of Imperial China. Here I erect this epitaph to sing praises to his virtues and for people of coming generations to read."

Written by Jia Yinghua at the Palace Museum on Qingming Festival, 1997

A piece of white cloud looked like a lonely sailboat coming slowly from the ends of the earth. It gradually disappeared into the immense sky. In the twinkle of an eye brilliant sunshine spread all over and turned orange. The brocade-like sunset glow focused on a corner of the tombstone to become a bright spot of dazzling white. It seemed time had stopped at the moment.

The clouds looked like a sea and the setting sun was as red as blood.

图书在版编目（CIP）数据

末代太监孙耀庭：英文/贾英华著；孙海晨译.
—北京：五洲传播出版社，2008.10（2013.6重印）
ISBN 978-7-5085-1407-9

Ⅰ.末… Ⅱ.①贾… ②孙… Ⅲ.孙耀庭（1902~1996）— 传记 — 英文
Ⅳ.①K828.9

中国版本图书馆CIP数据核字（2013）第123810号

策　　划　荆孝敏
责任编辑　张美景
装帧设计　刘　鹏　申真真

末代太监孙耀庭

五洲传播出版社
地址：北京市海淀区北三环中路31号生产力大楼B座7层
邮编：100088
电话：010-82007837，010-82005927
网址：www.cicc.org.cn

开本：160mm×230mm　1/16
印张：20.5
版次：2008年10月第1版　2013年6月第2次印刷
印刷：北京市全海印刷厂
书号：ISBN 978-7-5085-1407-9
09200